Understanding Business Statistics

An Active-Learning Approach

M.N.K. Saunders B.A., M.Sc., Ph.D., P.G.C.E.

Mark Saunders has been a statistician and researcher in local government and has taught on certificate and diploma professional management and personnel courses as well as BTEC higher national courses and degree courses in business studies.

He was previously Principal Research Officer for Hereford and Worcester County Council and is currently a Senior Lecturer in the Department of Management of the Business School at Cheltenham and Gloucester College of Higher Education.

Among his publications are distance learning material for companies and papers on research methods and teaching strategies.

S.A. Cooper M.I.P.M.

Stacey Cooper has worked as a trainer in the financial services sector. She has taught professional management and personnel courses and has developed competency based management programmes at NVQ levels 4 and 5. She is a qualified assessor and verifier and regularly acts as a consultant on portfolio development.

She is currently the Training Manager at RoyScot Trust Plc and a part time Lecturer in the Business School at Cheltenham and Gloucester College of Higher Education.

DP Publications Ltd
Aldine House, Aldine Place
142/144 Uxbridge Road,
London W12 8AW
1993

Acknowledgements

The authors would like to thank their partners (Jane and Keith) for looking after the children while this book was written, and colleagues in the Business School at Cheltenham and Gloucester College of Higher Education for their advice.

A CIP catalogue record for this book is available from the British Library

ISBN 1 85805 024 3

Printed by The Guernsey Press Co. Ltd.,
Braye Road, Vale,
Guernsey, Channel Islands

Preface

Aim

The aim of this book is to provide an activity-based introduction to Business Statistics.

Typical courses on which it can be used include:

- BTEC courses in Business Studies
- BTEC Certificate in Management (including NVQ4 M1)
- Accountancy foundation courses
- IPM Professional Management Foundation Programme
- BA Business Studies (level one)

It will also assist those students wishing to transfer to degree courses to obtain advanced standing for level one business statistics courses, as well as those taking advanced professional courses who need a revision course, or who want to make good any deficiencies in knowledge and understanding.

Need

The need was seen for a new type of book – one that could allow the lecturer to delegate a proportion of the teaching process to students themselves, enabling the lecturer to concentrate on managing students' self-teaching.

This book is flexible enough, however, to be used in any one of the following teaching modes:

a) as a support text for fully taught lessons;

b) as a self-teaching package with minimum, if any, lecturer support, ie as part of a distance/ open learning mode of study;

c) as a combination of (a) and (b), according to individual circumstances.

Approach

There are three main sections to the book:

Section 1 – Discovering Business Statistics
Section 2 – Information Bank
Section 3 – Developing Knowledge and Skills

Section 1 is the main driving force of the book. It comprises 25 units (which can be worked through sequentially or non-sequentially) following the experiences of a management trainee who comes across situations requiring the use of business statistics to solve problems that arise.

The scenarios set business statistical techniques in a 'real life' context; Quick Answer Questions (with answers on the following left-hand page) prompt problem recognition; and tasks motivate the reader to seek solutions (help lines direct the reader to Section 2: The Information Bank). Guidance is given where the use of spreadsheets for certain tasks would be advantageous. Answers to the tasks are given in an appendix.

Section 2 provides a concise summary of business statistical methods. Whilst it is organised in the same sequence as Section 1, it is not meant to be read in the same way as a conventional text book. ie the reader should consult this section in order to carry out the tasks in Sections 1 and 3.

Section 3 consists of a mixture of tasks with answers (to help the reader confirm his or her understanding) and tasks without answers. The latter, together with assignments, enables a lecturer to gauge the students' level of competence.

Note for lecturers

A Lecturers' Supplement is provided free of charge to lecturers adopting the book as a course text. This includes: outline answers to those tasks without answers; guidance notes for the assessment of the assignments; OHP masters of key diagrams; a formulae sheet; and guidance for group work.

How to use this book

The introduction to Section 1 includes an outline scenario of the company in which the 'heroine' is a management trainee. Each unit in Section 1 uses the scenario as a 'peg' on which to hang business statistical techniques or principles. If the book is being used for self-study, it would be logical to work through in sequence from the beginning, but it is not necessary.

If you are not going to work through in sequence it is helpful to treat the units as a number of distinct groups. Within each of these groups the later units rely heavily on earlier units to provide underpinning knowledge and understanding.

Data and information: units 1 and 2
Data sources: unit 3
Collecting data: units 4 and 6
Sampling: unit 5
Presenting data: units 7, 8, 9 and 10
Measures of central tendency: units 11 and 12
Measures of dispersion: units 13 and 14
Relationships between variables: units 17 and 18
Significance testing using chi square: unit 19
Index numbers: units 20, 21 and 22
Probability: units 23, 24 and 25

The planning chart on page vi is intended to help lecturers map out their courses, and students plan their revision.

Note: *Use in Open/Distance Learning*. Where a student is is studying largely on his/her own, this book provides a *stimulating* and *interesting* approach to learning the subject. For further support, wider reading and many more exercises with answers, *Business Mathematics and Statistics*, A Complete Course Text, by A. Francis (DP Publications 1993) makes an ideal companion text.

MNK Saunders & SA Cooper
July 1993

Contents

Study Planning Chart

To help with planning a course of study, you will need to know **where** all the topics in the Information Bank (Section 2) are covered.

The analysis below shows that all topics in the Section 2 Information Bank are covered by the parallel unit of Section 1, except in a very few cases. This will make course planning much easier.

The exceptions are where:

a) a task in a Section 1 unit requires an underlying knowledge of part of a particular other unit (indicated in brackets on the chart);

b) part of a unit is not covered in Section 1 but is covered by a task, with answer, in Section 3 (shown in the right hand column of the chart).

Section 2 – Information Bank Units	Coverage in	
	Section 1 units	**Section 3 topics (with answers)**
1. Data and information		
• Information and business	1	
• Business data	1	
• Business information	1	
2. The value and characteristics of information		
• The value of information	2	
• The characteristics of information	2	
3. Data sources		
• Primary data	3	
• Secondary data	3	
• Internal and external data sources	3	
• Sources of secondary data	3	
4. Deciding what data must be collected		
• Establishing what needs to be found out	4	
• Deciding what data is needed	4	
5. Populations, samples and sampling methods		
• Samples and populations	5	
• The need to sample, sampling frames	5	
• Random sampling	5	
• Systematic sampling	5	
• Stratified sampling	5	
• Multi-stage sampling	5	
• Quota sampling	5	
• Cluster sampling	5	
• Impact of sample size	5	
6. Collecting primary data: questionnaire and interview schedule design		
• Interviews, questionnaires and direct observation	6	
• Questionnaire and interview schedule design	6	
• Checking the sample is representative	6	
• Pilot testing	6	
7. Types of data and tabulating data		
• Types of data (categorical, quantitative, continuous, discrete)	7	
• Principles of good tabulation	7	
• Tally marks	7	
• Frequency distributions and cross tabulations	7	
• Deciding upon class intervals	7	
• Calculation of percentages	7	

Section 2 – Information Bank Units	Coverage in	
	Section 1 units	Section 3 topics (with answers)
8. Diagrams for categorical and discrete data: bar charts		
• Introduction to diagrams	8	
• Simple bar charts	8	
• Multiple bar charts	8	
• Stacked (component) bar charts	8	
• Percentage component bar charts	8	
• Misuse of bar charts	8	
9. Diagrams for categorical and discrete data: pie charts and pictograms		
• Pie charts and comparative pie charts	9	
• Pictograms	9	
• Misuse of pie charts and pictograms	9	
10. Diagrams for continuous and grouped discrete data: histograms and frequency polygons		
• Histograms for data with equal class widths	10	
• Histograms for data with unequal class widths	10	
• Frequency polygons (line graphs)	(12, 13, 15, 16)	
11. Measures of central tendency: means		
• Arithmetic mean from raw data	11, (12)	
• Arithmetic mean from a discrete frequency distribution	11	
• Arithmetic mean from a grouped frequency distribution	11	
• Harmonic mean	11	
• Geometric mean	11	
12. Measures of central tendency: medians and modes		
• Median from raw data	12, (13)	
• Median from a discrete frequency distribution	12, (13)	
• Median from a grouped frequency distribution (including ogives)	12, (13)	
• Mode	12	
• Interpretation: normal distribution, positive and negative skew	12	
13. Measures of dispersion: ranges, quartiles, deciles and percentiles		
• Range from raw data	13	
• Upper and lower quartiles and inter-quartile range from raw data	13	
• Percentiles and deciles	13	
• Quartiles and inter-quartile range from a discrete frequency distribution	13	
• Quartiles and inter-quartile range from a grouped frequency distribution (including ogives)	13	
• Interpretation: normal distribution, positive and negative skew	13	
14. Measures of dispersion: variance, standard deviation and coefficient of variation		
• Variance	14	
• Standard deviation (including computational formula) from raw material	14	
• Standard deviation from a grouped frequency distribution	14	
• Interpretation of standard deviation for normally distributed data	14	
• Coefficient of variation	14	
15. Time series: variations and moving averages		
• Simple time series	15	
• Components of a time series (long term trend, seasonal variations, cyclical fluctuations, residual influences)	15	
• Determining the trend: moving averages	15, (16)	

Section 2 – Information Bank Units	Coverage in	
	Section 1 units	Section 3 topics (with answers)
16. Time series: forecasting and seasonal variation		
• Forecasting from the moving average	16	
• Seasonally adjusting the trend	16	
• Forecasting using seasonal variation	16	
17. Relationships between variables: correlation		
• Types of relationship between two variables	17, (18)	
• Scatter graphs	17, (18)	
• Spearman's rank correlation coefficient	17	
• Pearson's product moment correlation coefficient	17	
18. Relationships between variables: regression		
• Regression equation	18	
• Interpreting the regression equation – interpolation and extrapolation	18	
• Coefficient of determination	18	
19. Testing for significance: the chi square test		
• Null hypothesis and hypothesis	19	
• Chi square test for frequency distributions (including Yate's correction)	19	
• Chi square test for two variable tables	19	
20. Index numbers using one item: quantity and price indices, value indices		
• Simple quantity (volume) index	20	
• Simple price index	20	
• Value (expenditure) indices	20	
21. Index numbers using more than one item: average index, Laspeyre's index and Paasche's index		
• Average quantity and price indices	21	
• Laspeyre's price index	21	
• Paasche's price index	21	
• Laspeyre's volume index		} 8.3
• Paasche's volume index		
22. Index numbers: chain based index, splicing indices, deflating a series		
• Selecting a suitable base period	22, (20)	
• Chain based index	22	
• Splicing (combining) indices	22	
• Deflating a series (including Retail Price Index)	22	
23. Theoretical and empirical probability		
• Types of event (mutually exclusive, dependent and independent)	23	
• Theoretical and empirical probability	23	
• Combining events (addition and multiplication rules)	23	
24. Expectation and conditional probability		
• Expectation – expected income	24	
• Expectation – expected profit		9.4
• Conditional probability, tabular method and Bayes' theorem	24	
25. Probability and the normal distribution		
• Properties of the normal distribution and probability	25	
• Calculation of z scores	25	

Section 1
Discovering Business Statistics

This section comprises 25 units describing the experiences of Liz Reynolds, a management trainee with Brunley's Ltd, who needs to use business statistics in her work. You are encouraged to learn through Liz's experiences, in particular through the task with which she has to deal.

Each unit contains scenarios, quick answer questions (QAQs) and tasks with help lines to Section 2 (The Information Bank). The earlier units are shorter, to enable you to gain confidence quickly, and it would be logical to work through from Unit 1 onwards. However, it is not necessary to do so as the units are generally self contained.

At the end of appropriate units, you are directed to those tasks in Section 3 which you could tackle at that point of your studies (if you so choose!).

Now read about Brunley's, below, and good luck with your studies!

Background to the scenarios

Brunley's is an old established supermarket chain located primarily in the South West of England. It is a private limited company with 40 major shareholders. It is well known in the trade as a caring employer, and many employees have worked for the company throughout their working life, often rising to positions of responsibility. Brunley's image to the customer is a family firm providing a traditional caring service in which the customer comes first.

Its head office is based in Cheltenham. There is also a central warehouse near this site close to the motorway where the company's own brand products are stored. Branches order own brand items from the central warehouse which are delivered by road.

Brunley's has 260 branches, 70 are located in prime sites in town centres; out of which 40 have large car parking facilities. There are 20 out of town sites and the remaining 170 branches are small shops situated in suburban housing developments. Brunley's main competitors are Tesbury, Springfield's, Gaterose and Greenland's.

In order to remain competitive the company has recently computerised its 70 town centre stores and the 20 out of town stores by installing bar code readers at the checkouts and electronic stock control (Electronic Point of Sale, EPOS). In addition the 20 out of town stores also have electronic payment equipment for customers (Electronic Funds Transfer at Point of Sales, EFTPOS). This has resulted in a wealth of sales data being collected automatically.

Two years ago the company started a management development programme taking on two or three graduates a year to train as future managers for the larger stores. The management trainees spend their first three months learning the ropes at one of the more modern stores, and then move to head office where they gain experience of a number of departments.

The main character in Section One of the book is Liz Reynolds, who has been employed by Brunley's as a management trainee. The situations and problems that she encounters in the course of her training programme provide the scenarios for the aspects of understanding business statistics covered in this book.

Section 1 Contents and outline

Unit 1: Liz Reynolds starts work at Brunley's

By the end of this unit you will:

- ❐ *be able to distinguish between data and information;*
- ❐ *know how data is transformed into information.*

Scenario:

It is Liz's first day working for Brunley's Supermarkets as a Management Trainee. She has reported to Gregory Woollons, the Manager of the Gloucester store, and is waiting with his secretary until she is called into his office. The intercom is buzzed and Liz is asked in.

Mr Woollons welcomes Liz and begins by reviewing the programme she will undertake as a Management Trainee.

'I thought you could spend an hour or so looking at recent management information reports produced in this store, and some computer printouts from our stock control system. They are all in these folders. I've also arranged for Jemma Douglas, the Deputy Manager, to take you on a tour of the store and introduce you to some of the staff. In particular I want you to meet the Stock Control Manager so you will be having lunch with him and spending the afternoon together. I'm off now to our weekly management meeting. If you have any queries, I'll answer them when I get back.'

Mr Woollons leaves the office and Liz starts looking at the folders she has been given.

QAQ 1.1

At the top of Liz's pile is a folder labelled 'Weekly Stock Control Report'. Inside are a series of computer printouts. Liz starts to read a printout (see extract below) but has difficulty understanding it. Liz thinks that this report is virtually useless and nobody could understand it.

Do you agree with Liz? Why do you think she has this view?

3245875543328	RED SHOE POLISH	8
4309754353033	CRYSTALLISED FRUITS	32
4355456464654	CARPET SHAMPOO	23
4696744650564	FROZEN RABBIT	8
5014213008031	MOLASSES	3
5085775438328	LEMON CHUTNEY	43
5424487324643	CHOCOLATE DOGGY DROPS	24
5433564646667	VANILLA SACHETS	13
5438735667834	FROZEN CREAM	32
5453059375573	FROZEN PHEASANT	14
5465664456644	FLY STRIP	11
5465732535533	ONION BREAD	25
5576456506437	SAFFRON	0
5847364365353	MARZIPAN	12
7653904932904	CHERRIES IN LIQUEUR	24

QAQ 1.2

Liz picks up the folder entitled 'Monthly Sales Report for Store Manager'. This contains a number of sheets of paper which Liz starts to read. After getting halfway through she begins to consider the recipient of the report, the Store Manager. She wonders if he would understand the report (see extract below).

What do you think?

Brunley's Monthly Sales Report January 199- Page 3 of 5

2. Sales Targets

Sales over the month of January have exceeded the store's target by 3%. The only department which failed to meet its target was Wines and Spirits. The performance of individual departments is shown below:

Fruit and Vegetables	+5%
Delicatessen	+2%
Meats and Poultry	+4%
Dairy	+2%
Frozen Food	+1%
Wines and Spirits	-1%
Overall	**+3%**

Discussion with the Departmental Manager suggests that the poor performance of the Wines and Spirits Department could be for three reasons:

1. Reduction in customer spending after Christmas.
2. Shortfall in stock on some of our most popular wines.
3. Strong marketing campaign by Tesbury promoting their wines.

■ Task 1.1

Towards the end of the hour Liz returns to the Weekly Stock Control Report. She realises that the computer printouts are a summary of the weekly sales taken from the Electronic Point of Sales System (E.P.O.S.) for each individual product line. Knowing that she will be having lunch with the Stock Control Manager she wonders what he makes of these computer printouts.

See *Section 2: The Information Bank* Data and information: Unit 1; page 57

Do you think the Stock Control Manager considers the Weekly Stock Control Report to be data or information? Why?

Give one example of data and one of information using the reports above.

Answer to QAQ 1.1

You will probably agree with Liz that the 'Weekly Stock Control Report' is useless. Liz thinks it is useless because it does not clearly state what the data is about.

Unit 2: Liz discovers different people need different information

By the end of this unit you will:

- ❐ *understand how information becomes valuable;*
- ❐ *understand why information is important to business;*
- ❐ *be able to assess the value of information against a range of characteristics.*

Scenario:

Liz is taken round the store by the Deputy Manager, Jemma Douglas. She is introduced to the departmental managers and their staff. Both the Stock Control Manager and the Personnel Manager spend some time explaining their job and duties to Liz. This includes explaining the data they currently collect and how they subsequently use it.

The Stock Control Manager explains the E.P.O.S. system to Liz.

'As each item passes over the laser scanner it is automatically recorded by the in-store computer. To help us in decision making the computer is already programmed to provide a number of management reports.'

He shows three of these reports to Liz, extracts of which are shown below:

Daily Balance of Stock and Reorder Report

BAR CODE	ITEM	SALES	STOCK	REORDER
5545345353535	WHITE BREAD	300	0	YES
4574354956333	BROWN BREAD	211	2	YES
5358735066033	TINNED TOMATOES	124	45	YES
5635786569533	CREAM CRACKERS	34	96	NO
3535646466666	SPRING WATER	22	145	NO
5353535567885	LEMONADE	23	178	NO
5397530560303	FROZEN SAUSAGES	45	550	NO
5743844867542	BAKED BEANS	230	900	NO

Weekly Report of Items Which Have Not Sold

ITEMS WHICH HAVE NOT SOLD	WEEK ENDING 6.01.9-
5492838345321	PURPLE SHOE POLISH
5759356309563	SMOKED VENISON
3456646657878	EXPENSIVE CHAMPAGNE
3575-35735555	IMPROVED HAIR RINSE
ENDS	ENDS

Value of Sales by Individual Departments over the past 6 months

BRUNLEY'S GLOUCESTER STORE	6 MONTHS ENDING DEC 199-
DEPARTMENTAL STOCK SALES	£'s
FRUIT & VEG	400230
DELICATESSEN	390321
MEATS AND POULTRY	612644
DAIRY	405222
FROZEN FOOD	555623
WINES & SPIRITS	893223
HOUSEHOLD	795890
OVERALL	4053153

QAQ 2.1

The Stock Control Manager tells Liz that only one of three information reports (see above) is valuable when he needs to reorder stock.

Identify this report and say in one sentence why you think it is valuable.

Scenario:

The Personnel Manager describes the Personnel Database to Liz.

'The in-store computer holds data about every employee. This includes personal details such as address, age and gender; payroll details such as salary and bank account number; sickness absences; and training courses attended. Unfortunately whilst the personal, payroll and sickness details are accurate I'm not so sure about the training details. Staff often forget to notify us when they have attended a training course. I don't think they view it as particularly important. Anyway, departmental managers never ask for reports on who has attended training courses, so I don't see bringing the data up-to-date as cost effective.'

QAQ 2.2

Do you think the Personnel Manager should use the data held on the Personnel Database to decide whether to send individual employees on training courses?

Give one reason why.

■ Task 2.1

The Store Manager, Gregory Woollons, tells Liz that the first two management information reports relating to Stock Control (see extracts above) are useless to him in his role of store manager.

HELP
See *Section 2: The Information Bank*
The value of information: Unit 2.1, page 59.
Base your answer on The Characteristics of information: Unit 2.2, page 60

Suggest reasons why he says this for each of the reports.

You are now ready to tackle the tasks and assignments in topic 1 of Section 3.

Answer to QAQ 1.2

As the report is entitled 'Monthly Sales Report for Store Manager', Gregory Woollons, the Store Manager, should understand this report and find it useful as he is the intended recipient.

Unit 3: Liz discovers the range of sources from which data can be obtained

By the end of this unit you will:

- ❐ *understand the difference between primary and secondary data;*
- ❐ *understand the difference between internal and external data sources;*
- ❐ *be able to explain the advantages and disadvantages of different data sources;*
- ❐ *appreciate the wide range of data sources available to businesses.*

Scenario:

It is the end of Liz's first day at Brunley's. Just before she left to go home, Gregory Woollons, the Store Manager gave her a copy of his annual report to read. After supper Liz settles down to read it. She notices that on all the tables, graphs and charts it states where the data has been obtained: – the source of the data. She is surprised by the number of different sources and begins to list them:

- Questionnaire Survey of Customers
- Local Authority Planning Department
- Personnel Database
- Daily Balance of Stock and Reorder Report
- Office of Population Censuses and Surveys County Report for Gloucestershire
- Published Market Research Report on Shopping Trends
- Discussion with store staff about this problem
- Value Added Tax Returns

■ Task 3.1

Categorise the list of data sources used in the Store Manager's Annual Report (above) into primary data and secondary data.

HELP: See *Section 2: The Information Bank* Introduction: Unit 3.1, page 61; Primary data: Unit 3.2, page 61; Secondary data: Unit 3.3, page 62

■ Task 3.2

Subdivide your list of secondary data sources (from task 3.1) into internal data sources and external data sources.

HELP: (Check your answer to task 3.1 first) See *Section 2: The Information Bank* Secondary data: Unit 3.3, page 62; Sources of secondary data (Internal data sources, External data sources): Unit 3.4, page 63

■ Task 3.3

Liz reads the conclusion to the Store Manager's Annual Report (see extract below). She wonders to which 'Survey Reports by Government Departments' Gregory Woollons is referring.

> **HELP**
> See *Section 2: The Information Bank*
> Base your answer on: Sources of secondary data (External data sources): Unit 3.4, page 63

Which government survey reports do you think are likely to be the most useful to the Store Manager for keeping abreast of national trends?

Give reasons for your choice of government survey reports.

Brunley's Supermarkets **Annual Report for the Gloucester Store** **Conclusion**

In order for the Gloucester Store to continue to operate profitably it is essential that we adapt to the changing retail environment.

We therefore need to maintain both a sound knowledge of our local customer base and be aware of national trends in the retail sector.

In house surveys conducted by store employees will continue to be an important means of gathering local knowledge. However, to keep abreast of national trends, the store needs to make more use of externally published data such as that found in Market Research Reports and Survey Reports by Government Departments.

Gregory Woollons
Store Manager, Gloucester

page 34

■ Task 3.4

Liz remembers that secondary data sources have disadvantages as well as advantages.

> **HELP**
> See *Section 2: The Information Bank*
> Secondary data: Unit 3.3, page 62

List the advantages and disadvantages of using sources of secondary data, such as those mentioned in the conclusion of the Store Manager's Annual Report (see extract above), to keep abreast of national trends.

Answer to QAQ 2.1

The 'Daily Balance of Stock and Reorder Level Report' is valuable to the Stock Control Manager when he needs to reorder stock. This is because it contains the information he needs and is produced often enough to enable him to reorder stock as soon as levels become low.

Answer to QAQ 2.2

The Personnel Manager should not use the Personnel Database to decide whether to send individual employees on training courses. This is because the data held on training courses attended by individuals is unlikely to be accurate.

Unit 4: Liz is asked to 'find out what the customers want'

By the end of this unit you will:

- ❒ *appreciate the importance of establishing precisely what is meant by any inquiry;*
- ❒ *be able to break down an inquiry into a series of detailed questions which need to be answered;*
- ❒ *be able to decide what data is needed to answer detailed questions.*

Scenario:

It is the Monday morning of Liz's second week at the store. As usual she reports to the Deputy Manager, Jemma Douglas. Jemma outlines what she wants Liz to do:

'I would like you to put your college training to use and find out what our customers want.' Liz is not sure what Jemma means by this so asks for clarification.

'I want to know what proportion of our customers would shop at the store if we opened on Sundays, and if they shop at any of our competitors' stores on Sundays or during the week. I would like to know which competitors' stores these were for the past month.' After a few moments thought Jemma adds:

'I would also like to know how much they think they would spend in the store each Sunday if they were to shop here and how they intend to get to the store. You can work in my office for the rest of the morning.'

QAQ 4.1

List the detailed questions for which Jemma Douglas has asked Liz to find the answers.

Scenario:

Half an hour later Jemma Douglas asks Liz how she is getting on. Liz shows Jemma the detailed questions which she thinks need to be answered. Jemma looks at them and adds a further question – How many times a week do customers visit the Gloucester store?

Then Jemma asks her to work out what data needs to be collected to answer these detailed questions. She also reminds Liz that Brunley's main local competitors are Tesbury, Springfield's, Gaterose and Greenland's.

■ Task 4.1

Using the detailed questions from the answer to QAQ 4.1 and the further question added by Jemma Douglas, decide for each:

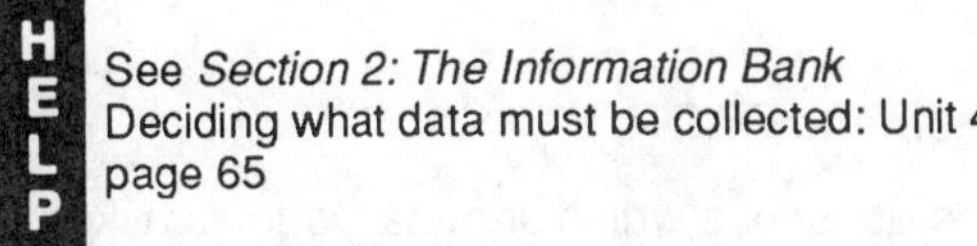

1. the data required to answer the questions.
2. how much detail is required of the data and the likely values or terminology this data could include.
3. the likely source(s) from which this data could be obtained.

Set out your answer as a table as shown in the information bank.

Unit 5: Liz decides to use sampling

By the end of this unit you will:

- ❐ *know the meaning of the terms: sample and population;*
- ❐ *know the advantages and disadvantages of sampling;*
- ❐ *understand random, systematic, stratified, multi-stage, quota and cluster sampling methods and be able to choose when to use them.*

Scenario:

Liz has given a lot of thought to the task set by Jemma Douglas (the Deputy Manager). This is to find Brunley's customers' views on Sunday opening of the Gloucester store. She has decided to undertake a survey of customers.

Jemma Douglas has told Liz that, although Brunley's do not have a list of their customers, there must be over 10,000 of them of whom over 90% live locally. Jemma has told Liz that she needs the results from the survey within the next two weeks. Although she can give Liz a small budget to cover printing and stationary, she will not be able to release any staff to help with a survey. She has also suggested that Liz collects the data on a weekday and a Saturday.

QAQ 5.1

List three factors that suggest Liz should only survey a proportion of those customers visiting the store.

Task 5.1

Can Liz define her sampling frame? Give one reason for your answer.

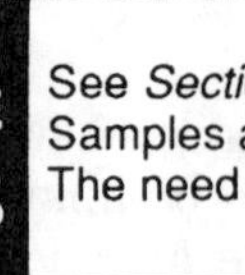

See *Section 2: The Information Bank*
Samples and populations: Unit 5.1, page 68;
The need to sample: Unit 5.2, page 68

Scenario:

Jemma Douglas has also given Liz a recently produced table which classifies the customers by age and gender (see below):

Answer to QAQ 4.1

The questions which Jemma Douglas asked Liz to find the answers for were:

1. What proportion of customers would shop at the Gloucester store on Sundays if it was open?
2. a. Do the Gloucester store's customers shop at any of Brunley's competitors on Sundays?
   b. Which competitors' stores were these (for the past month)?
3. a. Do the Gloucester store's customers shop at any of Brunley's competitors during the week?
   b. Which competitors' stores were these (for the past month)?
4. How much do the Gloucester store's customers think they would spend each Sunday if they were to shop at the store?
5. How do Gloucester store customers intend to get to the store to shop on a Sunday?

Gloucester Store: Estimated Proportion of Customers by Age and Gender

Age	Gender	Percentage	Age	Gender	Percentage
Under 20	Male	3	Under 20	Female	6
20 - 29	Male	6	20 - 29	Female	14
30 - 44	Male	9	30 - 44	Female	21
45 - 59	Male	7	45 - 59	Female	20
60 plus	Male	4	60 plus	Female	10

Source: Survey of Gloucester Store's Customers 199-

■ Task 5.2

Which one of the six methods of sampling (described in the information bank) should Liz use? Give one reason for your answer.

Making reference to the information in the table above describe the process that Liz will use to select her sample.

HELP See *Section 2: The Information Bank* How to sample: Unit 5.3, page 69

■ Task 5.3

As part of your answer to Task 5.2 you named the sampling method that Liz should use.

Give an example of when each of the remaining five methods of sampling described in the information bank might be used.

HELP See *Section 2: The Information Bank* How to sample: Unit 5.3, page 69; Sample size: Unit 5.4, page 74

You are now ready to tackle tasks 2.1 and 2.2 in Section 3

Unit 6: Liz designs an interview schedule

By the end of this unit you will:

- ❐ *be able to state the difference between an interview schedule and a questionnaire;*
- ❐ *know when to use interview, questionnaire and direct observation data collection techniques;*
- ❐ *be able to design an interview schedule and a questionnaire;*
- ❐ *understand and appreciate the importance of pilot testing.*

Scenario:

Liz has decided to collect the data from her sample using an interview schedule. She has already worked out exactly what data she needs to collect (Unit 4). Jemma Douglas, the Deputy Manager, shows her a questionnaire used 'a couple of years ago' to find out what staff felt about working at Brunley's Gloucester store. Jemma tells Liz that the questionnaire might be of some interest to her.

QAQ 6.1

The questionnaire that Jemma Douglas has given to Liz is shown below. Imagine that you are working for Brunley's Gloucester store and have just been given it to complete. Read through the questionnaire.

Do you think the questions are easy to understand or answer accurately?

Brunley's Gloucester Store: Staff Questionnaire

Feelings about work

1. Having regard to all the relevant facts, most employees like some aspects of their job at Brunley's, even though they dislike other facets.
   State here what you like about your job.
   State here what you dislike about it.

Working Conditions and payment

2. Your working conditions are unsatisfactory most of the time?

YES	
NO	

3. How long is your tea break? [ ] [ ] minutes
   e.g. for 10 minutes write [*1*] [*0*] minutes
4. In which way would you prefer to be paid?

BY CASH	
BY CHEQUE	
SOME OTHER	

Company Pension Scheme

5. If you are contracted in tick here.
6. How much does Brunley's contribute to your pension fund?

Canteen

7. What do you dislike about the canteen?
8. Do you think that the canteen gives poor value for money and provides a poor menu?

YES	
NO	

Your Union

8. Are you a member of the union YES
   If no please go to question 10 NO
9. Does your shop steward do all he can for you?
10. Do you think that Brunley's could arrange things so that it did not need to lay off workers during slack periods?

YES	
NO	
DON'T KNOW	

11. Do you favour clocking in for staff?

YES	
NO	

12. How many people would you say have left their jobs at Brunley's in the past month to take up other jobs?

0 – 5	
5 – 10	
10 – 15	
15 – 20	
20 – 25	

13. Would you like to see a strong fair minded union at Brunley's?

YES	
NO	

14. Which union are you a member of (if none write *'none'*)
15. As you all know, the law allows you to opt out of a Union.
    Do you think this is a good thing?

YES	
NO	

USING A COMPUTER FOR UNIT 6 TASKS

All the tasks can be done manually. However Task 6.5 will probably be easier if you can use a word processor. You will then be able to reword and rearrange the order of your questions with comparative ease.

■ Task 6.1

Liz has decided to collect the data from Brunley's customers using an interview schedule. Give one example of when Liz might use each of the following primary data collection methods whilst working at Brunley's Gloucester store.

1. Interview (using a check list of points).
2. Questionnaire.
3. Direct observation.

> **HELP**
> See *Section 2: The Information Bank*
> Introduction (Interview, Questionnaire, Direct observation): Unit 6.1, page 75

■ Task 6.2

Identify at least one example of each of the following types of question from the questionnaire (see above) given to Liz by Jemma Douglas.

1. Filter.
2. Open.
3. Pre-coded.
4. Self-coded.
5. Check.

> **HELP**
> See *Section 2: The Information Bank*
> Questionnaire and interview schedule design: an overview: Unit 6.2, page 76; Designing individual questions (Types of question): Unit 6.3, page 76

■ Task 6.3

List at least ten faults with the questionnaire given to Liz by Jemma Douglas (see above).

> **HELP**
> See *Section 2: The Information Bank*
> Designing individual questions (Wording of questions): Unit 6.3, page 78; Designing the survey form (Introducing the survey, The order and flow of questions, The layout of the survey): Unit 6.4, page 78

■ Task 6.4

What data will Liz need to find out about Brunley's customers to enable her to check that the sample is representative of all customers at the Gloucester store?

> **HELP**
> See *Section 2: The Information Bank*
> Checking the sample is representative: Unit 6.5, page 80
>
> Also reread the scenario in Unit 5, in particular the table 'Estimated Proportion of Customers by Age and Gender'.

■ Task 6.5

The answers to tasks 4.1 and 6.4 outline the data that Liz's interview schedule will need to collect.

Using these answers design an interview schedule to collect all the necessary data. Your interview schedule should include an introduction outlining the survey's purpose and giving assurances of confidentiality, and a variety of types questions.

> **HELP**
> Data the interview schedule needs to collect: Answers to tasks 4.1 and 6.4
>
> See *Section 2: The Information Bank*
> Designing individual questions: Unit 6.3,page 76; Designing the survey form: Unit 6.4, page 78; Checking the sample is representative: Unit 6.5, page 80

■ **Task 6.6**

Liz is not sure whether she should pilot test her interview schedule.

What advice would you give her? Give one reason for your answer.

HELP See *Section 2: The Information Bank*
Pilot testing: Unit 6.6, page 80

You are now ready to tackle the tasks and assignments in topic 2 of Section 3.

Unit 7: Liz starts to organise the data

By the end of this unit you will:

- ❐ *be able to distinguish between categorical and quantitative data;*
- ❐ *understand and apply the principles of good tabulation;*
- ❐ *be able to construct frequency distributions using tally marks;*
- ❐ *be able to construct tables for categorical data;*
- ❐ *be able to construct tables for continuous and grouped discrete quantitative data.*
- ❐ *be able to calculate percentages.*

Scenario:

Liz has administered her interview schedule (designed in Unit 6) and now has 120 completed forms to analyse. She decides to organise the responses into tables before showing them to the Deputy Manager, Jemma Douglas.

USING A COMPUTER FOR UNIT 7 TASKS

Task 7.4 can either be done manually or using a computer spreadsheet which has the facility to tabulate data. This is probably called 'crosstabs' or 'data distribution' in the manual. Task 7.5 is designed to be undertaken using a spreadsheet with the facility to cross tabulate data.

Answer to QAQ 5.1

Three factors which suggest Liz should only survey a proportion of those customers visiting the store are:

- There are over 10,000 customers, and Liz could not collect data from all of them on her own.
- Liz has only been given a small budget to cover printing and stationary. She could not afford to produce enough survey forms for 10,000 people.
- Liz has to have finished the survey and produced the results within two weeks. Even if she could collect data from 10,000 customers it would be impossible to analyse it and produce results in two weeks.

Answer to QAQ 6.1

Having read through the questionnaire you have probably found some of the questions difficult to understand or irrelevant. As an employee of Brunley's you would almost certainly have had difficulty in providing accurate answers to some of the questions.

■ Task 7.1

The table below has been constructed by Liz to show the competitors' supermarkets that Brunley's customers have shopped at on Sundays during the past month.

There are at least five errors in this table, what are they?

> **HELP** There are no numerical errors in this table.
>
> See *Section 2: The Information Bank* Principles of good tabulation: Unit 7.3, page 82

	Visited
Savers	22
None	50
Tesbury	18
Springfield's	10
Gaterose	30
Greenland's	8
Total customers	**120**

■ Task 7.2

Liz has noted down the responses to the question: 'Would you shop at this supermarket on a Sunday if it was open?' (see below).

Are these responses categorical data or quantitative data?

Construct a frequency distribution of this data using tally marks.

> **HELP** See *Section 2: The Information Bank* Introduction: Unit 7.1, page 81; Types of data: Unit 72, page 81; Tally marks: Unit 7.5, page 83

Y	Y	Y	Y	N	Y	N	Y	Y	N
N	N	Y	Y	N	D/K	Y	D/K	N	N
Y	D/K	N	Y	D/K	N	N	N	Y	Y
N	Y	N	Y	Y	Y	Y	D/K	D/K	D/K
Y	N	N	Y	Y	Y	Y	Y	D/K	N
N	N	N	Y	Y	Y	Y	N	N	N
Y	N	Y	Y	Y	N	N	Y	Y	Y
N	N	N	N	Y	Y	D/K	N	D/K	Y
Y	Y	Y	Y	Y	N	N	D/K	N	Y
N	N	Y	N	Y	Y	Y	N	D/K	N
Y	Y	Y	D/K	D/K	N	N	D/K	N	N
Y	N	Y	Y	Y	Y	Y	Y	Y	Y

N.B. Y = yes, N = no, D/K = don't know

■ Task 7.3

Add an extra column to the table you constructed for task 7.2 to show the percentage of customers who would shop on Sundays (including 'don't know').

> **HELP** See *Section 2: The Information Bank* Calculation of percentages: Unit 7.7, page 87

■ Task 7.4

Liz has noted down the responses to the question: 'How much do you think you would spend at this supermarket each Sunday if you were to shop here?' She has not included the responses from those customers who said that they would not shop at Brunley's on a Sunday.

> **HELP** See *Section 2: The Information Bank* Categorical and quantitative data: Unit 7.2, page 81; Tables for continuous and grouped discrete data: Unit 7.6, page 84

Are these responses categorical or quantitative data?

Use tally marks to construct a grouped frequency distribution of this data using ten equal class intervals with a width of £20. *(NB: the answers were recorded to the nearest pound.)*

10	25	17	80	90	130	180	**198**	20	100
20	30	45	56	70	60	20	30	40	70
60	23	21	19	50	**6**	70	33	44	21
38	42	55	65	90	35	35	40	76	13
15	28	30	46	50	50	25	55	70	45
20	67	89	20	27	11	58	15	25	24
30	28	50	67	15	80	64	59	15	63
140	130	30	46	19	93				

N.B. The highest and lowest data values are shown in bold and underlined.

COMPUTER TASK 7.5

Check that your computer spreadsheet has the facility to cross tabulate data. This is probably called 'crosstabs' or 'data distribution' in the manual.

HELP
See *Section 2: The Information Bank*
Cross tabulations: Unit 7.4, page 82

Enter the extract (below) of data from the survey into the spreadsheet and then use the appropriate spreadsheet commands to construct a cross tabulation.

Use the appropriate spreadsheet commands to label the table clearly.

The data on transport was collected from the question 'If this supermarket was open on a Sunday how would you usually get here?' (N.B. for the column labelled 'Gender' 1 = female, 2 = male; for the column labelled 'Transport' 1 = foot, 2 = car, 3 = bus, 4 = other).

N.B. For ease of data input row and column headings have been included on the extract of data. Although we could almost certainly construct this table more quickly by hand, this method is far quicker with large amounts of data.

	A	B
1	Gender	Transport
2	1	1
3	1	2
4	2	2
5	1	2
6	2	2
7	2	2
8	1	2
9	1	2
10	1	1
11	1	4
12	2	2
13	2	2
14	1	2
15	1	1
16	2	2
17	1	2
18	2	2
19	2	2
20	1	2
21	1	2

Unit 8: Liz prepares the findings for the Store Manager

By the end of this unit you will:

- ❒ *know when to use a bar chart;*
- ❒ *be able to recognise, interpret and construct simple bar charts, multiple bar charts, stacked (component) bar charts, and percentage component bar charts;*
- ❒ *be able to recognise and be aware of common misuses of bar charts.*

Scenario:

Liz has finished summarising the data from her customer survey as a series of tables (Unit 7). She finds Jemma Douglas, the Deputy Manager, and shows them to her.

'These are great', says Jemma 'but I doubt the Manager will like them. He prefers clear diagrams such as bar charts. If you do decide to use bar charts you had better make sure you add a few notes to each chart summarising what it shows.'

USING A COMPUTER FOR UNIT 8 TASKS

Tasks 8.4 and 8.6 can either be done manually or using the charting features of a computer spreadsheet. The use of a computer spreadsheet for these tasks will, with practice, enable you to achieve very high quality bar charts far more quickly than drawing them manually.

■ Task 8.1

Liz cannot remember whether a bar chart is the only sort of diagram that can be used for categorical and discrete data. She asks Jemma's advice. Draft Jemma's reply in not more than two sentences.

See *Section 2: The Information Bank*
Introduction to diagrams: Unit 8.1, page 88

Scenario:

Just before Jemma leaves she shows Liz a report which contains some diagrams. The report was produced by Brunley's Malvern store to illustrate the findings of their recent customer survey. Liz starts to read the report.

■ Task 8.2

The Bar Chart below is an extract from the Malvern store's customer survey report. Suggest at least three improvements to the chart.

See *Section 2: The Information Bank*
Introduction to diagrams: Unit 8.1, page 88

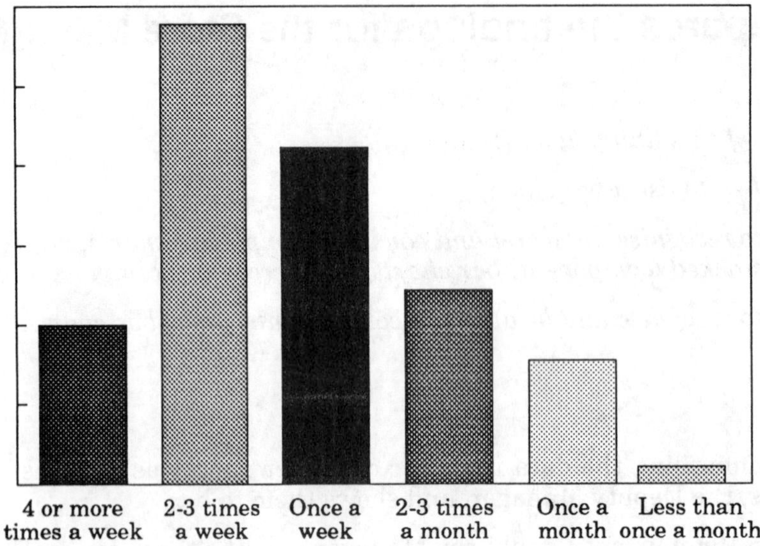

■ Task 8.3

The Bar Chart below is another extract from the Malvern store's customer survey report. Identify the way in which the chart distorts or misrepresents the data presented.

HELP See *Section 2: The Information Bank* Simple bar charts (Problems of scale): Unit 8.2, page 89

Percentage of Customers satisfied with Service at Stores

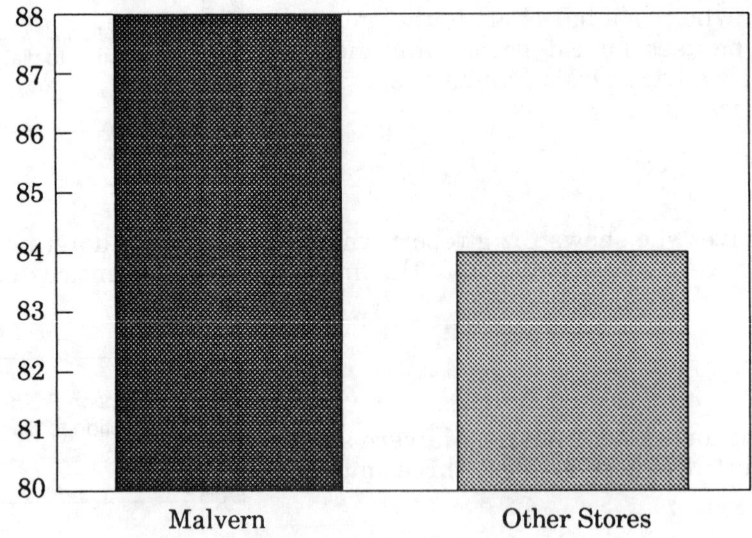

Source: Survey of Malvern Branch Customers 199-

Scenario:

Having decided that her diagrams will be better than those in the Malvern store's report Liz decides to start drawing her bar charts.

■ Task 8.4

The table (below) shows the competitors' stores visited by Brunley's customers on Sundays during the past month.

Draw a bar chart to illustrate this data and summarise what the bar chart shows in a few sentences.

> **HELP** See *Section 2: The Information Bank* Simple bar charts: Unit 8.2, page 89; Misuse of bar charts: Unit 8.6, page 94

Supermarkets at which Brunley's customers have shopped on Sundays over the past month

Supermarket	Frequency[1]
Gaterose	30
Greenland's	8
Savers	22
Springfield's	10
Tesbury	18
None	50
Total customers[1]	**120**

[1] Frequency will sum to more than the total customers as some customers visited more than one competitor's store

Source: Sample Survey of Customers 199-

■ Task 8.5

Liz looks at the table which combines the response to the question 'How often do you shop at this supermarket?' with the gender of the respondent (see below). She wants the reader to be able to compare the proportion of shoppers of each gender for each of the number of visits categories. She also wants to show the totals for each of the number of visits categories. She is unclear as to whether to draw a multiple bar chart, a percentage component bar chart or a stacked bar chart.

> **HELP** See *Section 2: The Information Bank* Multiple bar charts: Unit 8.3, page 91; Stacked bar charts: Unit 8.4, page 92; Percentage component bar charts: Unit 8.5, page 93

How would you advise Liz?

Give reasons for your answer.

Number of Visits to Brunley's Gloucester Store by Gender

Frequency	Gender	
	Male	**Female**
4 or more a week	0	11
2 to 3 a week	2	28
One a week	8	21
2 to 3 a month	9	11
One a month	6	11
Less than one a month	6	4
First time ever	2	1
Total	**33**	**87**

Source: Sample Survey of Customers 199-

■ **Task 8.6**

Liz decides to draw the chart to compare the proportion of shoppers of each gender for each of the number of visits categories, as outlined in task 8.5 (see above).

Draw this chart and summarise what it shows in a few sentences.

HELP See *Section 2: The Information Bank* Stacked bar charts: Unit 8.4, page 92

Unit 9: Liz shows the diagrams to the Deputy Manager

By the end of this unit you will:

- ❒ *know when to use pie charts and pictograms;*
- ❒ *be able to recognise, interpret and construct pie charts and pictograms;*
- ❒ *be aware of, and be able to recognise, common misuses of pie charts and pictograms.*

Scenario:

Jemma Douglas, the Deputy Manager, has just asked Liz how she is getting on with the diagrams. Liz shows her the bar charts she has drawn so far.

'These are great Liz, but have you considered how you are going to show all the data on the proportion of customers who would shop at Brunley's on Sundays? Maybe you could use a pie chart?' Jemma suggests.

The table of this data is shown below:

Percentage of Customers who would shop at Brunley's on Sundays (120 = 100%)

Shop on Sunday?	Percentage
Yes	50.8
No	36.7
Don't Know	12.5
Total	**100.0**

Source: Sample Survey of Customers 199-

USING A COMPUTER FOR UNIT 9 TASKS

Tasks 9.2 and 9.4 can either be done manually or using the charting features of a computer spreadsheet. The use of a computer spreadsheet for these tasks will, with practice, enable you to achieve very high quality pie charts and pictograms far more quickly than drawing them manually.

■ **Task 9.1**

Give one reason why you think Jemma suggested Liz used a pie chart to illustrate all the data on customers who would shop at Brunley's on Sundays (see table above).

HELP See *Section 2: The Information Bank* Pie charts: Unit 9.1, page 97

■ Task 9.2

Draw a pie chart to illustrate all the data on customers who would shop at Brunley's on Sundays (see table above).

Summarise what the pie chart shows in a few sentences.

> **HELP**
> See *Section 2: The Information Bank*
> Pie charts: Unit 9.1, page 97

■ Task 9.3

Liz and Jemma look at the comparative pie charts in the Malvern store's customer survey report (see extract below).

List two ways in which the reader is mislead by these charts.

> **HELP**
> See *Section 2: The Information Bank*
> Comparative pie charts: Unit 9.2, page 98;
> Misuse of pie charts: Unit 9.4, page 100

Feelings of Male and Female Customers about the Malvern Store

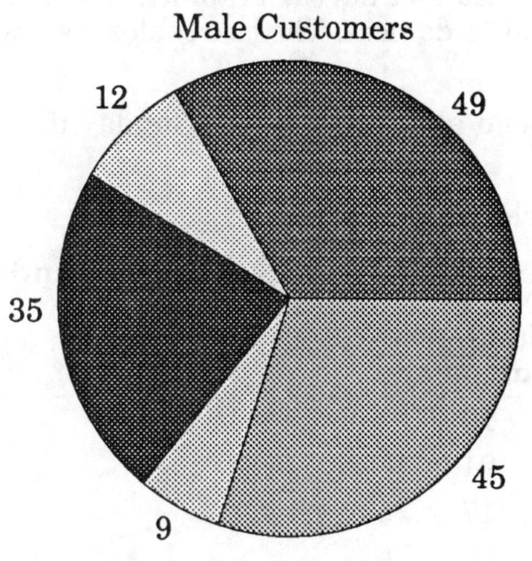

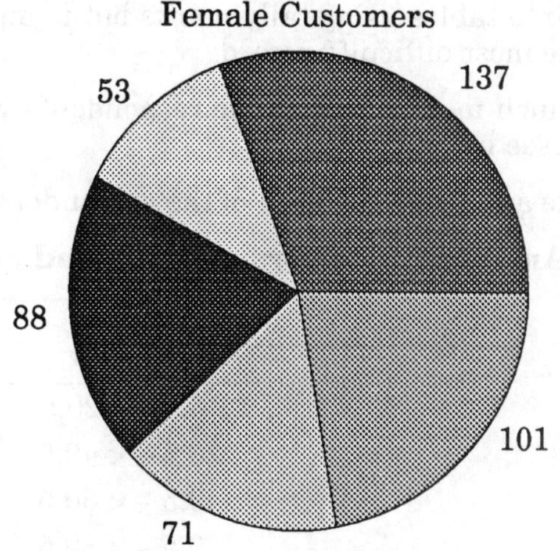

Scenario:

Liz shows Jemma the table 'Likely means of transport of customers who would shop at Brunley's on Sundays' (see below). Liz suggests that she illustrates this data using a pictogram, Jemma agrees.

Likely means of transport of Customers who would shop at Brunley's on Sundays
(N.B. excludes responses from those who would not shop on Sundays)

Transport	Frequency
Car	60
Foot	12
Bus	1
Other	3
Total	**76**

Source: Sample Survey of Customers 199-

■ Task 9.4

Draw a pictogram to illustrate the data of likely means of transport to Brunley's Gloucester store on Sundays (see table above).

Summarise what the pictogram shows in two sentences.

> **HELP**
> Use one picture to represent five people.
> See *Section 2: The Information Bank*
> Pictograms: Unit 9.3, page 99

Unit 10: Liz is unclear about histograms

By the end of this unit you will:

❐ *know when to use a histogram;*

❐ *be able to recognise, interpret and construct histograms for data with even and uneven class intervals;*

❐ *be able to recognise, and be aware of, common misuses of histograms.*

Scenario:

Liz is unsure how to present some of the data from her customer survey graphically. She has collated the data into tables using tally marks but is unsure what to do next. The two tables with which she is having the most difficulty record:

- how much money each of the respondents would spend at Brunley's each Sunday if they shopped there (see below).
- the age and gender of each of the respondents (see below).

Amount Customers would spend at Brunley's Gloucester Store each Sunday

Amount in £'s	Number of Customers
0.5 – < 20.5	16
20.5 – < 40.5	21
40.5 – < 60.5	17
60.5 – < 80.5	12
80.5 – < 100.5	5
100.5 – < 120.5	0
120.5 – < 140.5	3
140.5 – < 160.5	0
160.5 – < 180.5	1
180.5 – < 200.5	1

Source: Sample Survey of Customers 199-

Age by Gender of Customers shopping at Brunley's Gloucester Store

Age group	under 20	20 – 29	30 – 44	45 – 59	60 plus
Number of male respondents	3	7	10	8	5
Number of female respondents	8	17	26	24	12
Total respondents	**11**	**24**	**36**	**32**	**17**

Source: Sample Survey of Customers 199-

Scenario:

Gregory Woollons, the Store Manager, is passing so Liz asks him if he has any suggestions. Gregory looks at the tables.

'I see what you mean Liz, these are a bit complicated. As far as I can remember you need to use a histogram rather than a bar chart for this sort of data. It is something to do with relative frequency density. It was explained to me by a statistician friend when I showed him the Malvern store's customer survey report .'

QAQ 10.1

One of the tables above has unequal class widths, the other has equal class widths. Identify which table is which.

USING A COMPUTER FOR UNIT 10 TASKS

Task 10.3 can either be done manually or using the charting features of a computer spreadsheet. The use of a computer spreadsheet for this task will, with practice, enable you to achieve very high quality histograms far more quickly than drawing them manually. Task 10.4 involves constructing histograms with unequal class widths. A number of computer spreadsheets do not have this capability so check your spreadsheet manual prior to attempting this task.

■ Task 10.1

Give one reason why Gregory Woollons suggests Liz should use a histogram rather than a bar chart for the data in the tables above.

HELP
See *Section 2: The Information Bank*
The impact of data type: Unit 10.1, page 102;
Histograms for data with unequal class widths: Unit 10.3, page 104

Gregory Woollons also mentions relative frequency density. Why is it especially important to calculate this when constructing a histogram for data with unequal class widths?

■ Task 10.2

Liz has noticed a histogram based on similar data in the Malvern store's customer survey report (see below).

List at least two errors with this histogram.

HELP
See *Section 2: The Information Bank*
Histograms for data with unequal class widths: Unit 10.3, page 104

Age of Customers Shopping at Brunley's Malvern Store

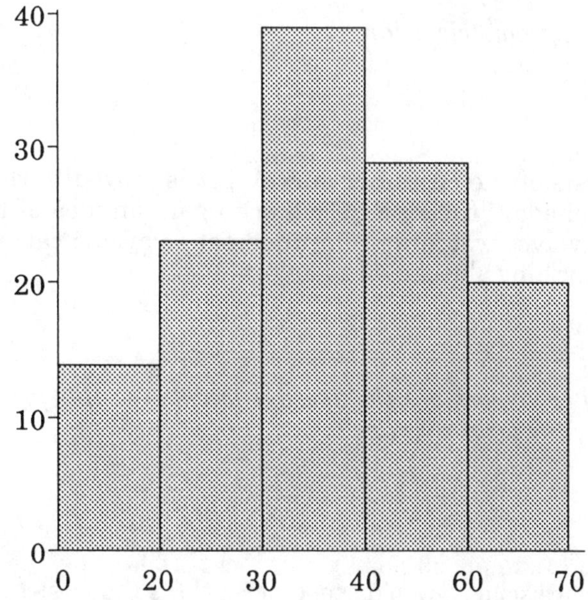

Source: Malvern Market Research Survey 199-

■ Task 10.3

Liz decides to draw a histogram of the data in the table 'Amount customers would spend at Brunley's Gloucester Store each Sunday' (see above).

Draw this histogram and summarise what it shows in a few sentences.

> **HELP**
> See *Section 2: The Information Bank*
> Histograms for data with equal class widths: Unit 10.2, page 102

■ Task 10.4

Draw two histograms using the data in the table 'Age by Gender of Customers Shopping at Brunley's Gloucester Store'. One histogram should be for male customers and the other for female customers.

What do these histograms tell you about the comparative age structure of male and female customers?

> **HELP**
> See *Section 2: The Information Bank*
> Histograms for data with unequal class widths: Unit 10.3, page 104

You are now ready to tackle the tasks and assignments in topic 3 of Section 3.

Unit 11: Liz spends a week with the Head Cashier

By the end of this unit you will:

- ❒ *know when to use the arithmetic mean;*
- ❒ *be able to calculate the arithmetic mean from raw data and from frequency distributions;*
- ❒ *know when to use the harmonic mean;*
- ❒ *be able to calculate the harmonic mean;*
- ❒ *know when to use the geometric mean;*
- ❒ *be able to calculate the geometric mean.*

Scenario:

After completing her analysis of the customer survey Liz is moved to the Accounts Department. For her first day she is told to 'shadow' the Head Cashier to gain an idea of the sort of work he does. The first part of the morning involves watching him undertake various calculations. Liz quickly becomes bored and asks if there is anything she can do to help.

QAQ 11.1

The Head Cashier asks Liz to work out the average weekly receipts for the past four weeks. What do you think he means by the term 'average'?

> Answer to QAQ 10.1
>
> The table titled 'Likely Amount Customers would spend at Brunley's Gloucester Store each Sunday' has equal class widths.
>
> The table titled 'Age by Gender of Customers shopping at Brunley's Gloucester Store' has unequal class widths.

USING A COMPUTER FOR UNIT 11 TASKS

Tasks 11.1, 11.2, 11.3, and 11.5 can be done manually or using a computer spreadsheet. However there is very little advantage for these tasks due to the small size of the data sets. You may need to use a computer spreadsheet for task 11.6 to work out the nth root as part of the calculation of the geometric mean.

■ Task 11.1

Using the data below calculate the mean receipts over the past four weeks.

> **HELP** See *Section 2: The Information Bank* Introduction to measures of central tendency; Unit 11.1, page 109; The arithmetic mean from raw data: Unit 11.2, page 109

Week 1	Week 2	Week 3	Week 4
£135,000	£151,000	£158,000	£165,000

■ Task 11.2

The Head Cashier gives Liz a table produced by the computerised Management Information System (see below). He asks Liz to work out the mean number of daily deliveries by external suppliers.

Calculate the answer.

> **HELP** See *Section 2: The Information Bank* The mean from a discrete frequency distribution: Unit 11.3, page 111

NUMBER OF DELIVERIES A DAY	NUMBER OF SUPPLIERS
1	25
2	15
3	7
4	2

■ Task 11.3

The Head Cashier tells Liz that the mean monthly receipts of the Gloucester Store are £609,000. He wants to know whether the Gloucester Store receipts are above or below average. He has received data from Brunley's Head Office detailing the receipts for 20 similar stores (see below). He asks Liz to work out the mean monthly receipts of these 20 stores.

> **HELP** See *Section 2: The Information Bank* The arithmetic mean from a grouped frequency distribution: Unit 11.4, page 112

Using the data below calculate the mean monthly receipts of these 20 stores.

Is their mean above or below the Gloucester store's mean monthly receipts?

Monthly Receipts in £,000's	Number of Stores
£450 – < £500	1
£500 – < £550	4
£550 – < £600	6
£600 – < £650	6
£650 – < £700	3

■ Task 11.4

After a while the Head Cashier becomes more friendly. He starts to explain how he uses statistics in his job. He tells Liz that he occasionally uses the harmonic mean and the geometric mean. Liz asks him to describe how these are used at Brunley's.

> **HELP** See *Section 2: The Information Bank* The mean of rates – the harmonic mean: Unit 11.5, page 113; The mean of proportional changes – the geometric mean: Unit 11.6, page 114

Suggest one example of how each of these means might be used by the Head Cashier.

■ Task 11.5

Brunley's has two home delivery vans which are mainly used for elderly customers' purchases. Each covers 500 miles a week. The driver of one van, Eddy, manages to get 25 miles per gallon, the other driver, George, only manages 20 miles per gallon. The Head Cashier asks Liz to use the harmonic mean to work out the average fuel consumption of the two vans.

> **HELP** See *Section 2: The Information Bank* The mean of rates – harmonic mean: Unit 11.5, page 113

Calculate the answer.

■ Task 11.6

The Head Cashier is keen to prove that, on average, sales at the Gloucester Branch have been rising steadily over the past 5 years. Each year he has calculated the percentage increase in sales over the previous year:

10.2%, 11.4%, 14.3%, 9.1%, 8.2%

> **HELP** If you intend to use a calculator for this task it will need to have an x^y key. Alternatively you can use a computer spreadsheet. See *Section 2: The Information Bank* The mean of proportional changes – geometric mean (including Helpful hints): Unit 11.6, page 114

He asks Liz to calculate the average percentage change over the past five years.

Decide which mean to calculate and then work out this average.

Unit 12: Liz meets the Personnel Officer and analyses employee data

By the end of this unit you will:

- ❒ *know when to use the median and the mode;*
- ❒ *be able to calculate the median and the mode from raw data and from a discrete frequency distribution;*
- ❒ *be able to calculate the median for a grouped frequency distribution using a cumulative frequency curve (ogive);*
- ❒ *understand the meaning of the terms normal, positive skew, and negative skew when referring to a frequency distribution;*
- ❒ *be able to interpret the mean, median and mode for a single data set.*

Answer to QAQ 11.1

The head cashier has used the term 'average' to describe the process of adding the weekly receipt figures for each of the past four weeks and then dividing them by the number of weeks (4).

Scenario:

Liz's final fortnight at the Gloucester store is with the Personnel Manager. After this her training will continue at Head Office in Cheltenham. She is looking forward to working with the Personnel Manager and analysing data relating to people. The Personnel Manager tells Liz that she will be helping with the analysis of a variety of employee data, mainly in preparation for the store's Annual Personnel Report.

USING A COMPUTER FOR UNIT 12 TASKS

Task 12.4 can either be done manually or using the charting features of a computer spreadsheet. The use of a computer spreadsheet for this task will, with practice, enable you to achieve a very high quality ogive far more quickly than drawing it manually.

Tasks 12.1 and 12.2 can also be done using a computer spreadsheet. This may include specific functions to calculate the median and the mode. However there is very little advantage for these tasks due to the small size of the data sets.

■ Task 12.1

The Personnel Manager needs to calculate the median salary of all store employees. At present the data is in alphabetical order. She asks Liz to calculate the median. Liz notes down the salary of the first six employees from the personnel database:

HELP
See *Section 2: The Information Bank*
The median from raw data: Unit 12.1, page 116

Name	*Annual Salary*
Denise	*£7,300*
Gillian	*£8,100*
Malcolm	*£13,800*
Martin	*£14,000*
Rosalie	*£7,300*
Sarah	*£7,400*

Use this data to calculate the median showing all your working.

■ Task 12.2

Data has also been extracted from the personnel database on the days usually requested as leave by all store employees.

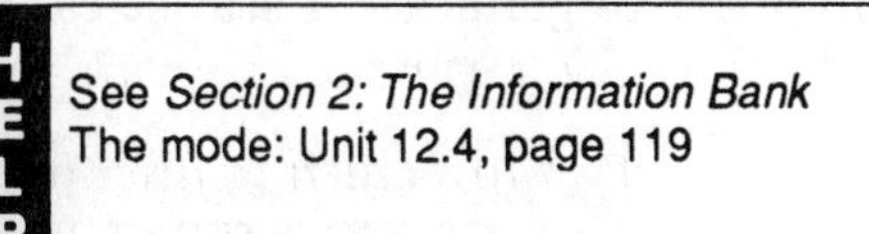
HELP
See *Section 2: The Information Bank*
The mode: Unit 12.4, page 119

GLOUCESTER STORE PERSONNEL DATABASE
LEAVE REQUESTS 199-

DAY	MON	TUES	WED	THUR	FRI	SAT
NO	200	120	100	90	150	100

Which 'average' should Liz and the Personnel Manager use to calculate the average day off? Give one reason for your answer.

Which day is the 'average' day off?

■ Task 12.3

The Personnel Manager tells Liz that it is likely that the union will be asking for an annual pay award based on 10% of average salary. Liz remembers that the majority of Brunley's Gloucester store employees are checkout operators and shelf stackers who earn low salaries.

> **HELP** See *Section 2: The Information Bank* The arithmetic mean from raw data: Unit 11.2, page 109; The Median from raw data: Unit 12.1, page 116; The Mode: Unit 12.4, page 119

Which 'average' should Brunley's use if they wish to keep the pay award to a minimum? Give one reason for your answer.

■ Task 12.4

Head Office has provided the Personnel Manager with a computer printout which contains the data on staff travel claims over the past month in a sample of Brunley's stores (see below). She knows the median staff travel claim at the Gloucester store is 10 miles but needs to state whether this is above or below the median for the sample of stores in her report.

> **HELP** See *Section 2: The Information Bank* The median from a grouped frequency distribution: Unit 12.3, page 118

TRAVEL CLAIM (MILES)	NUMBER OF EMPLOYEES (INCLUDING P-T)
0	2400
>0 – <10	1100
10 – < 20	900
20 – < 30	400
30 – < 40	280
40 – < 50	200

Draw an ogive and read off the median staff travel claim for the sample of Brunley's stores. Is it lower or higher than that of the Gloucester store?

■ Task 12.5

The Personnel Manager tells Liz that the personnel database can provide a statistical breakdown of some of the data held on employees. As Liz is interested she programs the computer to generate a statistical report on staff ages (see below).

> **HELP** See *Section 2: The Information Bank* Interpreting the mean, median and mode for a variable: Unit 12.5, page 120

GLOUCESTER STORE PERSONNEL DATABASE
STATISTICAL SUMMARY
EMPLOYEE AGE BY GENDER

GENDER	MEAN	MEDIAN	MODE
MALE	34	38	42
FEMALE	35	29	21

What do these statistics tell Liz about the distribution of the ages of males and females working for Brunley's?

You are now ready to tackle the tasks and assignments in topic 4 of Section 3.

Unit 13: Liz is transferred to Head Office, Transportation Department

By the end of this unit you will:

- *know when to use the following measures of dispersion: range, quartiles, deciles and percentiles;*
- *know how to calculate these measures of dispersion from raw and tabulated data;*
- *be able to interpret quartiles and the inter-quartile range in conjunction with the median for a data set.*

Scenario:

Liz has finished her three months initial training at the Gloucester Branch and has been transferred to the Head Office at Cheltenham. Fortunately for Liz she has not had to change her lodgings as Cheltenham is only 8 miles away. For the first two weeks at Head Office she has been placed in the Transportation Department working for John Johnson, the department's statistician.

John is in the process of considering a series of bids for the contract to transport Brunley's own label products from their warehouse to the stores. He asks Liz to help with some of the analyses based on data provided by the contractors. The first thing he needs to know is the extent to which the six bid prices (listed below) vary.

Contractor	Bid price
EJW	£29,500
Jay's Haulage	£21,000
Jeff's Haulage	£28,000
KAGR Transport Group	£31,000
Pete's Transport	£26,000
SA Ltd	£29,000

QAQ 13.1

Which contractor provides the lowest and which contractor provides the highest bid price?

USING A COMPUTER FOR UNIT 13 TASKS

Task 13.5 can either be done manually or using the charting features of a computer spreadsheet. The use of a computer spreadsheet for this task will, with practice, enable you to achieve a very high quality ogive far more quickly than drawing it manually.

Tasks 13.1 and 13.4 can also be done using a computer spreadsheet. This may include specific functions to calculate the median and the quartiles. However there is very little advantage for these tasks due to the small size of the data sets.

■ Task 13.1

John asks Liz to calculate the range of the six bid prices.

Undertake this calculation.

Using her initiative Liz also works out the median, lower and upper quartiles and the inter-quartile range.

Calculate these as well.

HELP: See *Section 2: The Information Bank* Introduction to measures of dispersion: Unit 13.1, page 123; The median from raw data: Unit 12.1, page 116; The range from raw data: Unit 13.2, page 123; Upper and lower quartiles and inter-quartile range from raw data: Unit 13.3, page 124

■ Task 13.2

John tells Liz that the median for last year's bid prices was £22,500, the lower quartile £18,900, and the upper quartile £24,100.

> **HELP** See *Section 2: The Information Bank*
> Interpreting the quartiles and median for a variable: Unit 13.7, page 128

Were these bid prices positively or negatively skewed?

Briefly justify your answer and explain what this means in terms of variation in the bid prices.

■ Task 13.3

Liz remembers something about percentiles and deciles but has forgotten how they divide the distribution. She asks John to remind her.

> **HELP** See *Section 2: The Information Bank*
> Percentiles and deciles: Unit 13.4, page 126

Briefly outline John's answer to Liz.

■ Task 13.4

The contractors EJW and SA Ltd have included data on the reliability of their lorry fleets in their contract bids. This has been summarised in a table (see below). This details the number of vehicles out of service over a 90 day period for each contractor.

> **HELP** See *Section 2: The Information Bank*
> The median from a discrete frequency distribution: Unit 12.2, page 117; Quartiles and inter-quartile range from a discrete frequency distribution: Unit 13.5, page 126

John thinks that the reliability data might aid the decision to whom to award the contract. He asks Liz to calculate the quartiles, inter-quartile range and the median number of lorries out of service for each contractor.

Undertake these calculations.

Which contractor's lorry fleet appears to be the most reliable?

Fleet Reliability of EJW Contractors and SA Ltd

Number of lorries out of service	Number of days occurred (EJW Contractors)	Number of days occurred (SA Ltd)
0	21	47
1	30	22
2	20	10
3	11	9
4	5	2
5	3	0

Source: Contractors' bids 199-

> Answer to QAQ 13.1
>
> The contractor with the lowest bid price is Jay's Haulage at £21,000. The contractor with the highest bid price is KAGR Transport Group at £31,000.

■ Task 13.5

John has received a letter and some data from a friend who works for a rival supermarket chain of a similar size to Brunley's (see below). He tells Liz the data will help to put the small number of bids they have received 'in some sort of context.' The data summarises the bids made by transport contractors for keeping the rival company's stores stocked.

> **HELP**
> Median and inter-quartile range of bids received by Brunley's: answer to task 13.1.
>
> See *Section 2: The Information Bank* Quartiles and inter-quartile range from a grouped frequency distribution: Unit 13.6, page 127

John asks Liz to calculate the median, lower and upper quartiles and the inter-quartile range using an ogive.

Undertake these calculations.

Are the median and inter-quartile range of these bids larger or smaller than those received by Brunley's?

Tesbury Supermarkets
Head Office • Bristol • Avon
Telephone: 0272 – 12345678

John Johnson
Departmental Statistician
Transportation Department
Brunley's Supermarkets
Head Office
Cheltenham
Gloucestershire

29th March 199-

Dear John,

As promised please find below the data on our recent transport contract bids. I can't give you the actual bid prices as the data is confidential. However I hope this is of some use.

Value of bid	Number of contractors bidding
£18,000 - < £20,000	1
£20,000 - < £22,000	1
£22,000 - < £24,000	2
£24,000 - < £26,000	3
£26,000 - < £28,000	5
£28,000 - < £30,000	0
£30,000 - < £32,000	1
£32,000 - < £34,000	1

I look forward to seeing you and Jean at the next Grocer's Benevolent Dance.

Kindest regards,

Mike

Unit 14: Liz analyses accident data using the standard deviation

By the end of this unit you will:

- ❒ *know when to use the following measures of dispersion: variance, standard deviation and coefficient of variation;*
- ❒ *know how to, and be able to calculate the variance and standard deviation from raw and tabulated data;*
- ❒ *be able to interpret the standard deviation in conjunction with the mean.*

Scenario:

John Johnson the Transportation Department's statistician, continues working on the bids for the Brunley's transport contract. He receives a short memo from the department's manager about the level of insurance claims made by staff with company cars (see below). As he is 'up to his ears in contract bids' John asks Liz to have a look at it.

BRUNLEY'S SUPERMARKETS

Memorandum

From: Alf Hattersley, Head of Transportation
To: John Johnson, Transportation Department Statistician
Subject: Insurance Claims - Company Cars
Date: 6th April 199-

I am worried by last month's high variation in claims for collisions which were the faults of 3rd parties. The three year mean value is £1115.88 with a standard deviation of £317.87. Please can you undertake a comparison. I attach copies of the relevant data.

Alf

Alf Hattersley

Enc.

USING A COMPUTER FOR UNIT 14 TASKS

Tasks 14.1 and 14.2 can either be undertaken by hand or using a computer spreadsheet. The calculations involved are, with practice, quicker and less prone to error using a spreadsheet.

■ Task 14.1

Liz examines the claims data which has been attached to the memo. The first table (below) shows claims for the previous month. As the data appears to be normally distributed Liz decides to calculate the standard deviation.

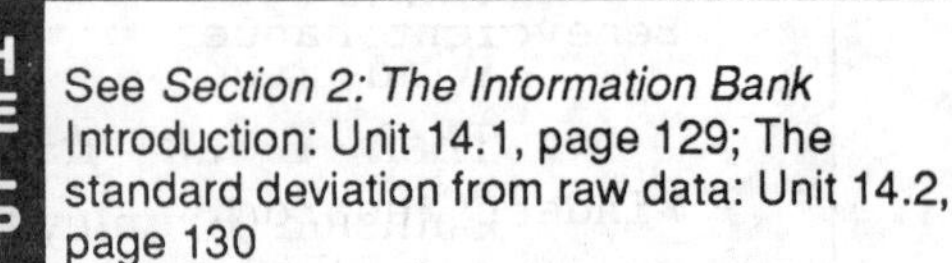

Give one reason why you think Liz calculated the standard deviation rather than the variance.

Calculate the mean and the standard deviation for this data.

How do these differ from those of three year average mentioned in the memo?

Claims for Collision (3rd party's fault) for March 199-

Vehicle	Amount claimed
J123 ABC	£1504.50
K234 BBC	£544.85
J345 CBC	£1275.00
K59 CBC	£1217.99
J19 XBC	£645.24
J452 MBC	£1501.45

Source: Brunley's Transportation Department

■ Task 14.2

Liz notices that a table which groups the data by claim category and size of claim for car park collisions is also attached.

Assume that this data is normally distributed.

Calculate the mean and the standard deviation for this data.

HELP See *Section 2: The Information Bank* Standard deviation from a discrete frequency distribution: Unit 14.3, page 132; Standard deviation from a grouped frequency distribution: Unit 14.4, page 134; Problems when calculating the standard deviation for large numbers: Unit 14.5, page 136; Interpreting the standard deviation for normally distributed data: Unit 14.6, page 136

What do these figures tell you about 95% of claims for car park collisions?

Fleet Vehicle Insurance Claims for Car Park Collisions (3 years ending March 199-)

Value of claim	Number of claims
£0 – < £250	3
£250 – < £500	11
£500 – < £750	13
£750 – < £1,000	3
£1,000 – < £1,250	1

Source: Brunley's Transportation Department

■ Task 14.3

The Transportation Manager has attached a table recording the mean and standard deviation for all insurance claims by type of claim over the past three years (see below). Assume that the data for each type of claim is normally distributed.

HELP See *Section 2: The Information Bank* The coefficient of variation: Unit 14.7, page 140

Calculate the coefficient of variation for each of the claim types listed in the table below. Which claim type has the least variation and which has the greatest variation?

Fleet Vehicle Insurance Claims by type for three years ending March 199-

Claim type	Mean	Standard Deviation
Windscreen	£178.25	£6.70
Theft / Break – in	£1984.78	£796.89
Collision (Brunley's fault)	£915.42	£280.76
Collision (3rd party's fault)	£1115.88	£317.87
Car – park	£528.23	£226.08

Source: Brunley's Transportation Department

You are now ready to tackle the tasks and assignments in topic 5 of Section 3.

Unit 15: Liz moves to the Corporate Sales Department

By the end of this unit you will:

- *understand what is meant by a time series;*
- *be able to distinguish and explain the main features of a time series: long term trend, seasonal variation, cyclical fluctuations and residual influences;*
- *be able to determine the trend by calculating a moving average.*

Scenario:

After two weeks in the Transportation Department Liz moves to the Corporate Sales Department (still at Head Office). Here she is given the corporate sales report for the past 4 years and left to her own devices as the person detailed to look after her is on sick leave!

CORPORATE SALES REPORT FINANCIAL REVIEW PAGE 6

Quality and Earnings
by
Ian Jones, Finance Director

The trading transformation of Brunley's is reflected in our financial achievements over the past four years. Over the past four years our profits have increased by more than the rate of inflation. This performance has meant that we have been able to increase the dividend to our shareholders for the seventh year running.

The performance for the last financial year was good with operating profits increasing consistently once seasonal variations have been taken into account. As in previous years sales were lowest in the April to June quarter and then rose steadily until Christmas. The January to March quarter experienced slightly lower sales than in October to December. However these were not as severe as we had expected.

The long term sales trend shows that, despite our competitors experiencing a decline in sales, Brunley's sales are still experiencing an underlying increase year after year. This is undoubtedly due to the hard work of all Brunley's employees and our ability to deliver the products the customers want at a price they can afford. We look forward to this continuing over the next five years.

BRUNLEY'S SUPERMARKETS

QAQ 15.1

Page six of the Financial Report (above) discusses recent trends in Brunley's sales over the past four years.

Find the terms 'seasonal variations' (paragraph two) and 'long term trend' (paragraph three). What do you think these terms mean in this report?

USING A COMPUTER FOR UNIT 15 TASKS

Task 15.2 can be either undertaken manually or using a computer spreadsheet. The calculation of the moving average is, with practice, quicker and less prone to error using a spreadsheet. The use of a spreadsheet's charting features will, with practice, enable you to achieve very high quality line graph far more quickly than drawing it manually.

■ Task 15.1

As Liz continues to read the report she is surprised that there is no mention of 'cyclical fluctuations' and 'residual influences'.

Give one example of a cyclical fluctuation and one example of a residual influence that could affect sales at a Brunley's supermarket.

HELP See *Section 2: The Information Bank* Introduction to time series: Unit 15.1, page 141; Simple Time Series (Cyclical fluctuations, Residual influences): Unit 15.2, page 141

■ Task 15.2

As Liz continues to read through the report she comes across a table of operating profit data (see below). As she feels the trend is not clear she decides to determine what it is by calculating the moving average.

HELP See *Section 2: The Information Bank* Determining the trend (moving averages): Unit 15.3, page 144

Undertake this calculation.

Plot the raw data and the moving average on the same line graph.

Describe the overall trend in one sentence.

N.B. If you are using a computer spreadsheet save your worksheet for use in Unit 16.

CORPORATE SALES REPORT OPERATING PROFITS PAGE 17

Table 12.1 Operating Profits in £'s million 1989 to 1993

Year	Quarter 1	Quarter 2	Quarter 3	Quarter 4
1989		£22.7	£28.3	£31.4
1990	£27.3	£23.8	£30.0	£30.8
1991	£28.9	£25.6	£31.5	£33.8
1992	£31.0	£27.4	£36.0	£38.5
1993	£34.1			

BRUNLEY'S SUPERMARKETS

Unit 16: Liz forecasts future operating profits using time series data

By the end of this unit you will:

- ❒ *understand the need for forecasting in business.*
- ❒ *be able to forecast the trend from the moving average.*
- ❒ *understand and be able to explain the term seasonally adjusted.*
- ❒ *be able to forecast taking seasonal variations into account.*

Scenario:

On her second day in the Corporate Sales Department Liz is pleased to notice that her mentor for the next few weeks has returned from sick leave. Tim Price greets Liz and after a brief chat explains the immediate task.

Tim explains that, although the Corporate Sales Report contains data on quarterly operating profits over the past four years, it does not contain predictions of future operating profits. For the next Brunley's shareholders' meeting the Finance Director has requested that a prediction of future quarterly operating profits over the next two years is made available to the shareholders.

USING A COMPUTER FOR UNIT 16 TASKS

Tasks 16.1 and 16.4 can be either undertaken manually or using a computer spreadsheet. The calculations involved are, with practice, quicker and less prone to error using a spreadsheet. The use of a spreadsheet's charting features will, with practice, enable you to achieve a very high quality line graph far more quickly than drawing it manually.

■ Task 16.1

Liz remembers she has already calculated the moving average from the operating profit data (see answer to task 15.2). She knows she can forecast future sales based on these calculations.

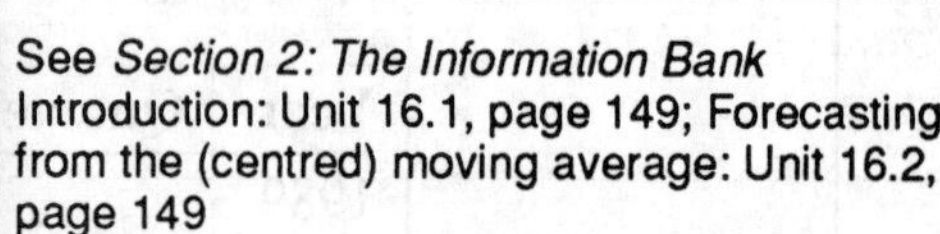

Use the answer to task 15.2 as your base from which to calculate the long term trend and forecast future quarterly sales until the last quarter of 1994.

N.B. If you saved your computer spreadsheet from task 15.2 you can continue on the same worksheet for this task.

Answer to QAQ 15.1

Seasonal variations describe movements that recur year after year in the same quarters. In this case the Finance Director was describing seasonal variations in operating profits.

The long term trend is the underlying movement over a number of years. In this case the Finance Director was describing long term trend in value of sales.

■ Task 16.2

See *Section 2: The Information Bank*
Taking seasonal variation into account: Unit 16.3, page 151

Liz shows her forecasts to Tim who comments

'That's all very clever Liz, but what do we say when the shareholders ask about seasonal variations?' Liz thinks for a few minutes and replies

'Don't worry, I'll seasonally adjust the data and then forecast using the seasonal variation.' She then goes on to explain to Tim what is meant by seasonally adjusted data.

In one paragraph write what you think Liz would have said.

■ Task 16.3

HELP

See *Section 2: The Information Bank*
Forecasting using the seasonal variation: Unit 16.5, page 154; Forecasting from the (centred) moving average: Unit 16.2, page 149

Tim listens to Liz's explanation and asks

'What do you mean by forecasting using seasonal variation?' Liz decides to explain by contrasting forecasts using seasonal variation with those using the moving average.

What is the main difference between these two methods of forecasting?

■ Task 16.4

HELP

See *Section 2: The Information Bank*
Taking seasonal variation into account: Unit 16.3, page 151; Seasonally adjusting the trend: Unit 16.4, page 153; Forecasting using the seasonal variation: Unit 16.5, page 154

Tim and Liz decide that the best way to show shareholders predicted operating profits is by using a line graph with a couple of sentences of explanation.

Use the operating profit data from table 12.1 of the Corporate Sales Report (Unit 15) to calculate the corrected seasonal variation.

Forecast operating profits for the next two years using this seasonal variation.

Present the data as a line graph showing actual and predicted operating profits on the same graph.

Explain what the line graph shows in one or two sentences.

You are now ready to tackle the tasks and assignments in topic 6 of Section 3.

Unit 17: Liz investigates likely sales of a new snack

By the end of this unit you will:

- ❒ *be able to recognise positive, negative, and perfect correlation from a scatter graph;*
- ❒ *know when to use Spearman's Rank Correlation Coefficient and Pearson's Product Moment Correlation Coefficient;*
- ❒ *be able to calculate and interpret Spearman's Rank Correlation Coefficient and Pearson's Product Moment Correlation Coefficient.*

Scenario:

Liz has completed the sales forecasts so Tim Price, Liz's mentor in the Corporate Sales Department, introduces the next project. Brunley's has decided to sell a new kind of snack in a number of their stores. Early trials at 10 of the stores suggest that sales of this snack are related to the sales of dry roast peanuts. The data is shown below:

Sales of Dry Roast Peanuts and New Snack

Trial Store	Dry Roast Peanuts Sales ('000s)	New Snack Sales ('000s)
Malvern	1.80	1.95
Worcester	3.50	3.20
Kidderminster	0.20	0.35
Hereford	3.70	3.60
Cheltenham	4.50	5.30
Tewkesbury	2.00	1.80
Gloucester	4.00	3.50
Stroud	1.50	1.10
Cirencester	2.80	2.70
Evesham	0.60	0.10
Total	**24.60**	**23.60**

Source: Brunley's Trials in 10 Stores 199-

QAQ 17.1

Liz looks at the sales data (above) and notices that there is a relationship between dry roast peanut and new snack sales.

Describe this relationship in one sentence.

Into which stores would you recommend Brunley's introduce the new snack?

USING A COMPUTER FOR UNIT 17 TASKS

Tasks 17.2 and 17.3 can either be undertaken manually or using a spreadsheet. The calculations involved are, with practice, quicker and less prone to error using a spreadsheet. The use of a spreadsheet's charting features will, with practice, enable you to achieve a high quality scatter graph far more quickly than drawing it manually.

■ Task 17.1

Tim asks Liz how she would test the strength of this relationship. Liz replies that she could use either Spearman's Rank Correlation Coefficient or Pearson's Product Moment Correlation Coefficient to test the strength of the relationship between these two variables.

HELP
See *Section 2: The Information Bank*
Introduction to relationships between variables: Unit 17.1, page 155; Spearman's rank correlation coefficient: Unit 17.3, page 157; Pearson's product moment correlation coefficient: Unit 17.4, page 160

Is Liz correct?

Give one reason for your answer.

■ Task 17.2

Liz decides to calculate Pearson's Product Moment Correlation Coefficient for this data.

HELP
See *Section 2: The Information Bank*
Types of relationship between two variables: Unit 17.2, page 156; Pearson's product moment correlation coefficient: Unit 17.4, page 160

Draw a scatter graph of this data and undertake the calculation.

What does the correlation coefficient you have calculated tell you about the relationship between sales of the two products?

Does this support your answer to QAQ 17.1?

■ Task 17.3

Tim asks Liz to explain rank correlation to him. Liz searches for some suitable data and finds the table below in a report:

> **HELP**
> See *Section 2: The Information Bank*
> Spearman's rank correlation coefficient:
> Unit 17.3, page 157

Top ten selling fruits at the Malvern and Worcester Stores 199-

Product	Malvern	Worcester
Apples	1	1
Bananas	2	4
Pears	3	2
Oranges	4	3
Grapefruit	5	5
Melons	6	7
Grapes	7	6
Kiwi Fruits	8	9
Cherries	9	8
Fresh Figs	10	10

Source: Store Returns

Calculate Spearman's Rank Correlation Coefficient using this data.

What does the correlation coefficient tell Tim and Liz about sales of fruit at the two stores?

Unit 18: Liz predicts likely sales

By the end of this unit you will:

- ❐ *know when to use regression;*
- ❐ *be able to calculate and interpret a regression equation;*
- ❐ *understand and be able to explain the terms interpolation and extrapolation;*
- ❐ *be able to calculate and interpret the coefficient of determination.*

Scenario:

Tim Price is very pleased with Liz's work on the New Snack Product and the way she uses statistics. He asks her if she would use her statistical knowledge to try and predict the annual turnover of new stores. Liz asks him what data is available. Tim shows Liz the following extract from the Corporate Sales Report:

CORPORATE SALES REPORT TURNOVER STATISTICS PAGE 26

Table 18.4 Mean Weekly Turnover by Floor Area 199- to 199-

Store	Floor area ('000 sq. ft)	Turnover (£'000s)
Monmouth	7.990	71.9
Bristol	18.500	145.0
Ross on Wye	5.850	46.8
Chippenham	4.000	28.0
Trowbridge	3.075	24.6
Bath	14.500	199.0
Wells	3.400	27.2
Bridgewater	9.200	82.8
Swindon	12.000	179.0
Marlborough	2.100	16.8

Source: Store Returns

BRUNLEY'S SUPERMARKETS

QAQ 18.1

Examine the extract from the Corporate Sales Report above.

Do you think that floor area is more likely to affect the level of sales of a store, or that the level of sales is more likely to affect the floor area of a store?

USING A COMPUTER FOR UNIT 18 TASKS

Tasks 18.3 and 18.4 can either be undertaken by hand or using a computer spreadsheet. The calculations involved are, with practice, quicker and less prone to error using a spreadsheet. The use of a spreadsheet's charting features will, with practice, enable you to achieve a very high quality scatter graph far more quickly than drawing it manually.

■ Task 18.1

Liz decides to use regression to predict likely sales. She tells Tim that the regression equation will be of the form $y = a + bx$.

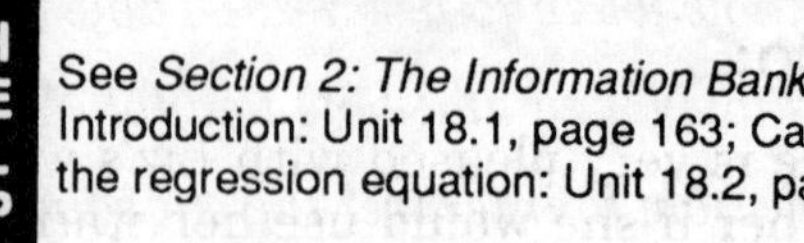

Explain the meaning of each of the letters in this equation using a diagram.

How do the letters y and x relate to the data in the extract from the Corporate Sales Report (above)?

Answer to QAQ 17.1

The relationship the data shows is that as sales of dry roast peanuts increase so do sales of the new snack. You have probably recommended that Brunley's introduce the new snack into stores which already have high sales of dry roast peanuts.

■ Task 18.2

Liz tells Tim that the regression equation, once calculated, will be 'fine for interpolation, but a bit dodgy for extrapolation.'

> **HELP**
> See *Section 2: The Information Bank*
> Interpreting the regression equation: Unit 18.3, page 165

With reference to the data in the extract of the Corporate Sales Report (above) explain in two or three sentences what is meant by the terms 'interpolation' and 'extrapolation'.

Give one reason for Liz's comment.

■ Task 18.3

Tim asks Liz to predict the value of weekly sales for two stores that Brunley's are to open shortly. Their floor areas are 8,000 square feet and 15,000 square feet. Liz decides to plot a scatter graph of the floor area and turnover data first and then calculate the regression equation.

> **HELP**
> See *Section 2: The Information Bank*
> Scatter graph: Unit 17.4, page 160;
> Calculating the regression equation: Unit 18.2, page 163; Interpreting the regression equation: Unit 18.3, page 165

Use the data in the extract from the Corporate Sales Report (above) to plot a scatter graph; then calculate the regression equation.

Use the regression equation to predict the value of sales for floor areas of 8,000 and 15,000 square feet.

■ Task 18.4

Liz also calculates the coefficient of determination for her regression equation.

> **HELP**
> N.B. you have already calculated the majority of the components for the calculation of the coefficient of determination in task 18.3.
> See *Section 2: The Information Bank*
> Calculating and interpreting the coefficient of determination: Unit 18.5, page 166

Calculate the coefficient of determination.

Describe what this tells you about your regression equation in one or two sentences.

Unit 19: Liz moves to the Marketing and Promotions Department

By the end of this unit you will:

- ❒ *know when to use and be able to calculate a chi square test for a frequency distribution;*
- ❒ *know when to use and be able to calculate a chi square test for a contingency table;*
- ❒ *know when and how to apply Yate's correction;*
- ❒ *be able to interpret the chi square statistic.*

Scenario:

After a month in the Corporate Sales Department Liz's training takes her to the Marketing and Promotions Department (at Head Office). The first task she is given involves analysing the impact on sales of a recent trial promotion for Brunley's own brand mayonnaise at ten stores. Data has been collected on the number of sales of own brand mayonnaise before and after the promotion period. This data has been recorded as a table (see below).

Number of Sales of Own Brand Mayonnaise at 10 stores

Before promotion	After promotion	Total
230	320	**550**

Source: Mayonnaise promotion data 199-

Data has also been purchased from a Market Research Company on the social class of customers and whether they purchase salad cream or mayonnaise (see below). Brunley's hope to use this information to enable them to target their future promotions to different groups of their customers. Liz is told that she will also be expected to analyse this data.

Number of purchasers of Salad Cream and Mayonnaise by Social Class

	Salad Cream	Mayonnaise	Total
Upper class	60	90	150
Middle class	175	210	385
Lower class	220	150	370
Total	**455**	**450**	**905**

Source Market Research Company 199-

QAQ 19.1

Examine the table recording the number of sales of own brand mayonnaise (above).

What was the impact of the promotion on the number of sales of own brand mayonnaise?

QAQ 19.2

Examine the table recording the number of purchasers of salad cream and mayonnaise by social class (above).

Are purchasers of salad cream more likely to be upper or lower class?

Are purchasers of mayonnaise more likely to be upper or lower class?

Scenario:

Prior to introducing their own brand mayonnaise to the rest of the stores, the Marketing and Promotions Department need to know if the trial promotion has resulted in a significant increase in the number of sales. Liz is asked to calculate whether the increase in number of sales of own brand mayonnaise is significant. She decides to use the chi square test.

USING A COMPUTER FOR UNIT 19 TASKS

Tasks 19.1 and 19.3 can either be undertaken by hand or using a computer spreadsheet. The calculations involved in task 19.3 are, with practice, quicker and less prone to error using a spreadsheet.

Answer to QAQ 18.1

Floor area is more likely to affect the level of sales than the other way around. This means that sales are, at least partially, dependent upon the floor area.

■ Task 19.1

State Liz's null hypothesis and hypothesis.

Use the data in the table 'Number of Sales of Own Brand Mayonnaise at 10 stores' to calculate the chi square statistic using Yate's correction.

> **HELP** See *Section 2: The Information Bank* Introduction: Unit 19.1, page 168; Chi square test for frequency distributions: Unit 19.2, page 168; Problems with the chi square test (Yate's correction): Unit 19.3, page 170; Critical values of Chi Square: Appendix 4

Brunley's will only introduce the promotion into their other stores if they can be at least 95% certain of it altering the number of sales.

Should Brunley's introduce this promotion to their other stores?

■ Task 19.2

Give one reason why Liz needed to use Yate's correction in the calculation of the chi square statistic for task 19.1.

> **HELP** See *Section 2: The Information Bank* Problems with the chi square test (and Yate's correction): Unit 19.3, page 170

■ Task 19.3

The Marketing and Promotions Manager asks Liz if there is a significant relationship between the social class of potential customers and whether they purchase salad cream or mayonnaise.

> **HELP** See *Section 2: The Information Bank* Chi square test for two variable tables: Unit 19.4, page 170; Critical values of Chi Square: Appendix 4

State Liz's null hypothesis and hypothesis.

Calculate the chi square statistic using the data in the table 'Number of purchasers of Salad Cream and Mayonnaise by Social Class'.

Brunley's will only target their mayonnaise promotion by social class if they can be at least 95% certain that mayonnaise purchases are associated with certain social classes.

Should Brunley's target this promotion by social class?

If the answer is 'yes', which social classes do you think they should target?

You are now ready to tackle the tasks and assignments in topic 7 of Section 3.

Unit 20: Liz is asked to examine changes in purchasing patterns

By the end of this unit you will:

- *understand how simple index numbers can be used in business;*
- *be able to calculate and interpret simple quantity indices, simple price indices and value or expenditure indices;*
- *understand the importance of selecting a suitable base period for calculating indices.*

Scenario:

The Marketing and Promotions Manager shows Liz a recent market research report which discusses trends in sales of a number supermarket goods over the past eight years. These include electrical items as well as more traditional supermarket goods such as fruit and vegetables and frozen foods. He asks Liz to examine the sales data for blank video tapes (see extract below) to discover if the trend in sales experienced by Brunley's is similar to the national trend.

M.J. MARKET RESEARCH SUPERMARKET PRODUCT SALES 1986 – 1993 page 59

Table 19.8: Index of number of video tapes sold in supermarkets (1986 = 100)

	1986	1987	1988	1989	1990	1991	1992	1993*
Pre-recorded	100	101	103	104	109	115	120	121
Blank	100	102	103	105	108	111	114	115

* 1993 figures are estimates

QAQ 20.1

Examine the table 'Index of number of video tapes sold in supermarkets' from the Market Research Report (see extract).

Do you think that the number of blank video tapes sold in supermarkets over the period 1986 – 1993 has increased or decreased?

■ Task 20.1

Liz discovers that Brunley's stores have sold blank video tapes since September 1984. She notes down their sales for the years 1984 to 1992 from the sales database (see below) and calculates the quantity index for each year using 1985 as the base year.

HELP See *Section 2: The Information Bank* Index numbers in business: Unit 20.1, page 174; Selecting a suitable base period: Unit 22.1, page 187; Simple quantity index: Unit 20.2, page 174

'84 = 45,000; '85 = 171,000 '86 = 175,000; '87 = 180,000; '88 = 190,000;
'89 = 195,000; '90 = 200,000; '91 = 206,000; '92 = 213,000

Give one reason why you think Liz has decided not to use 1984 as the base year.

Calculate the quantity index for each year using 1985 as the base year.

■ Task 20.2

Liz decides to compare the quantity index for sales of blank video tapes in Brunley's stores with that for sales in all supermarkets. She notices that the base year for the index numbers in the market research report is 1986.

HELP See *Section 2: The Information Bank* Simple quantity index: Unit 20.2, page 174

Recalculate the index numbers for blank video tape sales in Brunley's stores for each year (see task 20.1 for data) using 1986 as the base year.

Have sales of blank video tapes at Brunley's stores increased more or less rapidly than those at all supermarkets since 1986?

Answer to QAQ 19.1

The number of sales of own brand mayonnaise had increased by 90 after the promotion.

Answer to QAQ 19.2

Purchasers of salad cream are more likely to be lower class.

Purchasers of mayonnaise are more likely to be upper class.

■ Task 20.3

Liz notices that the report also contains data on the prices of other products such as baked beans (see extract below). She wonders whether the price of Brunley's own brand baked beans has increased more or less rapidly since 1988 than that of the market leader, Hugo's baked beans.

HELP
See *Section 2: The Information Bank*
Simple price index: Unit 20.3, page 174

Using 1988 as the base year calculate the price index for 1992.

Which brand of beans has experienced the largest price increase over the period 1988 – 1992?

M.J. MARKET RESEARCH SUPERMARKET PRODUCT SALES 1986 – 1993 page 60

Table 20.1: Baked bean prices

	1986	1987	1988	1989	1990	1991	1992	1993*
Brunley's	–	–	18p	21p	23p	25p	27p	28p
Hugo's	–	–	24p	25p	27p	30p	32p	35p

* 1993 figures are estimates

■ Task 20.4

The average Brunley's customer purchased 68 cans of Brunley's baked beans in 1988 and 49 cans in 1992. They purchased 36 cans of Hugo's baked beans in 1988 and 27 in 1992.

HELP
See *Section 2: The Information Bank*
Value or expenditure index: Unit 20.4, page 176

Using the data on baked bean prices from the Market Research Report (see extract above) calculate two expenditure indices (one for Brunley's beans and one for Hugo's beans) with 1988 as the base year and 1992 as the period of interest.

Has the average customer's expenditure on Brunley's baked beans increased or decreased over the period 1988 – 1992?

What has happened to the average customer's expenditure on Hugo's baked beans over the same period?

Unit 21: Liz compares weekly shopping basket costs over time

By the end of this unit you will:

- ❐ *know when to use and how to calculate the average price index;*
- ❐ *be able to calculate and interpret Laspeyre's price index;*
- ❐ *be able to calculate and interpret Paasche's price index;*
- ❐ *understand the limitations of Laspeyre's and Paasche's price indices.*

Scenario:

It is now Liz's third week in the Marketing and Promotions Department at Head Office. Briony, one of Liz's colleagues, shows her a recent advertising leaflet from Gaterose. This states that the price of a weekly shopping basket has increased less at Gaterose than any other supermarket (see below).

Gaterose keeps weekly shopping prices low!!!!

Five years ago we looked at the price of your weekly shopping at four leading supermarkets. This year we looked again. The price of your weekly shopping basket has increased by less at Gaterose than all other local supermarkets.

If your shopping basket had cost £100 five years ago it would now cost

over £145 at Greenland's
over £142 at Brunley's
over £138 at Tesbury
only £129 at Gaterose

Gaterose where prices rise least !!!!

Based on a weekly shopping basket of baked beans, milk, corn flakes, butter, bread, coffee, cola, beef.

Briony is certain that prices cannot have increased by this much at Brunley's. She asks Liz to help her calculate the true increase in the cost of the weekly shopping basket at Brunley's. Liz's first task is to gather data on the price and weekly quantity purchased for each of the weekly shopping basket items (see below).

Unit Price and Quantity Purchased for each of the items in the Gaterose Advertisement

	5 years ago		Today	
Item	**Unit Price**	**Quantity**	**Unit Price**	**Quantity**
Baked Beans (434 g tin)	£0.22	3	£0.28	2
Milk (pint)	£0.20	4	£0.26	3
Corn flakes (500 g packet)	£0.99	1	£1.29	1
Butter (500 g pack)	£0.45	2	£0.63	1
Bread (large loaf)	£0.54	4	£0.69	4
Coffee (200 g jar)	£1.19	1	£1.59	1
Cola (2 litre bottle)	£0.49	2	£0.59	3
Beef (per pound)	£3.99	3	£5.99	2

USING A COMPUTER FOR UNIT 21 TASKS

Tasks 21.1, 21.2 and 21.3 can either be undertaken by hand or using a computer spreadsheet. For all tasks the calculations are, with practice, quicker and less prone to error using a spreadsheet. The spreadsheet for task 21.1 can, with some thought, be adapted for the subsequent tasks.

Answer to QAQ 20.1

The number of blank video tapes sold in supermarkets over the period 1986 – 1993 has increased.

■ Task 21.1

Briony thinks that Gaterose might not taken into account the quantities consumed when calculating the average price increase of the weekly shopping basket. Liz suggests that they calculate the average price index to see if this is the case.

HELP
See *Section 2: The Information Bank*
Introduction: Unit 21.1, page 178; Average indices: Unit 21.2, page 178

Using the data in the table (above) calculate the average price index for the shopping basket.

Does this calculation give the same increase as suggested by the Gaterose advertisement?

■ Task 21.2

Liz thinks that it is more likely that the Gaterose calculation takes into account the actual quantities of each item purchased. They decide to calculate a base weighted price index.

HELP
See *Section 2: The Information Bank*
Weighted average indices: Unit 21.3, page 180; Laspeyre's price index: Unit 21.4, page 181

Using the data in the table (above) calculate Laspeyre's price index for the weekly shopping basket.

Does this calculation give the same increase as suggested by the Gaterose advertisement?

■ Task 21.3

Calculate Paasche's price index for the weekly shopping basket.

HELP
See *Section 2: The Information Bank*
Paasche's price index: Unit 21.5, page 183

Does this calculation give a lower or higher increase than that suggested by the Gaterose advertisement?

Which price index do you think Liz would use to show the increase in the price of Brunley's weekly shopping basket to the best advantage for Brunley's Supermarkets?

You are now ready to tackle task 8.3 in topic 8 of Section 3.

Unit 22: Liz helps analyse the checkout operators' pay claim

By the end of this unit you will:

- ❒ *be able to calculate and interpret a chain based index;*
- ❒ *be able to combine (splice) two or more indices where the bases differ;*
- ❒ *know when and how to deflate a series of data.*

Scenario:

For the final part of her management training Liz is placed in the Corporate Personnel Department. The Deputy Personnel Officer, Barry Bacon, introduces her to the personnel department staff. He tells Liz that, for the next few days, she will be working on the checkout operators' pay claim.

Barry tells her that checkout operators are paid a basic rate of £4.19 an hour with time and a half for Sundays. Brunley's have offered an increase of just under 2% which is in line with the current rate of inflation. This will take the hourly rate to £4.27. The checkout operators' union negotiator feels that this is insufficient as pay has fallen in real terms since 1989. Barry asks Liz to examine the claim in further detail. He gives Liz a sheet of paper with the following data:

Year	Inflation Index	Hourly rate
1981	155	£1.98
1982	171	£2.18
1983	180 (=100)	£2.30
1984	105	£2.43
1985	111	£2.67
1986	116	£2.86
1987	121	£3.12
1988	125	£3.41
1989	135	£3.75
1990	145 (=100)	£3.89
1991	109	£4.04
1992	112	£4.19
1993	114	pending

USING A COMPUTER FOR UNIT 22 TASKS

Tasks 22.1, 22.2 and 22.3 can either be undertaken by hand or using a computer spreadsheet. The calculations for all tasks are, with practice, quicker and less prone to error using a spreadsheet. The spreadsheet for task 22.1 can, with some thought, be adapted for the subsequent tasks.

■ Task 22.1

Barry suggests that the reason the union negotiator is basing the pay claim on 1989 is because checkout operators had their last large pay rise in that year.

Calculate a chain based index for the hourly rate data on Barry's sheet of paper (above).

Is Barry's suggestion correct?

> **HELP**
> See *Section 2: The Information Bank*
> Introduction: Unit 22.1, page 187; Chain based index: Unit 22.2, page 187

■ Task 22.2

Barry asks Liz to find out if the union negotiator's claim that pay rises have been below the rate of inflation since 1989 is true. To do this she decides she needs to splice the inflation index and then deflate the checkout operators' hourly rate to 1990 prices.

> **HELP**
> See *Section 2: The Information Bank*
> Splicing indices: Unit 22.3, page 187;
> Deflating a series: Unit 22.4, page 189

Briefly explain what is meant by 'splice the inflation index' and 'deflate the checkout operators' hourly rate to 1990 prices'.

■ Task 22.3

Barry asks Liz to calculate the checkout operators' hourly rate at 1990 prices for the years 1981 – 1993 inclusive (see Barry's sheet of paper above for data).

Undertake the necessary calculations.

> **HELP**
> See *Section 2: The Information Bank*
> Splicing indices: Unit 22.3, page 187;
> Deflating a series: Unit 22.4, page 189

Has the hourly rate for checkout operators fallen behind the rate of inflation since 1989?

Why do you think the union negotiator chose 1989, rather than any other year between 1981 and 1992, as the year on which to base the pay claim?

You are now ready to tackle the tasks and assignments in topic 8 of Section 3.

Unit 23: Liz investigates accidents at work

By the end of this unit you will:

- ❐ *understand the meaning of the terms mutually exclusive, dependent and independent with reference to probability of events occurring;*
- ❐ *be able to distinguish between problems requiring theoretical probability and problems requiring empirical probability;*
- ❐ *be able to calculate the theoretical probability of an event occurring;*
- ❐ *be able to calculate the empirical probability of an event occurring;*
- ❐ *know how to combine probabilities using the addition and the multiplication rules.*

Scenario:

The Deputy Personnel Manager, Barry Bacon, has received a memo from the Brunley's Health and Safety Committee requesting information on the likelihood of different categories of employees being involved in accidents (see below). Barry gives the memo to Liz and asks her to find the answers.

BRUNLEY'S SUPERMARKETS

Memorandum

From: Fred Smith, Health and Safety Committee
To: Barry Bacon, Personnel Department
Subject: Employee Accidents
Date: 17th June 199-

Further to our recent discussion I would be grateful if you could supply me with the following information:

1. The probability of a store employee having had an accident in the past year.
2. Given that a store employee has had an accident in the past year, the probability that the employee was:

   a checkout operator;
   a shelf stacker;
   a member of administrative staff;
   a manager.
3. If an accident occurred at a store during the past year what was the probability it was at:

   a town centre store;
   a suburban store;
   an out of town store.
4. Given that 70% of our store employees are female the probability that an accident occurs at an out of town store and involves a female employee.

I look forward to receiving your reply

Fred Smith

■ Task 23.1

Liz reads the first question on the memo. She remembers that last year Brunley's employed 22,700 people in their stores. She checks on the personnel computer and discovers there have been 832 accidents in stores over the past year.

> **HELP** See *Section 2: The Information Bank* Introduction to probability: Unit 23.1, page 191; Theoretical and empirical probability (Empirical probability): Unit 23.3, page 192; Types of event (Mutually exclusive events): Unit 23.2, page 191

What is the probability of a store employee having had an accident in the past year?

Is the probability of a store employee having had an accident a mutually exclusive event? Why?

■ Task 23.2

Liz hopes the personnel computer can provide data on the number of accidents by employees' job category to help her answer the second question on the memo. Unfortunately this data is not available. As the computer can sum total stores' employees by their job categories Liz obtains this data as a computer printout (see below).

> **HELP** See *Section 2: The Information Bank* Theoretical and empirical probability (Theoretical probability): Unit 23.3, page 192

Given that a store employee has had an accident in the past year, calculate the probability that the employee was:

a checkout operator;
a shelf stacker;
a member of administrative staff;
a member of managerial staff.

What is the probability that the accident involved either a checkout operator or a shelf stacker?

BRUNLEY'S SUPERMARKETS CENTRAL PERSONNEL SYSTEM
STORE EMPLOYEES' REPORT

JOB CATEGORY	NUMBER OF EMPLOYEES
MANAGERIAL STAFF	250
ADMINISTRATIVE STAFF	1600
SHOP FLOOR – CHECKOUT OPERATOR	11000
SHOP FLOOR – SHELF STACKER	9850

■ Task 23.3

Liz reads questions three and four from Fred Smith's memo again. From her earlier interrogation of the personnel computer she knows that it will not hold data about the number of accidents in each category of store. However it does hold data on the number of employees at each type of store. Liz types the appropriate commands into the personnel computer and notes down the numbers of employees:

> **HELP** See *Section 2: The Information Bank* Theoretical and empirical probability (Empirical probability): Unit 23.3, page 192; Combining events: Unit 23.4, page 195

Town centre: 10,050 Suburban: 9,100 Out of town: 3,550

If an accident occurred at a store during the past year what is the probability that it was at:

a town centre store;
a suburban store;
an out of town store?

Given that 70% of Brunley's store employees are female what is the probability that an accident occurs at an out of town store and involves a female employee?

■ **Task 23.4**

Barry is delighted with Liz's work and asks her to draft a reply to Fred Smith's memo providing the information he requested.

Draft the reply.

> **HELP** Use the answers to tasks 23.1 – 23.3. Write your reply in a similar style to the memo received from Fred Smith.

Unit 24: Liz is asked to help by the Corporate Transportation Department

By the end of this unit you will:

- ❒ *understand what is meant by the term expectation and be able to apply this understanding to problems involving probability;*
- ❒ *understand what is meant by conditional probability;*
- ❒ *be able to calculate the conditional probability of an event occurring using the tabular method;*
- ❒ *be able to apply Bayes' theorem to problems involving conditional probability.*

Scenario:

As soon as Liz arrives at work she is called into the Deputy Personnel Manager's Office. He tells her that John Johnson, from the Corporate Transportation Department, has just telephoned. John has requested Liz's help for the next few hours to continue the analysis of accident claims. Liz telephones John and is asked to go to his office straight away.

John explains the problem to Liz. The Manager of the Transportation Department has asked him to find the answer to three questions by lunch time:

1. What is the mean insurance claim that Brunley's expect their company car drivers to make?
2. What is the probability of car drivers who are aged under 35 having an accident?
3. Given a company car driver is aged 35 or over what is the probability of them having an accident?

John gives Liz a sheet of paper listing the data which he has obtained by telephoning various people (see below). He asks Liz to gather the remaining data she will need to answer these questions and work out the answers as quickly as possible.

Probability of various types of claim over the past 3 years:

Windscreen: 0.08
Theft / Break - in 0.27
Collision (Brunley's fault) 0.26
Collision (3rd party's fault) 0.25
Car - park 0.14.

120 of Brunley's company car drivers are aged under 35, the remaining 80 are aged 35 or above.

95 of Brunley's 200 company car drivers have had an accident in the past year.

Good luck Liz!

USING A COMPUTER FOR UNIT 24 TASKS

Task 24.1 can either be undertaken by hand or using a computer spreadsheet. The calculations are, with practice, quicker and less prone to error using a spreadsheet. Tasks 24.2 and 24.3 are quicker by hand using a calculator.

■ Task 24.1

Liz remembers that she has already calculated the mean value of insurance claims for each claim type (see below).

Use this data and the relevant data from John's sheet of paper to calculate the mean insurance claim that Brunley's expect their company car driver's to make.

HELP

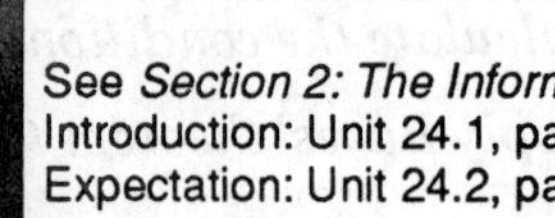

See *Section 2: The Information Bank*
Introduction: Unit 24.1, page 196;
Expectation: Unit 24.2, page 196

Fleet Vehicle Insurance Claims by type for three years 199- to 199-

Claim type	Mean
Windscreen	£178.25
Theft / Break – in	£1984.78
Collision (Brunley's fault)	£915.42
Collision (3rd party's fault)	£1115.88
Car – park	£528.23

Source: Brunley's Transportation Department

■ Task 24.2

Use the data on John's sheet of paper to calculate the probability of each of the following occurring:

HELP

See *Section 2: The Information Bank*
Conditional probability (Tabular method):
Unit 24.3, page 198

- **a company car driver aged under 35 having an accident;**
- **a company car driver aged 35 or over having an accident;**
- **a company car driver aged under 35 not having an accident;**
- **a company car driver aged 35 or over not having an accident.**

You should use the tabular method of calculation.

What is the probability that, given an company car driver is aged 35 or over, they have an accident?

■ **Task 24.3**

Liz shows her answers to John who is pleased. He tells her that she can check the answer to the third question using Bayes' theorem.

> **HELP**
> See *Section 2: The Information Bank*
> Conditional probability (Bayes' theorem):
> Unit 24.3, page 198

Given the probabilities below use Bayes' theorem to check your answer to the question 'Given a company car driver is aged 35 or over what is the probability of them having an accident?'

The probability that a company car driver has an accident is 0.475;

The probability that a company car driver is aged 35 or over given they have an accident is 0.4;

The probability that a company car driver is aged over 35 is 0.4.

You are now ready to tackle task 9.4 in topic 9 of Section 3.

Unit 25: Liz looks at possible redundancy packages

By the end of this unit you will:

- *know the properties of data that is normally distributed;*
- *be able to calculate the z score for a specified value given the mean and the standard deviation;*
- *be able to calculate the probability of an event using z scores.*

Scenario:

Brunley's are now seeing the impact of new technology in their stores. Unfortunately one major impact is that a number of checkout operators are now surplus to requirements. The Personnel Department has been asked to have a look at the checkout operator numbers. Barry Bacon, the Deputy Personnel Manager, explains to Liz three possible scenarios which could be used to reduce checkout operator numbers:

1. Encourage checkout operators to take early retirement by offering added years.
2. Make recently employed checkout operators compulsory redundant.
3. Offer voluntary redundancy to all checkout operators.

Barry tells Liz that if sufficient added years were offered he is sure that virtually 100% of checkout operators would take early retirement. He also says that a recent staff survey suggests that voluntary redundancy would appeal to few staff.

The personnel computer at Head Office has a hardware fault so Liz is unable to obtain data on individual checkout operators' ages. However Barry shows Liz an extract from a recent personnel report which contains some summary information (see below).

BRUNLEY'S SUPERMARKETS PERSONNEL REPORT APPENDIX 2

2.2 Summary Service Statistics

Employee Category	Number of Employees	Mean Length of Service	Standard Deviation
Checkout operator	11,000	20 years	7 years

* 1993 figures are estimates

■ Task 25.1

Barry tells Liz that Brunley's will make up the pensions for all checkout operators with over 30 years service.

Use the data in the extract from the Personnel Report (above) to calculate the z score for a length of service of 30 years.

What is the probability that a checkout operator will have over 30 years service?

As Brunley's employs 11,000 checkout operators how many would be eligible to take early retirement?

HELP
See *Section 2: The Information Bank* Introduction: Unit 25.1, page 201; The normal distribution and probabilities: Unit 25.2, page 201; Calculation of the *z* score: Unit 25.3, page 201; The probability of the *z* score being greater than that calculated: Unit 25.5, page 203; Values of the Standard Normal Distribution: Appendix 5

■ Task 25.2

The second possibility on Barry's list is to make some staff compulsory redundant.

Use the data in the extract from the Personnel Report (above) to calculate the z score for a length of service of 3 years and a length of service of 5 years.

What is the probability that a checkout operator will have less than or equal to 3 years service?

What is the probability that a checkout operator will have less than or equal to 5 years service?

As Brunley's employs 11,000 checkout operators how many would be made redundant if all checkout operators with less than or equal to 3 years service, or alternatively less than or equal to 5 years service, were made redundant?

HELP
See *Section 2: The Information Bank* Calculation of the *z* score: Unit 25.3, page 201; The probability of the *z* score being less than that calculated: Unit 23.4, page 202; The probability of the *z* score being greater than that calculated: Unit 25.5, page 203; The problem of negative z scores: Unit 25.6, page 203; Values of the Standard Normal Distribution: Appendix 5

■ Task 25.3

Calculate the probability of a checkout operator keeping their job if Brunley's decides to make all staff with less than or equal to 3 years service compulsory redundant and all staff with over 30 years service take early retirement.

As Brunley's currently employs 11,000 checkout operators how many checkout operators will be left after the compulsory redundancies and early retirements?

HELP
Use your answers to tasks 25.1 and 25.2 to help answer this task.

See *Section 2: The Information Bank* The probability of a value between two z scores: Unit 25.7, page 203; Values of the standard normal distribution: Appendix 5

You are now ready to tackle the tasks and assignments in topic 9 of Section 3.

Postscript

BRUNLEY'S SUPERMARKETS
Head Office, Cheltenham, Gloucestershire
TELEPHONE: 0242 987654

Ms Elizabeth J Reynolds
324, Goodson Road North
Gloucester
Gloucestershire

4th July 199-

Dear Ms Reynolds

Departmental Manager – Wines and Spirits

Following the successful completion of your management training I am delighted to offer you the post of Departmental Manager (Wines and Spirits) at our Malvern Store.

I would be most grateful if you could confirm your acceptance of this post by returning the enclosed contract to me as soon as possible.

I take this opportunity of wishing you a very happy future with Brunley's Supermarkets.

Your sincerely

Barry Bacon

Barry Bacon
Deputy Personnel Manager

Enc.

Congratulations. You have completed Section 1. You are now ready to tackle all the tasks and assignments in Section 3, including those in topic 10.

Section 2
The Information Bank

This section contains a summary of business statistical methods It follows the same sequence as Section 1 for the sake of convenience, but you are not expected to read through it from the first page to the last page. Rather, you will be directed from tasks in Sections 1 and 3, to solve problems on a 'need to know' basis. Once you have covered all the tasks in the book however, you will have been directed to all parts of the Information Bank, ie you will have covered all the business statistical methods you need for your course.

References are provided for you to pursue topics further if you so wish.

Section 2 Contents and outline

Unit 1: Data and information

1.1 Information and business

In all but the smallest businesses managers rarely observe everything that is happening. Their understanding of what is happening, and the actions they decide to take on the basis of this understanding, are based upon the information they can obtain. Within everyday speech the terms *data* and *information* are used interchangeably. However within business they have distinct and separate meanings.

1.2 Business data

All businesses collect and store vast amounts of data. These are facts which have been obtained by the business and subsequently recorded. The key points are that data consists of:

- facts
- obtained
- subsequently recorded

Usually they are termed *raw data* as the data is recorded and stored in its raw form.

The types of data with which a business is concerned will include:

- data regarding levels of performance, costs, overheads, profits and losses, cash flows, stock, production;
- data relating to the organisation of the work force: employee levels, payroll, managers' spans of control and responsibilities;
- data relating to the performance of competitors;
- data relating to social, political and economic factors.

We can therefore see that data will record, amongst other things, the day to day performance of the business. For example, a manufacturer producing bicycles will collect and store data about the number of bicycles they produce each working day. This data will be collected as the total number of bicycles produced and stored as a single figure, along with data about the day, like this:

Number of bicycles produced on: Monday 57

Other data that our Bicycle Manufacturer could collect and store from within the factory (*internal sources*) on a regular basis include details relating to raw material purchases, sales invoices, maintenance costs of their factory, as well as data about employees such as payment method, national insurance number, age and gender.

Data would also be collected and stored from outside the factory (*external sources*). This data would include bank statements, price of the company shares, and the prices of competitors' bicycles.

We can therefore see that the term data refers to facts, events, and transactions which have been collected and recorded. Data is collected from sources both internal and external to the business.

1.3 Business information

The term *information* is more complicated than its use in everyday speech would suggest. Information is data that has been interpreted, understood and is useful to the person who has received it.

The key points here is that for data to become information it must have been:

- interpreted by
- understood by, and
- useful to

} the recipient.

Or put another way, it must have been interpreted and understood by the person using it.

The Production Manager at our Bicycle Manufacturer receives the daily bicycle production data for the previous week every Monday, it looks like this:

Monday	57
Tuesday	58
Wednesday	64
Thursday	62
Friday	38

For this to become information it must be understood, interpreted, and useful to him. If the manager receives the data and does not look at it then it will remain data. However he may look at the data, understand it, and then interpret it to answer the question: 'Has the level of production remained constant throughout the past week?'. He will see that production on Friday was much lower than on the previous four days, a potentially useful finding. As the data has now been processed it has become information.

The Finance Department of the Bicycle Manufacturer produces a monthly statement detailing the previous month's Sales. This data is subsequently analysed and processed and forms part of the 'Information Report' which is presented to the Finance Manager, and is shown below:

Finance Department: Information Report for the month of March 199- **page 7 of 18**

3. Sales Analysis

Bicycle type	Sales this month last year	Sales this month this year	Percentage change
Mountain	400	440	+10.0%
Racing	300	340	+13.3%
Touring	150	125	-16.7%
Child	300	320	+6.7%
Total	**1150**	**1225**	**+6.5%**

Overall sales have increased by 6.5% compared to the same month last year. The largest proportional increases were in the sales of our Racing and Mountain Bike models.

Sales of Touring Bikes continue to decline. The impact of this must be considered in conjunction with our high stock levels for these bikes (see page 15).

Although this report is called an Information Report, it only becomes information if it is understood by the person who receives it, in this case the Finance Manager. It is the user who determines whether a report contains information or processed data. It is therefore very important that all data (including reports) is presented clearly, is easily understood, and is in the format most suited to the recipient. This will help to ensure that information is derived from it.

1.4 Summary

- Business data consists of facts which have been obtained and subsequently recorded.

- For this to become business information it must be interpreted, understood and useful.

Help: See Section 2 – The Information Bank
Data sources: Unit 3

Further Reading:

Management Information Systems (Chapter 2), Lucey T, DP PUBLICATIONS (1991)

Unit 2: The value and characteristics of information

2.1 The value of information

Information within a business has no value in its own right. The value comes from the decision that is made based upon the information. If the cost of the information is greater than the value of the decision, then the information is too costly. When considering the cost of information we must remember that our calculations will need to include the costs of data collection, recording and analysis upon which the information is based.

We can illustrate this as shown in the diagram below. If the costs of producing the information are greater than the value derived from the changes based upon the decision (below the diagonal line) then the information is too costly. If the costs of producing the information are less than the value derived from the changes based on the decision (above the diagonal line) then the information is valuable.

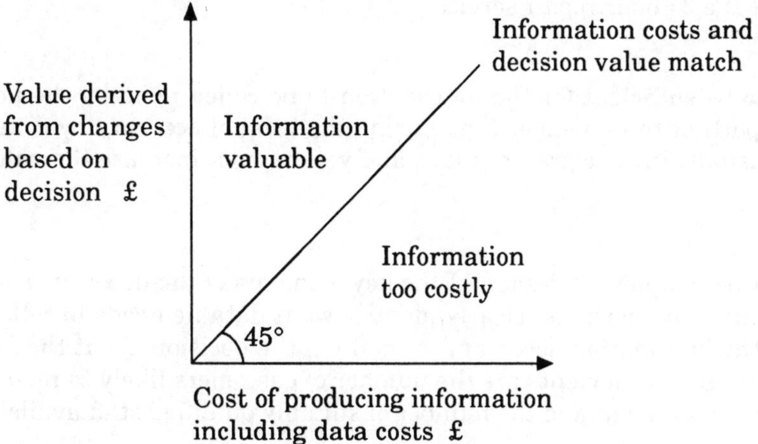

The value and cost of information

Business people often assume that the more accurate and more up to date the information upon which they base decisions the better. However this may not be the case. It is better only if it improves the resulting decisions and, of equal importance, only if the value of the decision to the business is more than the costs of producing the information upon which it is based.

The Manager of a Computer Company which assembles and sells micro computers has to decide whether or not to offer customers a 24 hour computer repair service. In effect he needs to answer the question 'Should we offer customers a 24 hour computer repair service?'. To answer this question the company could obtain very accurate information about customer demand by undertaking a survey of existing customers. Alternatively it could produce a reasonable estimate of likely demand based upon published market research data about the demand for 24 hour computer repair services. Whilst the latter is likely to be less accurate, the information will be far less costly to produce and it may be of sufficient accuracy for the decision. In summary, the choice of data collection methods and subsequent analyses will be influenced by their impact on the relative costs of producing the information and the value of the decision to the company.

2.2 The characteristics of information

To ensure that information does have value it must possess a number of characteristics. These can be summarised as:

- relevant and current
- sufficiently accurate
- complete
- reliable
- timely
- at the right level of detail
- understandable by the user

Relevance and currency
Relevance is the single most important quality of business information. If we consider the information needs of our Computer Company Manager's decision we can see that only certain information will be relevant. For example, information about sales of computer software will probably be irrelevant to his decision about a repair service.

Often management reports contain tables, charts and text which are irrelevant to the report and do little to aid the user's understanding. A common cause of irrelevance is the inclusion of data which is too out of date to be of any use. If our Computer Company Manager could only obtain Market Research Reports which were published 10 years ago, they would be of little relevance to his decision about the 24 hour repair service.

Accuracy
Accuracy needs to be sufficient for the information to be relied upon by the person making the decision. It is important to remember that raising the level of accuracy by collecting the data in more detail will usually involve greater costs, and yet may not increase the value of the information.

Completeness
Information must be complete in respect of the key elements of the decision. This means that our Computer Company Manager must clearly identify what data he needs to collect and analyse in order to provide the information necessary for making the decision about the 24 hour repair service. In this case these key elements are the number of customers likely to require such a service, frequency of their requirement and the number of suitably qualified staff available.

Reliability
The source of the information will affect the confidence the user has in the information. This becomes more obvious when we realise that the information will ultimately be used to justify a decision. Confidence is based upon the perceived reliability of the source: external sources of information, such as market research conducted by large established consumer research companies, may well be perceived as more reliable than equivalent data obtained from a smaller unknown company. In some cases confidence in the information will be enhanced if the information source is known to be independent of the decision maker as it is less likely that the information has been biased by the decision maker. Often information from various sources is cross checked to increase confidence in its reliability.

Timeliness
Timeliness refers to the time between the information being received and the time when the decision is taken. Obviously if data is received too late to be used for a particular decision, it cannot

be considered as information even if it is interpreted and understood. This is because one of the properties of information is that it is useful. Information that is not timely is useless!

Level of detail

Information only needs to contain sufficient detail to enable the decision to be made. For example, if our Computer Company Manager wishes to project long term sales demand to plan capacity of the assembly plant, then annual sales figures would be more useful than monthly sales figures. By contrast, monthly sales figures would be needed to show the seasonality of sales, so as to plan short term capacity fluctuations.

Understandability

Understandability, like timeliness, is one of the factors that transforms data into information. If the data is not understood it cannot be used and so cannot add value. It is therefore important that information is presented clearly and in a form which is easy to understand.

2.3 Summary

- Information needs to be presented in an understandable and suitable format at the right time and at the right level of detail.
- Information must be considered to be sufficiently reliable by the person using it.

Further reading:

Making Management Decisions (Chapter 12), Cooke S and Slack N, PRENTICE HALL (1984)
Management Information Systems (Chapter 2), Lucey T, DP PUBLICATIONS (1991)

Unit 3: Data sources

3.1 Introduction

The main reason for collecting and analysing data in business is to provide the information to answer questions and on which to base decisions. Business statistics are concerned with the analysis and understanding of data and before we can begin any analysis we obviously need data. The source of our data is important because the validity of any analysis we subsequently undertake depends on the reliability of the data that is used.

We can divide the data we use into two types:

- primary
- secondary

Primary data is raw data that is collected through some survey or enquiry and used for the specific purpose for which it was collected. *Secondary data* is data, perhaps already processed, that was originally collected for some totally different purpose to that which we now wish to put it. Secondary data may have been collected within the organisation (*internal*) for some other purpose or *external* to the organisation now undertaking the survey or enquiry.

Statistical analyses can use either primary data, secondary data or a combination of the two.

3.2 Primary data

Primary data is therefore data for which the collector specifies the purpose for which it is being collected. A retailer will be interested in their weekly sales of each of the products in their shop to enable them to reorder items as stock levels become low. A manufacturer of a luxury item will be interested in their monthly sales returns in order to enable them to produce sufficient items to meet demand. Both might have a 'gut feeling' for what they feel is happening but to base any decisions on such a feeling would be foolish. They need to collect the primary data which they can subsequently analyse statistically and interpret to provide them with the information to make a logical, business decision.

The main advantages of primary data are:

- we can specify exactly what data we require;
- we have control over the method of collection;
- it is likely to be more up to date than secondary data.

However, against this we must remember the disadvantages of collecting our own data:

- it will be relatively expensive in terms of both time and money;
- we may not have access to the data we require and so will need to use secondary (external) sources.

Because of these, in some cases it may be preferable to use secondary data.

3.3 Secondary data

A prime example of secondary data used by business is the large amount of official statistics that are published every year by the Government. Because government imposes a statutory requirement on organisations and people to provide certain details about wages, hours worked and so on they ensure a coverage which it would be impossible for us to obtain if we were undertaking our own data collection. It also has at its disposal vast resources devoted to the collection and processing of statistical data. Thus the Census of Population, for example, possesses a coverage (virtually 100% of the population) and level of detail which we could not possibly emulate. Such statistics can be vital to businesses.

We must remember that secondary data also includes data collected by people other than government including organisations, businesses, and individuals. Consumer Research Companies collect data which is subsequently used for analytical and marketing purposes for a number of different clients. Trade organisations such as the Federation of Motor Traders may ask their members to supply data such as monthly sales which, when published, we may be able to use. Whilst Motor Traders would be unwilling to provide this for their competitors they will supply it to the trade organisation for the benefit of the entire industry. They know that their confidentiality will be maintained and the data will only be published anonymously as part of an aggregation of data referring to a number of traders. Individual companies hold data on their employees for pay roll purposes, which can also be analysed for other purposes such as human resources planning.

There are a number of advantages to using secondary data; these include:

- having access to complex data which we could not hope to collect ourselves as primary data;
- not having to spend the time or effort in data collection.

However, there are also disadvantages of which, even if we can do nothing about, we need to be aware. These include disadvantages such as:

- the data may not always be up-to-date. Some official statistics, such as the 'Monthly Digest' are as the name suggests produced monthly. Other statistics take much longer to collect, must then be processed and finally printed and distributed. This means the data may be out-of-date for our purposes by the time we receive it;

- the data may not be entirely suitable for what we want to do, for example it may not be in sufficient detail;

- often we do not know how the secondary data was collected and we must therefore assume valid techniques were used. This will usually be a fair assumption with published official statistics. However, some data must be viewed critically. It may have been collected using too small a sample or using a poorly designed questionnaire. Alternatively it may have been analysed selectively in order to make a particular point;

- some terms used might have a number of possible meanings. For example does 'employees' refer to the number of full and part time employees, just full time employees or the number of full time equivalent employees?

- it often happens that we need data from a variety of sources. Because the data may have been collected and processed in different ways there can be problems of 'mixing' data and the conclusions we draw may not be valid;

- published data may also contain errors due to typing or printing. This is unlikely to occur in data that has been thoroughly researched and checked, but data appearing in some magazines and newspapers may need careful checking.

3.4 Sources of secondary data

We can divide secondary data sources into those which are internal and those which are external to the organisation using the data.

Internal data sources

Internal data sources will differ depending upon the business which we are looking at. However in most business we would expect to find data already collected for the following purposes:

- Payroll
- Accounts of Sales of Goods or Services
- Value Added Tax Returns

If we were working for the business which had collected this data, but we wished to undertake an analyse for some purpose other than that for which the data were originally collected these would be termed *internal secondary data*.

External data sources

As we discussed earlier (3.3) external data sources cover a wide range of possibilities. However the most important are without doubt those provided by the Central Statistical Office and other Government Departments. The more frequently used will be often be available in college libraries as well as the reference section of larger public libraries. Within the United Kingdom they include:

> **Guide to Official Statistics:** this is published periodically by the Central Statistical Office. Whilst it is often not a source of secondary data in its own right it is probably the most useful single book. It provides a reference to what statistics have been compiled as well as an index of where they have been published. It covers all official statistics, and some significant non official ones, published over the last ten years.
>
> **Census of Population Reports:** these have been published since the 19th Century for every population census by the Office of Population Censuses and Surveys in England and Wales and General Registrar's Office in Scotland. There are a series of reports cover-

ing a range of economic, social and demographic topics for the United Kingdom, England, Scotland, Wales, Standard Regions, Counties and County Districts.

Annual Abstract of Statistics: this has been published for over 150 years and provides tables of data on social, economic and industrial life including population, social services, justice, crime, education, manufacturing and agricultural production, transport and communications. This along with a less detailed summary, the **Monthly Digest of Statistics**, is published by the Central Statistical Office.

Financial Statistics: this is published monthly by the Central Statistical Office and brings together financial and monetary statistics over a wide range of topics. These include financial accounts for sectors of the economy, Government income and expenditure, banking statistics, money supply and domestic credit expansion.

United Kingdom National Accounts (The CSO Blue Book): this is published annually by the Central Statistical Office and contains data on national product, income and expenditure split in a variety of ways. In addition it contains detailed definitions and explanatory notes.

United Kingdom Balance of Payments (The CSO Pink Book): this is published annually by the Central Statistical Office and is the basic reference book for all balance of payments statistics.

Economic Trends: this is also published monthly by the Central Statistical Office and contains the main economic indicators illustrated with graphs and charts.

Regional Trends and **Social Trends:** these are both published annually by the Central Statistical Office. The former presents a wide range of government statistics by Standard Regions covering social, demographic and economic topics. The latter concentrates on statistics about many aspects of life in the United Kingdom and also provides a descriptive analysis of the data. Both publications contain graphs and charts to illustrate the data.

Family Expenditure Survey and **National Food Survey**: these are both published annually. The former appears in a report of the same name and covers household spending on the full range of goods and services. The results of the National Food Survey are published in 'Household Food Consumption and Expenditure'. It contains statistics and a brief analysis of the consumption and expenditure on the main food groups by household composition, income group and region.

Employment Gazette: this is published monthly by the Employment Department and includes many summary statistics on employment, unemployment, wages, retail prices. It also contains an Employment News feature and in depth feature articles.

In addition a wide range of quality daily newspapers, business publications, academic journals, on-line computer databases and market research data may also be useful as external sources of secondary data.

Further reading:

The most useful further reading you can undertake for this unit is to visit a library and examine as many of these secondary data sources as you can. The following books are useful guides to data sources:

Guide to Official Statistics, Central Statistical Office, HMSO (1990)
UK Statistics: A Guide for Business Users, Mort D, ASHGATE (1992)

Unit 4: Deciding what data must be collected

4.1 Introduction

Within any business it is important that the data we collect, be it primary or secondary, will enable us to answer the questions or inquiries we have. The data we collect must therefore be capable of being turned into information.

In order to decide what data we need to collect, we need to be clear about how we are going to use the data and the information produced from it. We can think of this as what we need to find out; the questions or inquiries we want to answer once we have collected and analysed the data.

4.2 Establishing what we need to find out

Often in business what we want to find out is dictated by a manager. The manager of a lawnmower manufacturing company might ask us: 'How well has our company performed over the last three months?'. We then have to establish exactly what is meant by their inquiry. This often involves further discussion so that we have a clear understanding of what needs to be found out.

For example, the manager might have meant 'performed' in terms of how many goods have been produced or how many have been sold. In addition he might require a comparison with the company's competitors involving data from the same three month period one year previously.

Often further discussion will result in the initial inquiry being sub divided into a number of more detailed questions, all of which will also have to be answered. If we take the initial inquiry:

- 'How well has our company performed over the last three months?'

This might sub divide into:

- 'How many lawnmowers has our company produced and sold over the last three months?'
- 'How many lawnmowers did our company produce and sell in the same three month period last year?'
- 'What has happened to the number of lawnmowers produced and sold when these two periods are compared for our company, and our main competitor?'.

4.3 Deciding what data we need and where it will come from

Once we have established what needs to be found out we can decide what is the most appropriate data to enable us to do this and where it will come from. This can often be seen more clearly if we consider four areas:

- **detailed question**. Here we list all the detailed questions fully. It is especially important when we are working in groups to ensure that each member has the same understanding of what is meant by each question. There could be any number of detailed questions from say three to over thirty.
- **data required.** We should list, in as much detail as possible, the data that needs to be collected to answer each of the inquiries.
- **likely values.** Here we state, for each item of data, the sorts of values and terms the data could include, this is especially important if we are going to design our own survey. In some cases, such as a person's age, this is relatively straight forward as age is unlikely to be outside the range 1 to perhaps 110 years. In others it is more difficult, for example persons' attitudes to ethnic minority groups or a particular government policy. For any survey we need to understand how respondents think and talk about the issues – the con-

cepts and words that they use. This provides valuable guidance as to how individual survey questions should be phrased and the more probable responses.

- **source.** This states where the data will be obtained, this could be internal or external secondary sources. In other cases we may have to design a survey and collect the data ourselves (primary sources).

These areas can be shown in a table such as the one given below, which uses one of the questions from our example in section 4.2.

Detailed question	Data required	Likely values	Source
How many lawn-mowers has our company produced and sold over the last 3 months?	Number of lawn-mowers produced over 3 month period April to June	Actual number 200 – 300	Production Department's monthly statistics (Secondary Data, internal source)
	Number of lawn-mowers sold over 3 month period April to June	Actual number 400 – 600	Sales Department's monthly statistics (Secondary Data, internal source)

We can approach inquiries involving the collection of primary data in exactly the same manner. For example, the Manager of the Service Department might want to know: 'Were customers who used our repair service in the past year satisfied with the speed of the service?'.

Using the four areas our table would look like this:

Detailed question	Data required	Likely values	Source
Were customers who used our repair service in the past year satisfied with the speed of service?	(For each customer)		
	Used repair service in period January to December last year	Yes / No	Sales Department Records (Secondary Data, internal source)
	Satisfaction with speed of service	Very satisfied, Satisfied, Dissatisfied, Very Dissatisfied	Survey of Customers who used repair service (Primary Data)
	Actual speed of the repair from receipt to collection in days	Same Day, or actual number of days	Survey of Customers who used repair service (Primary Data)

If the Sales Department Manager asks 'What do customers think is the best feature of our lawnmowers?', this would prove more difficult. Although a list could be obtained from the sales department of the lawnmower's features it would not answer the query. As a preliminary stage a list is required of the lawnmower's features. However, information is also needed of how customers refer to each of these features and how they define the term 'best'. The likely range of data is at present unclear and further discussion would be helpful.

The detailed question 'What is the role of the Senior Sales Manager in the provision of the after sales service?', is even less straightforward. This is because a wider range of data is required to provide the answer. In this case it would be advantageous to establish exactly what is meant by 'role'. At the moment it is not clear whether the detailed question refers to interaction with other Sales Department employees, interaction with people receiving the after sales service, or indeed a range of other possible interactions. Once again further discussion would be helpful.

Finally, once we have decided what data is needed and where it will come from it is important that we check that what we intend to collect will enable the inquiry to be answered fully. If we look at the table above we may decide that the data outlined on speed of repair service will not be sufficient to answer our detailed question. At present we are planning to record speed as the 'actual speed of the repair from receipt to collection in days'. This does not enable us to distinguish between the length of time taken for the lawnmower to be repaired and the subsequent length of time the lawnmower remained in the repair shop awaiting collection by the customer. We may therefore wish to amend this to include both repair and awaiting collection time.

If this is not done and the omission is only discovered at a much later date it is likely to be impossible to obtain the originally omitted data.

4.4 Summary

Before collecting data it is important to establish:

- exactly how the data is going to be used;
- what data is required;
- the level of detail required;
- and the likely data sources.

Further Reading:

Management Research – An Introduction (Chapters 1 & 2), Easterby-Smith M, Thorpe R and Lowe A, SAGE (1991)
Surveys in Social Research (Chapter 3), deVaus DA, ALLEN AND UNWIN (1991)

Unit 5: Populations, samples and sampling methods

5.1 Samples and populations

In business we often have to collect data to enable us to answer questions. However in many cases it would be impossible to collect and use all the data available to us due to a lack of time and money.

Sampling is the method we can use to collect data, and at the same time reduce the time and money element. It is used in many areas of business, including market research, surveys of employees and product testing. It forms a basis for making some estimation of the characteristics of the whole group from which the sample has been selected. For example, if a sample of employees was asked what they thought of the food provided by the company's canteen and 80% said that they thought it was poor value for money you might infer that 80% of all employees felt this way.

We call the group from which the sample is taken the *population*. If there were 100,000 people living within a shopping centre's catchment area, then they would be the 'population' for a survey of potential customers. We might select 1,000 of them as our sample, the theory being that the 1,000 were representative of the population as a whole.

The term population is not used in its normal sense. In sampling a population does not necessarily refer to people. If we were obtaining data about electric light bulbs produced in a factory, then the light bulbs produced in the factory would be the population. A motor vehicle manufacturer might wish to undertake a survey of warranty claims on a particular model of car. In this case the population would be the total number of cars of that particular model manufactured.

5.2 The need to sample

The advantages of sampling are clear:

- it is often impossible to survey the whole population and so we simply have to take a sample. For products which are tested to destruction such as in the crash testing of motor vehicles it would be economic suicide to test all products!

- in other cases we might theoretically be able to survey the whole population but time and cost would prevent it. Quality control often works by checking every 1,000th item for faults, as it would be too costly and time consuming to check every single item for quality;

- sampling allows results based on a subset of the population to be available more quickly than if data had been collected from the entire population. This is an important consideration when there are tight deadlines;

- sampling is usually less expensive.

If our sample is to be a reliable substitute, it must be a *representative* sample, that is it must represent the variability in the population as closely as possible. A university lecturer who has invented a new product and undertakes a survey of people within the university to gauge their reaction to it will not be surveying a representative sample. She might argue that the sample was composed of:

- males and females
- a wide range of age groups
- a wide range of classes (cleaners, maintenance men as well as professors)

However, the sample would only consist of people connected with that university, located within a particular town or city, and would not represent the population of the country as a whole. It would not, for example, represent anyone:

- from manufacturing industry
- from the armed forces
- under the age of 17
- over the age of 65 (probably).

To produce a completely representative sample we have to choose it in such a way to ensure that every single item in the population that is being sampled has an equal chance of being selected. We may still end up with no one from manufacturing, the armed forces, under 17 or over 65 years of age, but the important fact is that all these groups will have had an equal chance of being selected which they did not have in the university sample.

Before selecting a sample there are a number of 'ground rules' that need to be followed:

1. The *sampling frame* must be defined. This is simply a complete list of all the items in the population from which the sample will be drawn. For a sample survey of a Doctor's patients the sampling frame would be a complete list of patients' names. We would then select our sample from this list. The important point is that every item (in this case patient) in the population has an equal chance of selection because they have all been included in the sampling frame.

2. Clearly the list we use must be accurate. Sometimes we may have to compile our own but often a list is already available. If, for example, we were surveying a bank's employees we could probably obtain a list from the personnel section. However we would still need to check how up-to-date it was.

3. Bias should be avoided at this stage. If we were conducting a survey of UK householders, a telephone directory might appear to provide a good sampling frame of typical householders. However, any single telephone directory will only deal with people in a particular area. Unless our survey aims to look at just one area, we are introducing a form of bias. Another bias is that our sample would only contain people who had telephones and who had their number in the directory. The bias is therefore towards telephone owning members of society and against ex-directory subscribers.

4. The person selecting the sample must do so using a technique that is without, and can be seen to be without, bias. If we select from the sampling frame using personal judgement, then bias is almost certain to occur due to subjective selection. Even if bias has not occurred, it is very difficult to prove this is the case. The usual way of ensuring the sample is selected without bias is to use a mechanistic method.

5.3 How to sample

Having chosen a suitable sampling frame we need to select the most appropriate method for selecting a representative sample. The perfect sample is one that exactly represents the population from which it is drawn. If 90% of a sample said they would purchase a new product, and subsequently the proportion of the total population who purchased this product once it became available was 90%, then we would have chosen a sample which perfectly represented the total population for new product sales.

So any sample we take should ideally reflect the characteristics of the population as a whole. If 20% of the population have a certain feature then 20% of the sample should have the same feature. For this reason it is important that we analyse any refusals to respond. It may be that people who refuse to respond are different from those who do respond, thereby introducing bias into our sample.

There are six main methods we can use to select a representative sample:

- random
- systematic
- stratified random
- multi-stage
- quota
- cluster

Random sampling

Suppose we have a population of 1,000 customers. They have all purchased one of our new products and we wish to find out why they chose this particular product. There is no time to interview all of them and so we decide to take a sample – 10%, or 100 customers. How would we choose the 10%? One random way would be to put 1,000 names in a hat and pull out 100.

Alternatively we can either use tables of published random numbers or use a computer program that can generate random numbers.

Here is an extract from the Random Number Tables in Appendix 3:

Extract from Random Number Tables

33865	04131	78302	22688	79034	01358	61724	98286	97086	21376
09356	**09387**	52825	93134	21731	93956	85324	68767	49490	11449
98243	37636	64825	43091	24906	13545	90172	31265	81457	93108
99052	61857	33938	86339	63531	77146	33252	81388	28302	18960
00713	24413	36920	03841	48047	04207	50930	84723	07400	81109
34819	80011	17751	03275	92511	....				

Source: Appendix 3

If we were using these to pick 100 customers out of 1,000 we would first need to number our 1,000 customers. In order for each number to be made up in the same way we would use 1,000 3-digit numbers which would run from 000-999. So, number 6 would actually be represented as 006.

It is usual to start at a randomly chosen point (closing your eyes and stabbing the page with your finger is as good a way as any). This ensures that the sets of random numbers obtained for different samples are not the same – otherwise patterns which are random but identical will be produced.

If for example we had selected the value 09387 in this manner (shown in bold on the table), starting with this we could read off the random numbers:

093 875 282 593 134 217 319 395 685

and so on until 100 customers were selected.

The numbers are taken from the table by reading systematically from the table. The process continues until the sample is complete.

If we select a customer's number twice it must be disregarded the second time as we need 100 different customers. This means we are not putting the customers names (numbers) back into the sampling frame once we have selected them. Because the customer numbers are not replaced in the sampling frame once they have been selected, this is called sampling *without replacement*.

If selecting a 25% sample from a sampling frame of 6,244 customers we would have to number our customers from 0000 – 6243. We would then read off the random numbers until 1561 (25%) of our customers had been selected. It is likely that we would read off some random numbers outside our range of values (for example 6459). In these cases we would disregard the random number and continue until 1561 customers had been selected.

Because random numbers allow us to select a sample without bias, the sample can be said to be *representative* of the total population. However it is possible, especially with samples below a few hundred items, that simply by chance certain parts of a population are over or under represented. For example assume that we have 100 tins of baby food and we suspect that some of them may be contaminated. We decide to take a random sample of 20% of the cans to check them and so number the cans 00 to 99. From random number tables we select 20 numbers for the cans we will check. These are:

64, 82, 54, 30, 91, 24, 90, 61, 35, 45, 17, 23, 12, 65, 81, 45, 79, 31, 10, 89

The actual contaminated cans are:

3 44 83 33 21

If we had chosen two, three or more numbers that matched we would be worried that a great deal of the sample is contaminated. As none of our numbers matched up we might think there is no problem. In fact, the sample, if it were a true representation, would suggest that 5% of all cans are contaminated. This example illustrates that even random sampling can give unsatisfactory results; so care must always be taken.

Systematic sampling

A systematic sample is one in which our selection is made from the sampling frame at regular intervals. For example, selecting every tenth patient in a Doctor's Practice would give us a 10% sample; every fifth patient a 20% sample.

However, on its own, this would not be a random selection because every tenth patient (or fifth patient) would be bound to be selected and it is important that everyone in the population should have an equal chance of selection. The way round this is to select the starting point randomly. Usually the first item from the sampling frame is selected using a random number and subsequent items systematically from there.

For example for a 10% sample of patients in our Doctor's Practice we would select the first person using the first digit of a random number (say 3). Subsequent patients selected would be the 13th, 23rd, 33rd, 43rd and so on until we had gone right through the complete list (i.e. the sampling frame).

The advantages of systematic sampling are that it is easier to understand and it is a simpler and quicker method than random sampling. In addition it gives a uniform coverage of the population. Random samples tend to include 'clusters' or, on the other hand leave 'gaps', unless the random sample is particularly large.

But there are disadvantages. This method depends on the population being randomly distributed and this is not always the case. If it is not, then the systematic sample may be biased. For example, a list of customers may be listed by family. If we sampled the second person in each family it might give a high proportion of female customers because males are usually placed at the head of the family.

Stratified sampling

This method divides the population by a series of attributes or strata which are considered significant to our investigation. In effect we divide or stratify our sampling frame into a series of subsets, from which we draw separate samples. For example, a company is made up of the following categories of employee:

	Branches	Head Office	Total
Management	200	500	700
Administration	800	400	1200
Sales	2100	0	2100
Research and Development	0	1000	1000
Total	**3100**	**1900**	**5000**

We are administering a survey to find out overall what the employees think about a diversification programme which will affect everyone, head office staff as well as branch staff.

10% of the population is to be surveyed, in other words, 500 employees.

We could simply sample using random numbers to obtain a representative result of the views of the total company. However, it might mean that the employees in smaller categories might not be represented at all, due to the clustering effect of random sampling.

Stratified sampling can help because it allows separate samples to be drawn from each sub-set. Under this process we would sample 10% of each subset. The numbers in our sample for each subset would be as follows:

	Branches	Head Office	Total
Management	20	50	70
Administration	80	40	120
Sales	210	0	210
Research and Development	0	100	100
Total	**310**	**190**	**500**

We still have sampled 10% of the population but the results, once we have combined our subsets, will be far more representative of the structure of the population we are dealing with. The general procedure we use is therefore:

1. Stratify the population into separate subsets.
2. Take the same proportion as a sample (e.g. 10%) from each subset.
3. Combine the results to provide the stratified sample.

The main advantage of this method is that the sample is free from bias yet at the same time it takes account of significant attributes (strata) in the population. However it is only possible to do this as we are aware of these attributes and can easily distinguish them. It is probable that such a survey will be more expensive to conduct.

Multi-stage sampling

This method is very useful for national surveys where the population is widely spread. Suppose we wanted to interview 1,000 people from the United Kingdom's population. Choosing them randomly we would probably get 1,000 people dispersed throughout the United Kingdom. The time and cost of visiting the sample would be enormous.

Multi-stage sampling allows us to overcome this. First of all we split the country into geographically discrete areas. These might be counties or local authority districts. A small number of these discrete areas are selected at random. Sub sample selection of the 1,000 people to be interviewed from the sampling frame is then confined to these randomly selected areas. The procedure we adopt is:

1. Split the area into geographically discrete smaller areas.
2. Select a small number of these smaller areas at random.
3. Select the sub sample from each of these areas proportional to the total population of the area.

Using this method we can 'randomly' select 1,000 people but also ensure they are in a few discrete geographical areas.

The main advantage of multi-stage sampling is that it minimises the amount of travel required for interviewing and hence reduces the time and cost of any survey. Disadvantages are that the final areas selected may be unrepresentative in some way and so bias may enter the process. In addition, the method is not truly random as once we have selected our discrete areas, no member of the population in any other area can be selected for our sample.

Quota sampling

Quota sampling is entirely non-random. The population is split into groups and then the exact number (or quota) is specified for each group to build the sample. These quotas are calculated from available data about the population so that, for example, the age, gender and social class are represented in the sample in the same proportions. Quota sampling is often used for market research projects where it is not possible to list every member of the sampling frame.

Using the quota sampling method the interviewer can decide whom they interview until they complete the number of interviews required and fulfil their quota. For example, an interviewer may be given the following quota:

Age	Gender	Social Class	Quota
16 – 19	Female	Low	20
16 – 19	Male	Middle	20
20 – 29	Female	High	30
20 – 29	Male	Middle	20
60 plus	Female	High	25
60 plus	Male	Middle	20

This quota would then be combined with the quotas from other interviews to provide the full sample. This method is therefore not random, although it does ensure the sample contains members of the population in the desired proportions.

We may have been part of a quota sample if we have been stopped in the street by an interviewer who wishes to ask some questions. However we have not been randomly selected because people walking in another street had no chance of being selected for the survey. Despite this limitation quota sampling can be very accurate especially when:

- quotas are correctly identified;
- the interviewer fills the quotas correctly.

Cluster sampling

This is another non-random method of sampling which has the advantage that it can be used when no sampling frame exists. It is often used for populations that have a large geographical spread. Individuals are not identified but rather areas or 'clusters' are selected as being potentially representative of the population. All members of the population within the cluster are then sampled. If we were seeking to survey firms who used drink vending machines we might select three distinct areas perhaps an inner city, a suburb, and a rural area. We would telephone each firm in each area to establish if they used drink vending machines. The sample would subsequently be those who used drink vending machines.

5.4 Sample size

The size of our sample is as important as the method we choose. The sample needs to be large enough to be reasonably representative but obviously the cost of collecting the data increases with the number in the sample! Although there is no universal formula for calculating sample size there are a number of factors we need to consider:

- amount of time and money we have available;
- the degree of accuracy required. The greater the accuracy required the larger the sample. For large populations a sample of 100 may be sufficient for a quick market research exercise requiring an accuracy of plus or minus 10%. A sample size of 500 would be required for an accuracy of plus or minus 5%. For sampling where an accuracy of plus or minus 1% is required the sample size will need to be approximately 10,000;
- the size of the population. For small populations smaller size samples are needed to obtain the same level of accuracy;
- the number of sub-samples required. When a stratified sample is being used it is important that the smaller groups within the sample contain sufficiently large numbers to be significant.

As a rough rule of thumb a sample size of less than 30 is unlikely to be large enough, even for small populations.

5.5 Summary

- A sample is used as a basis for making some estimation of the characteristics of the whole group from which the sample has been selected.
- Sampling is used as an alternative to collecting data from the entire population. This is usually either because it is impossible to obtain data from the population, or it is too costly and time consuming.
- A sample should represent the whole population fairly, that is it should not be biased to any part of the population.
- In order that samples can be seen to have been selected without bias a mechanistic method of sample selection is often used.
- Different sampling methods are appropriate to different situations.
- The size of sample selected will always be a trade off between the need for an accurate representation of the total population and the amount of time and money available.

Further reading

Business Mathematics and Statistics (Chapter 2), Francis A, DP PUBLICATIONS (1993)
How to lie with Statistics (Chapter 1), Huff D, PENGUIN (1973)
Quantitative Approaches in Business Studies (Chapter 2), Morris C, PITMAN (1989)
Survey Methods in Social Investigation (Chapter), Moser KA and Kalton G, GOWER (1979)

Unit 6: Collecting primary data: questionnaire and interview schedule design

6.1 Introduction

In the previous unit we examined a number of different ways in which we can obtain our sample. If secondary data is not available or is not suitable for some reason, maybe because it is out of date, biased or based on particular assumptions, we may have to collect our own primary data. Usually this will involve sampling. So, having selected a sample from the population how are we going to collect the data?

Before we made a decision on how we are going to collect the data we need to have considered three key questions:

1. What are we actually trying to find out?
   Unfortunately it is very easy to start a survey without thinking it through, until it is too late! So to avoid this error it is worth asking ourselves what we are trying to find out and why? Is the data available from existing sources? Is there any other useful data we could collect at the same time? (This is discussed in unit 4).

2. What are our constraints?
   All surveys take time and cost money. Are we clear about the resources we have at our disposal? Will the data be confidential?

3. How will we collect the data?
   In view of the aims of the survey and the constraints, which we have established from answering the first two questions, what method will work best?

The three main methods for collecting primary data from a sample are:

- interview
- questionnaire
- observation

Interview

Many surveys rely on personal interviews. One of the advantages is making personal contact with the person who is being interviewed. This helps the communication process and means any difficulties or misunderstandings can often be cleared up. It also means that the response rate is likely to be higher than might be expected with questionnaires.

Data is either collected using an interview schedule or a checklist of points. In the majority of cases interview schedules are used when we want to ask the same questions to a large number of people, whereas checklists are used for more in depth interviews with a smaller number of people. The interviewer asks the questions and also records the responses.

The greatest danger with this method is that the interviewer may bias the responses, however unwittingly. Interviews are also expensive, due to the time they take.

Questionnaire

Questionnaires are used in similar situations to interview schedules. The main difference between a questionnaire and an interview is that for a questionnaire the person answering the questions (the *respondent*) records their own answers. They provide a cheaper way of collecting data and there is no built-in interviewer bias, although there could be bias in the ways the questions are phrased. However, response rates tend to be lower, questions may be misunderstood and there is no way of knowing whether the answers are serious or not.

Questionnaires are often distributed by post.

Observation

The final method you can use to collect data is by observation. Direct observation involves watching people or processes and noting what happens but with no interference.

Obviously, the method we use to collect data depends on what the data is. Simple facts and figures such as the amount of time it takes a machine operator to do a certain task can usually be observed. Data on feelings or attitudes is easier to obtain through interviews or questionnaires.

6.2 Questionnaire and interview schedule design: an overview

Let us assume that we have decided what data we need to collect (unit 4) and that the only possible way to collect it is either through a questionnaire or an interview schedule. We have also selected our sample (unit 5) but want to make sure that it is representative.

Although we are looking at questionnaire design, the same rules apply to interview schedules. This is because the main difference is that a questionnaire needs to be even more easily understood as an interviewer is unavailable to help. By contrast in an interview we can make use of the interviewer by, for example, using visual prompt cards as part of the schedule.

The accuracy of the data we collect using the questionnaire, and the response rate, depends to a large extent on how we word the questions and how the questionnaire is laid out on the page. We can split the design process into two parts:

- designing the individual questions;
- putting it all together – designing the complete questionnaire or interview schedule.

6.3 Designing individual questions

Types of question

There are five main types of question which are used in questionnaires: filter, open, pre-coded, self coded and check.

- *Filter* questions are used to make sure which question is answered by whom. The first question is the filter and predetermines if the second question is answered. For example:

  1. Do you have a paid job? Yes ☐

     No ☐

  (if 'yes' go to question 2, if 'no' go to question 7)

  2. Please describe your job in the space below...

  In this case question 1 is the filter question and predetermines whether or not the respondent will answer question 2.

- *Open* questions are used when we are unsure of the response we are going to receive, when we require a detailed answer, or when we want what is upper most in the respondents mind. Question 2 (above) is an example of an open question. Here is another:

3. Please list the factors that made you choose Zappo Washing Powder below...

A major problem with open questions is that we will receive different amounts of information from different respondents. In addition the data collected may be difficult to summarise, and will need to be coded prior to numerical analysis.

- *Pre-coded* questions are used when there is a well established range of possible answers. In effect the information is coded by the respondents. These questions are often used to discover respondents' opinions:

4. Was the service you received? Good ☐ Reasonable ☐ Poor ☐

This can be expanded to record finer shades of opinions. In addition you can ensure the respondent does not 'sit on the fence', by omitting a middle value:

5. Was the service you received? Very Good ☐ Good ☐ Poor ☐ Very Poor ☐

Pre-coded questions are also used when the range of possible answers is well established and limited:

6. Which of the services provided by this bank do you use?

	Use	Don't Use
Current Account	☐	☐
Deposit Account	☐	☐
Credit Card	☐	☐
Foreign Currency	☐	☐

Other (please describe) ....

....

As can be seen in question 6 (above) it is useful to include the category 'other' in case we have missed out one of the 'services' or the respondent does not feel that their response fits into any of the categories given. This means we can subsequently check and, where appropriate, recode these responses.

- *Self coded* questions are used to save time and effort as the respondent codes the answer. These are particularly useful when the data is going to be analysed by computer as it means our data is already in the correct form for typing it in. However it is important that the instructions are clear. Here is an example of a pre-coded question:

7. What is your year of birth?

1	9		

(e.g. for 1959 write)

1	9	5	9

- *Check* questions are often included to make sure the respondent is answering consistently. They are usually separated by a number of other questions and are used predominantly in long interview schedules. The check question below could be used to check the response to question 7 above. If the respondent put the current year in question 7 this would be immediately clear. If we are entering the data into a computer it is usually possible to program the computer to compare responses with check questions.

32. How old are you? [|] Years [|] Months

(e.g. for 33 years and 9 months write) [3|3] Years [0|9] Months

Wording of questions

Each question in a questionnaire or interview schedule needs careful consideration. Here are some points that we need to consider when writing questions:

- the words we use should be familiar to those filling in the questionnaire. It is no good asking small children 'to list the artefacts they have discovered on vacation'. So, level of language is important. Also, avoid jargon, abbreviations and colloquialisms;
- avoid words which sound alike as this might cause confusion;
- avoid too many information carrying words;
- all questions should be clear and unambiguous. 'Are you happy to travel?' is a poor question as it may have more than one meaning. Questions with numbers can also be ambiguous. If we ask people how much they earn and pre-code their answer into three overlapping groups (up to £10,000, £10,000 to £20,000, and £20,000 and over) they will be unclear which group to choose if they earn £10,000 or £20,000;
- questions should be short, precise and accurate. Long questions are difficult to understand and often result in no response at all: 'Have you, or have you ever had (within the last three years) occasion to complain about the way you (or your colleagues) have been treated (vis-a-vis your work) by your superiors (or other staff)?'
- avoid multiple questions. Ask one question at a time: 'Have you, or your colleagues, ever been cold in the open plan office?' This question would be difficult if there was a Yes/No answer required and you had never been cold but your colleague had;
- avoid the double negative as this often creates confusion: 'Isn't it true that you haven't always been on time?'
- avoid questions about abstract topics which will have no meaning to the respondent;
- avoid embarrassing the person responding to the survey. People are likely to, at best, refuse and at worst punch us in the face or throw our survey in the bin!
- avoid bias by implying the right answer in your question: 'Do you think, like all reasonable people, that .... '
- try to limit the possible responses so that the respondent gives a clear-cut answer. We are unlikely to find out much if any individual can respond with a long list of possible and correct answers.

6.4 Designing the survey form

Introducing the survey

At the start of any questionnaire, or interview schedule, we should explain clearly and concisely why we want the survey to be completed. In other words, communicate our objectives. Also we should give some idea of how long the person will need to spend answering the questions and, where appropriate, assurances of confidentiality.

> 'This survey of staff attitudes is being carried out by the Management Services Department to try and improve office layout. Your co-operation will be extremely useful, the forms are anonymous and confidential and should only take you 10 minutes at most to complete.'
>
> 'If you have any questions or queries please contact John Smith on 0123-456789'

As indicated above, it is useful to have a contact name and telephone number, so that if the respondent has any queries or questions they have a contact point. For interviews the interviewer should always carry and show some form of identification.

The order and flow of questions

When constructing the questionnaire it is a good idea to give some thought to the order of the questions, there are a number of key points we need to consider:

- start with straightforward questions that are easy to answer. This will put the respondent at their ease and allow them to get quickly into the questionnaire;
- put any more complex questions towards the middle of the questionnaire. By this stage respondents should be confidently completing the survey but not yet tired or bored;
- personal questions should come towards the end (age, occupation, income). On seeing these the respondent may refuse to answer any more questions, if they are at the end of the survey we will still have collected the rest of the data;
- any sensitive questions should come at the end. This allows time to gain the respondent's confidence but, if they are not completed, at least the majority of the survey will have been.

The questions should be put in a logical order so that the questionnaire has its own flow and internal order. This may involve filter questions, or phrases such as....

'I am now going to ask you about....'

to lead the respondent into a new topic.

The layout of the survey

Layout is particularly crucial for questionnaires as it is our only form of communication with the respondent and it will affect the response we get. The following points are important:

- type the survey in a typeface that is easy to read;
- avoid the use of *italics* or CAPITALS. **Semi-bold** characters are often preferred, especially by the partially sighted;
- avoid excessively long or short lines as this reduces legibility;
- avoid the questions being cramped up on the page as this puts readers off answering it. A thick pile of paper is equally off putting;
- print the survey, especially questionnaires, on good quality paper to give a good image. Colour plays an important part in achieving a good response rate. Warm pastel shades such as yellow and pink will generate more responses than cold colours such as blue or green. Bright colours are best avoided and white is a good neutral colour;
- use different types of question to maintain respondents interest;

- (if it is a questionnaire) make sure that it is easy to understand and contains detailed instructions to the respondent on how to fill it in;
- (if it is an interview schedule) make sure it is only printed on one side of the paper and that all instructions to the interviewer are included. Remember the interviewer only has two hands!

Finally, remember to thank the respondent for completing the survey.

6.5 Checking the sample is representative

When undertaking a sample survey it is a good idea to include a question, or questions, to enable us to check that the sample is representative of the total population. If we are undertaking a survey of all adults living in a town data will probably be available from the local authority giving the number of males and females in that town split by age groups

Age	Male	Female
18 – 19		
20 – 29		
30 – 39		
40 – 49		
50 – 59		
60 – 64		
65 plus		

If we include questions about age and gender in our survey we can then compare the age and gender of those who responded to our survey with the total population. This will enable us to check if our sample is representative of the total population in terms of the age and gender.

6.6 Pilot testing

It is always necessary to 'pilot test' a questionnaire or interview schedule before using it to collect data. This can easily be done with a small group of people selected to represent the target population. The aim of *pilot testing* is to detect any errors or problems in the layout and design of the questionnaire and the nature of the data it is actually collecting. It is much better to make mistakes at the pilot stage, when they can be rectified, than notice them after the data has been collected!

As with sampling there is no rule about the number of people upon which to conduct a pilot test. However for a small market research survey of, say, 100 people, you should pilot test the questionnaire or interview schedule on between five and ten people. Larger surveys will require much more extensive pilot testing.

6.7 Summary

- Questionnaires are designed to be filled in by the person answering the questions (respondent). They are often administered by post.
- Responses to interview schedules are filled in by an interviewer who asks the questions.
- The process of designing a survey can be divided into designing the questions, and designing the survey form.
- Wherever possible a variety of questions should be used. Attention should be paid to the order and flow of the questions as well as the overall layout of the survey.
- Where necessary questions should be included to check that the sample is representative.
- Surveys should always be pilot tested.

Further reading:

Survey Methods in Social Investigation (Chapter 13) Moser KA & Kalton G, GOWER (1979)
Statistics (Chapter 15) Owen F & Jones R, PITMAN (1990)

Unit 7: Types of data and tabulating data

7.1 Introduction

Often in business when we receive raw data, be it from primary or secondary sources, we need to organise the data into a more easily understandable form. The way in which we do this depends upon the type of data: categorical or quantitative, the latter being subdivided into continuous or discrete. We will discuss these terms in further detail later in this unit. The most common method of organising and summarising data used in business is the table. This can either be done manually or, as is increasingly common, using a computer spreadsheet or statistics package. Whichever way we choose to generate our table it is important that the table is presented so that it is easy to understand and interpret.

7.2 Types of data

Let us suppose we work for a company manufacturing baby products for use in United Kingdom hospitals and wish to conduct a survey to see if our incubators are improving the current survival rate of new born babies. Our population is therefore all United Kingdom births over a period and as it has a definite number, we term this *finite*. There are also *infinite* populations such as the repeat results of a scientific experiment. It is not feasible to collect data on every birth in the United Kingdom, not even for a single year, therefore the data needs to be collected from a sample, one which we expect to be representative of the total population.

The choice of what data we collect is obviously important. The items about which we need to collect data are called *variables*. The variables we need to collect data on for each birth include:

- weight at birth;
- gestation period;
- number of babies born to the mother prior to this birth;
- whether or not our company's incubators were used.

These, like all data, can be classified into two main types:

Categorical: categorical data consists of values which cannot be expressed numerically but can be grouped into categories. In our example the data we collect on whether or not our company's incubators were used is categorical. This data has two possible categories: used and not used.

Quantitative: quantitative data consists of values that can be expressed numerically as quantities. In our example this could be data recording weight at birth and gestation period.

Quantitative data can further be sub divided into two groups:

Discrete, where individual items of numeric data can have one of a finite number of values within a specified range, such as number of babies born to the mother prior to this birth. The value can usually be counted and it changes in discrete units, in this case whole numbers.

Continuous, where numeric data is not restricted to specific values and is usually measured on a continuous scale. In our example the weight of a baby at birth would be continuous data and would probably fall somewhere along a continuous scale from 1 kilogram to 6 kilograms, see diagram below. When dealing with continuous data there are limitations on the precision of measurement and, as a result, a degree of approximation is used.

1 kg *Baby's weight somewhere along here* 6 kg

7.3 Principles of good tabulation

Tables serve two main purposes:

- to provide results in a compact form. These should be easy to understand and quick to digest;
- to summarise data for the 'business person' so that they do not have to sift through the raw data to answer every question.

To aid this it is a good idea to make sure that every table:

- has a title that is brief but descriptive. Many tables are photocopied and presented away from the accompanying text. Without a title it is impossible to know to what the data refers;
- has brief descriptive headings to both rows and columns;
- states clearly the units used, for example 'thousands' or '000's', and explains what these mean where necessary: 'passenger miles = total miles travelled by passengers;'
- states the source of the data used in the table;
- places columns and rows in a logical sequence, for example: '0-5 years, 6-10 years, 11-15 years.'

It also aids interpretation if:

- when there is a large volume of data to be shown a number of small tables are used rather than one big one;
- footnotes are used to explain individual data entries further if required. This is especially useful for irregularities such as 'figure represents two weeks due to Christmas close down;'
- tables are enclosed in a box or a frame.

7.4 Tables for categorical and discrete data

As we have discussed the easiest way to summarise data is by constructing a table. Presentation is extremely important: a messy cramped table is unlikely to convey information especially to those unfamiliar with the subject area. When secondary data is used it is often already tabulated. The example below tabulates the number of dependants of employees who work for a small company. The variable on which we have collected data is the number of dependants, and this has been split into six discrete components, one for each of the possible numbers of dependants. This has been summarised as the number of employees (the frequency) who have 0, 1, 2, 3, 4, or 5 dependants (the discrete variable). This form of table is called a *frequency distribution*.

Number of Employees with Dependants: June 1993

Number of Dependants	Number of Employees
0	12
1	16
2	18
3	10
4	1
5	2
Total	**59**

Source: The New Computer Company Personnel System

This information is easy to understand in this format and it is easy to transfer to a diagram.

The other main form of table presents data for two or more variables in the same table. This is sometimes referred to as a *cross tabulation* or *contingency table* to indicate dependence between the variables. The table below shows a cross tabulation of number of car accidents by gender of employee.

Number of Car Accidents by Gender of Employee 1992-3

	Male	Female	Total Employees
0 accidents	15	20	35
1 accidents	15	2	17
2 accidents	7	0	7
Total accidents	37	22	59

Source: The New Computer Company Personnel System

7.5 Tally marks

If we are using primary data, it may need organising before it is useful. For example, a survey collects data from each respondent about their marital status (categorical data). The results when abstracted from each survey form look like this:

> Married, Widowed, Divorced, Single, Single, Married, Widowed, Separated, Married, Divorced, Married, Widowed, Divorced, Single, Single, Married, Widowed, Separated, Married, Divorced, Married, Widowed, Divorced, Single, Single, Married, Widowed, Separated, Married, Divorced, Single.

These will form the variable marital status which will have five components (categories), one for each of the possible states. To construct a frequency distribution we would:

1. Draw up a list of all possible values, these will form our components;
2. Work through the data placing a *tally mark* against the appropriate component, building up '5-bar gates' as we go to give us the *class frequency*;
3. Add up the tally marks to give the class frequencies and tidy the table up.

Marital Status of Respondents 1993

List	Tally	Frequency
Single	~~IIII~~ II	7
Married	~~IIII~~ IIII	9
Separated	III	3
Divorced	~~IIII~~ I	6
Widowed	~~IIII~~ I	6

Source: Survey conducted by Market Research Company

7.6 Tables for continuous and grouped discrete data

When a continuous or a discrete variable has a large number of different data values, it is unlikely that a frequency distribution using all the components will summarise the data sufficiently to enable us to easily interpret it. In many cases the table would take up a number of pages, and although it would be better than looking at the raw data the format would be confusing. For example, a frequency distribution showing the number of days absent (discrete data) over the past year for employees of a large manufacturing company might include a component for each of the values from 0 to 365. It is likely that this would cover at least five pages and would be in far too much detail to understand the overall pattern of absence.

It is for this reason that we sometimes group discrete values together and form a *grouped frequency distribution* which arranges the values into groups which do not overlap. We treat data which is continuous in the same way.

For example: We work for the Quality Control Department of a manufacturing company which tests (to destruction) a sample of 100 long life batteries each month. Their lives in hours (continuous data), are listed below to the nearest hour (for ease of interpretation the minimum and maximum values are **<u>in bold and underlined</u>**):

90	101	122	84	60	99	115	142	126	116
128	105	93	91	68	106	107	91	101	113
140	62	76	138	114	103	95	92	99	63
98	87	103	126	99	92	114	124	64	85
94	105	117	82	117	107	96	97	81	89
112	133	105	73	94	116	**<u>145</u>**	92	119	108
79	80	**<u>54</u>**	91	69	85	125	104	124	101
89	102	110	96	97	109	121	77	80	114
85	124	136	96	88	92	128	56	90	71
102	96	108	98	110	82	94	76	100	95

It would not be very beneficial to look at the frequency distribution for each of the individual values above, so we will group the values into equal width groups which do not overlap These are termed *class intervals*, and they are sub-divisions of the total range of possible values of the variable 'battery life'.

So to review these terms:

- *class interval* is a sub-division of the total range of values which a variable may take;
- the *class frequency* is the number of variables whose values fall within a given class interval;
- therefore the *frequency distribution* of a variable is the set of class-intervals for that variable together with the associated class-frequencies.

Deciding on the class intervals

We have established that we wish to group the battery data (above) into a series of equal width class intervals. The use of equal width class intervals is often necessary if we are using a computer spreadsheet as many can only cope with equal width class intervals.

To create sensible groupings we need to:

1. establish the way in which the data was collected.

   In this case the actual life of each battery was rounded to the nearest whole hour. This means that the first value, recorded as 90, was in fact either 89.5 or above but less than 90.5. As the data is continuous and we must remember how the data was rounded.

   The range of possible values for the following battery lives (rounded to the nearest hour are therefore:

   101 either 100.5 or above but less than 101.5
   122 either 121.5 or above but less than 122.5

2. establish what the lowest and highest values are.

   Lowest 54
   Highest 145

For ease we will use 10 equal width class intervals of 10 hours. The *class width* is the difference between the two boundaries of a class interval.

There are four (main) class interval structures which we could use for our battery life data but only one is suitable:

1. **Class interval**
   50 – 59
   60 – 69
   70 – 79
   :
   :
   140 – 149

   There is no ambiguity but this structure is **not suitable** for continuous data because of the gap between class intervals. If we take the value 69.75. It will have been rounded to 70 and hence put in the class interval 70 – 79 where it does not really belong. There is no place for the value in this structure as it lies somewhere between the first and second class intervals.

2. **Class interval**
   50+
   60+
   70+
   :
   :
   140+

   This is sometimes written as 50 – < 60 which means 50 to less than 60. Although this is a continuous scale it is **not suitable** for our battery life data. If we consider the value 69.75 it should belong in the 60+ class interval, but as it has been rounded it has been placed in the 70+ class interval which is incorrect. This structure could be used **if** the data was not rounded prior to recording.

3. **Class interval**
   50 – 60
   60 – 70
   70 – 80
   :
   :
   140 – 150

   This is **not suitable** for continuous data as there is ambiguity in the cases 60, 70, 80 etc., since we do not know which class interval to put them in. However, these class intervals are used in some business tables (and diagrams) with the footnote: '50 – 60' means 50 and over but less than 60.'

4. **Class interval**
   49.5 – < 59.5
   59.5 – < 69.5
   69.5 – < 79.5
   :
   :
   139.5 – < 149.5

   In order that each data item is placed in the correct class interval we must therefore **use this structure**. Unlike the structures in 2 and 3 this is unambiguous despite data rounding to whole numbers. In effect we have taken the first structure and *bridged the gap* to make it continuous. This is not the same as structure 3 as, even though the data has been rounded at collection, there is no ambiguity.

Class boundaries

The values used to delimit classes are called *class boundaries.* The left-hand (lower) ones are called *lower class boundaries (LCB)* and the right-hand ones are called *upper class boundaries (UCB).* The data values in each class will always be less than the upper class boundary.

If we group the battery data into 10 groups with class width 10, using structure 4, we obtain the following:

Life expectancy in hours of Batteries tested to destruction (1993)

Class Interval life expectancy)	LCB[1]	UCB[2]	Group Frequency (f) (number of batteries tested)
49.5 – < 59.5	49.5	59.5	2
59.5 – < 69.5	59.5	69.5	6
69.5 – < 79.5	69.5	79.5	6
79.5 – < 89.5	79.5	89.5	13
89.5 – < 99.5	89.5	99.5	26
99.5 – < 109.5	99.5	109.5	18
109.5 – < 119.5	109.5	119.5	13
119.5 – < 129.5	119.5	129.5	10
129.5 – < 139.5	129.5	139.5	3
139.5 – < 149.5	139.5	149.5	3

1 = Lower Class Boundary, 2 = Upper Class Boundary

Source: Quality Control Department

The advantages of grouping data are that:

- it makes subsequent calculations quicker (and easier) as we will see in unit 10.
- it is easier to understand and interpret the distribution of the data and any overall trends once any small irregularities have been smoothed by grouping.

However a disadvantage is the loss of detail due to grouping.

Helpful hints when constructing class boundaries

1. If given continuous data to subdivide into class-intervals, try to obtain between 6 and 12 classes of equal width as this usually leads to a reasonable graphical representation of the data.

2. Try and use class widths in multiples of 10, 5 or 2 units as people find these easier to understand.

3. a. If given *rounded* data which is, in reality, continuous construct class boundaries which 'bridge the gap' (to make the structures continuous) and overcome the rounding problem.

This usually requires the introduction of half-values. This strange procedure is needed not only to accommodate some computer spreadsheets but also to enable the production of the correct graphical representation (as we will see in unit 10).

b. The one exception is when the variable is age. When we ask someone their age they will always tell you their age last birthday (except in the case of a young child or someone who always replies '21'). This means that even on the eve of their 40th birthday they are 39. So the normal rules of rounding do not apply to age, and groupings such as:

16 – 20, 21 – 29, 30 – 39, 40 – 59, 60 – 74

whilst allowable in a frequency table, are converted to

16 – 21, 21 – 30, 30 – 40, 40 – 60, 60 – 75

to give a continuous structure for use in a diagram. A note must be included that the upper class boundaries themselves are not included in the group i.e. for 16 – 21 we read 16 or over but under 21.

In this example the class widths vary. This is quite common with age data as groupings are chosen to reflect life cycle stage.

4. Some tables have *open* first or last (or both) class intervals. Again this is common for age data, for example:

under 16
75 and over.

Unfortunately many computer spreadsheets ask you to state the maximum and minimum values for your class boundaries.

A commonly used method is to give the open-ended class interval the same width as the interval adjacent to it. Thus for our age data 'under 16' becomes '11 -< 16' (i.e. a width of 5 like the 16 – 21 class interval). These are also the boundaries which would be used in any diagram of the data.

7.7 Calculation of percentages

Often with tables we wish to display each class frequency as a percentage of the total of the class frequencies for that variable. If we take the marital status table created in section 7.5 we can see how this is done.

Marital Status of Respondents 1993

Components	Frequency	Percentage[1]
Single	7	22.6
Married	9	29.0
Separated	3	9.7
Divorced	6	19.4
Widowed	6	19.4
Total	**31**	**100**

1 = Percentages rounded to 1 decimal place so may not sum to 100

Source: Survey conducted by Market Research Company

Total the component frequencies, in this case 31.

Take each component frequency and divide by the total component frequency, for 'Single' this would be:

$$\frac{7}{31} = 0.2258$$

Multiply the answer to this by 100, for 'Single' this would be:

$$0.2258 \times 100 = 22.6\%$$

when rounded to one decimal place.

7.8 Summary

- Data can be categorised as categorical and quantitative. Quantitative data can be further sub divided into discrete and continuous data.
- Often secondary data is presented in the form of tables.
- Tables must be clearly labelled in order to be understood.
- When constructing tables with quantitative data it is important to choose the correct class boundaries based upon how the data was collected. For the purpose of constructing tables continuous and grouped discrete data can be treated in the same way.

Further reading:

Management Information and Statistics (Chapter 4), Bee R & Bee F, IPM (1990)
Quantitative Approaches in Business Studies (Chapter 3), Morris C, PITMAN (1989)
A First Course in Business Mathematics and Statistics (Chapter 6), Rowe RN, DP PUBLICATIONS (1991)

Unit 8: Diagrams for categorical and discrete data: bar charts

8.1 Introduction to diagrams

Although the easiest way we can present business data is by using a table it is often not the most effective. Diagrams register a far more immediate and greater impression with little effort required from the reader.

Within business diagrams are a means of communication. The choice of diagram depends upon the type of data, the likely audience and what we are trying to say. Diagrams are unlikely to provide information as precisely as a table but can give a quick overall impression of the findings. This makes them a very powerful tool which should not be abused.

When presenting data using diagrams there are, like with tables, some general rules that should be applied:

- there should always be a title stating clearly what is being shown. If the title is missing or not clear the reader cannot be certain what the diagram is about. A good title would be 'Seasonally adjusted number of unemployed people in the United Kingdom, 1981 to date;'
- diagrams should always include a statement of the source of data, for example: 'Source: Department of Employment Unemployment Statistics.' If the source of data is missing we should be wary of the data that is illustrated;

- the axes should always be clearly labelled, stating what is being shown and, where appropriate, the units. If percentages are used then some indication of the absolute values should be given for example '100% = 2,800,000.'

There are several different methods of presenting data available, some of the most common for categorical and discrete data are:

- bar charts or column charts
  - simple bar charts
  - multiple bar charts
  - component or stacked bar charts
- pie charts
- pictograms

in this unit we are going to look at bar charts, and in unit 9 pie charts and pictograms.

8.2 Simple bar charts

The *bar chart* is perhaps the most commonly used and easiest to draw of all the diagrams. The technique of constructing a bar chart will be demonstrated by using the data in the following table:

Number of Families with Children

Number of Children per Family	0	1	2	3	4	5
Frequency	8	15	23	9	7	3

Source: Survey of Households 1992

A bar chart has two axes, one for the variable and other for the frequency. The *variable axis* is usually horizontal and is split into the components of the variable. The *frequency axis* is usually vertical and is given a scale. Both axes should be clearly labelled. So, in our example the blank chart will look like this:

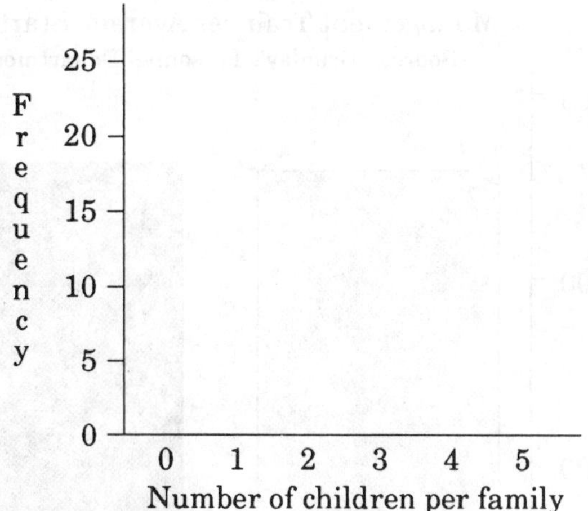

There are three basic rules which we should follow when drawing the bars:

1. The width of each bar should be the same.
2. A gap should be left between the bars (the amount of space is a matter of personal preference, although half a bar width is usual).
3. The height of the bar is determined by the frequency.

Here is the completed bar chart. You will notice that a title and a source of data have also been added.

Number of Families with Children

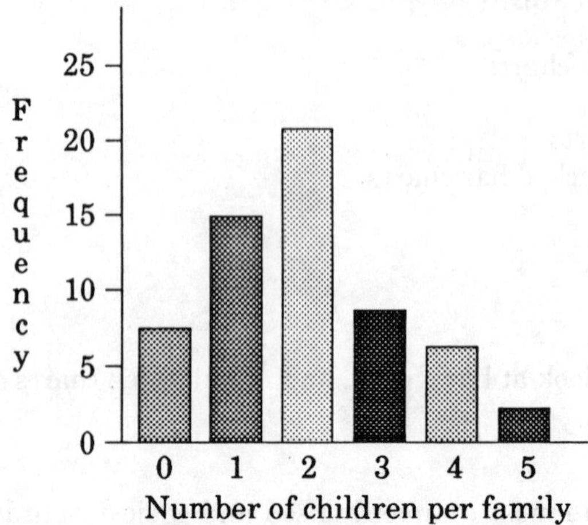

(Source: Survey of Households 1992)

Problems of scale

Often the frequencies of each component are very large compared to the size of the differences between them. To fit the bar chart on the page the frequency axis has to be drawn in such a way that small differences may not easily be seen. If we try to use a large scale to enable differences to be seen easily, then the diagram will become too large to fit onto the page.

We have collected data recording the average start pay of management trainees. In 1992 it was £12,945 whilst in 1993 it was £13,227. The bar chart illustrating this (below) fails to show this increase in average start pay clearly:

BRUNLEY'S SUPERMARKETS
Management Trainees Average Start Pay
(Source: Brunley's Personnel Department)

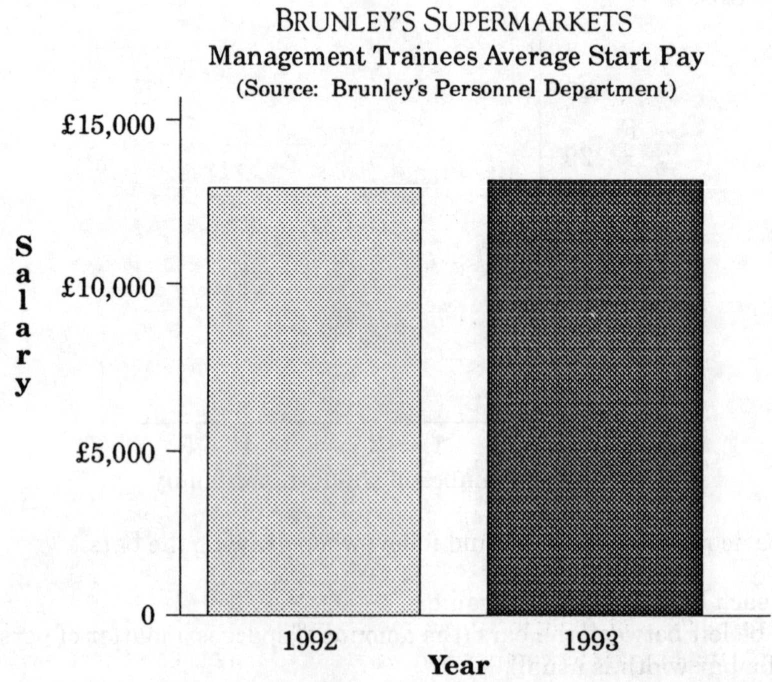

The solution is to put a break in the frequency axis. We must still remember to always start the frequency axis scale at zero. Then we place a break, represented by a zig-zag line, in the axis below the lowest frequency in the data. Breaking the scale like this is particularly important when dealing with large figures. For example if the lowest value was 12,945,000 an extremely tall graph would be needed to illustrate the data. The result of including a break in the scale can be seen below for our average start pay data. Notice how the difference in column heights is larger than in the previous bar chart.

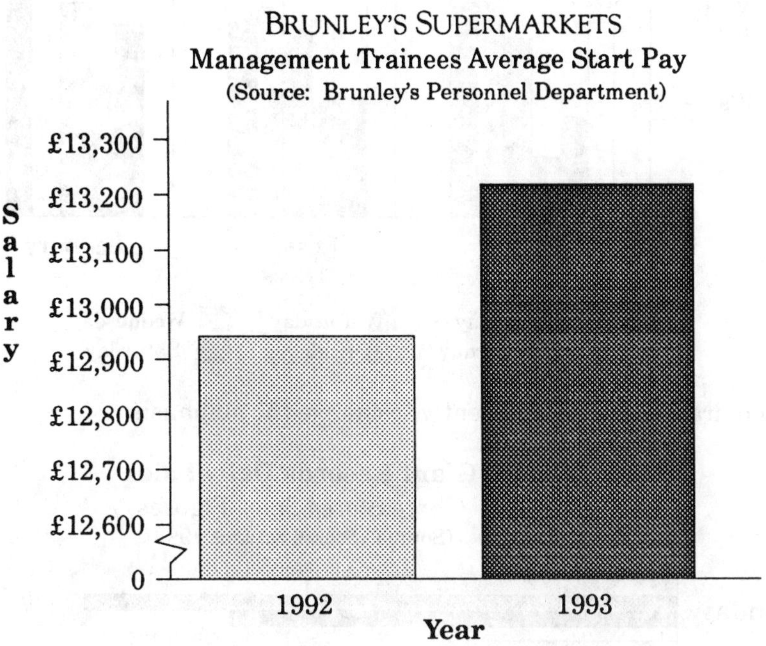

8.3 Multiple bar charts

We construct *multiple bar charts* in the same way as a simple bar chart. This time we use two or more bars to illustrate the data for each component of our variables.

Let us consider the sales figures for three record stores belonging to the company Giant Records:

Giant Records Daily Sales – 3 Stores Sales Figures (£'s)

Day	Malvern	Ross	Ledbury
Monday	8,891	15,740	11,983
Tuesday	5,091	6,073	9,671
Wednesday	3,071	5,871	6,791
Thursday	8,971	14,897	10,891
Friday	13,602	12,894	9,261
Saturday	15,753	10,005	13,002
Total	**55,379**	**65,480**	**61,599**

Source: Stores Returns 1993

There are two distinct ways of constructing a multiple bar chart using this data. The choice of which one to use depends upon the comparison we want to make. The chart below is designed to make the comparison between days easy within each of the three branches.

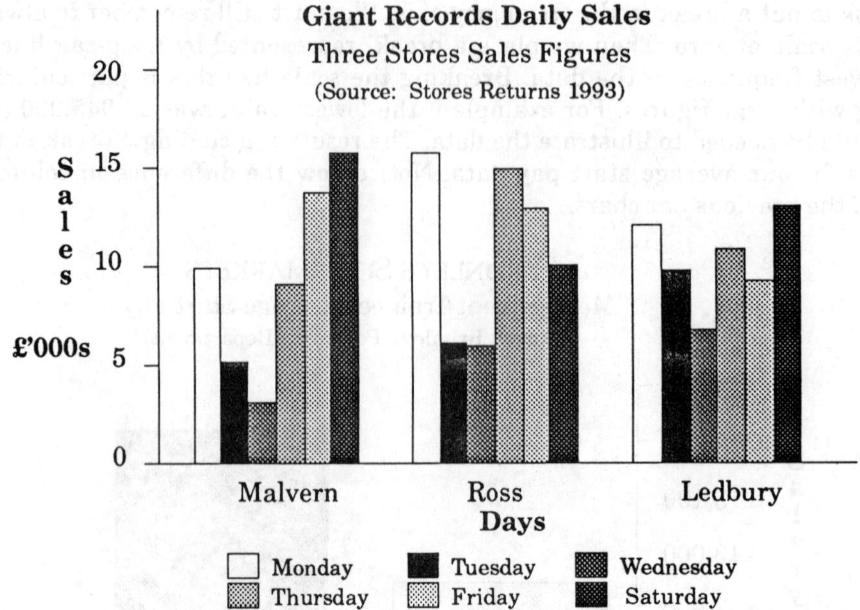

However, we could draw the chart differently to change the emphasis:

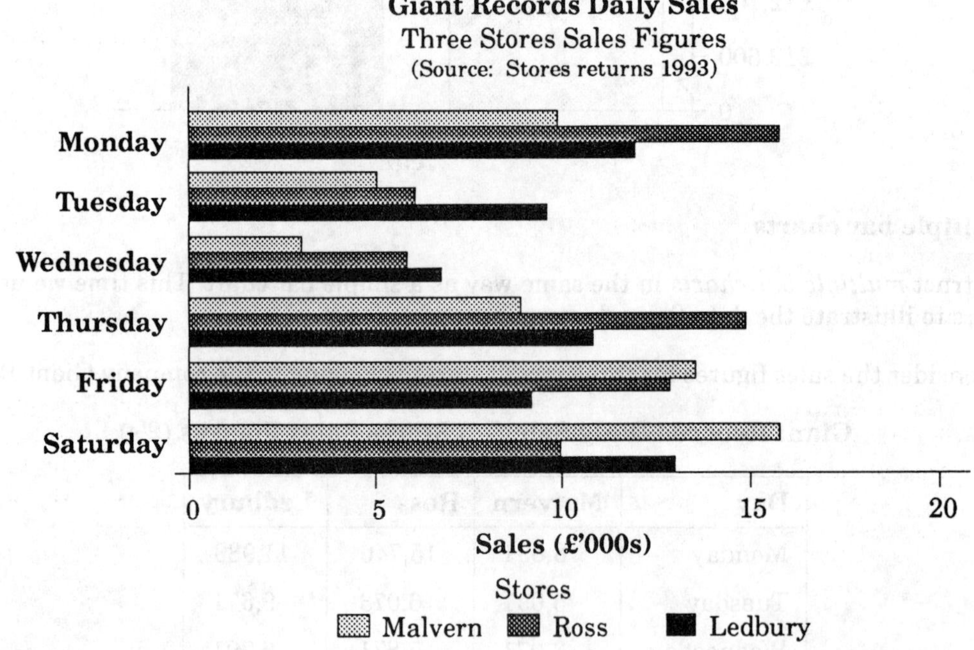

This chart presents exactly the same data as the first one but emphasises the comparison between stores rather than days. In addition we have drawn it as a horizontal bar chart.

8.4 Stacked (or component) bar charts

We can also display our Giant Records' daily sales data using a *stacked bar chart*. We take the individual components, in this case daily sales figures, and 'stack' them on top of each other to provide a single bar for each store. The advantage of this is that it provides a picture of the total sales of the store whilst still including the split of sales between days.

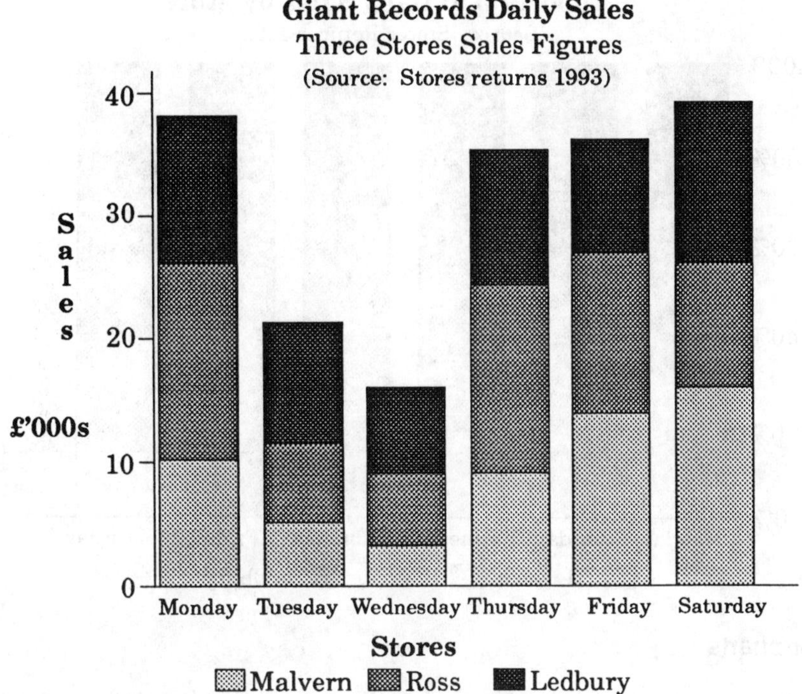

Each bar represents the total sales for the day for all stores, the three components representing the three stores.

When drawing stacked bar charts it is important that:

- the components are stacked in the same order throughout;
- a key (legend) identifies the components;
- not too many components are included in the interests of clarity.

8.5 Percentage Component Bar Charts

Percentage component bar charts are often used in business publications. These diagrams are similar to the stacked bar chart except that each bar represents 100% and the components change proportionately within the bar. The percentage component bar chart is used to compare the proportion of each component to the total and to show changes in this proportion. It does not show any of the original data, this is replace by the proportions (percentages). It is therefore only used when proportions are more important than the actual magnitude of the data.

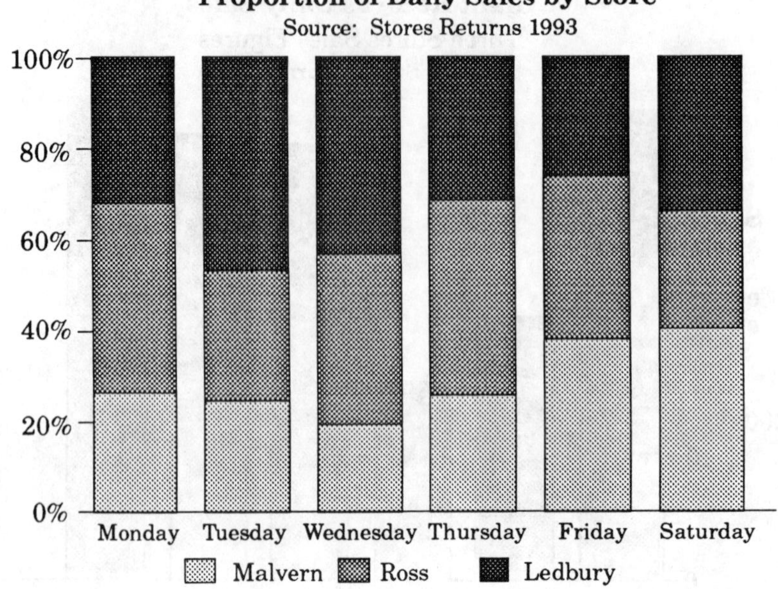

8.6 Misuse of bar charts

Bar charts are used a great deal in newspapers and business publications and, as we have already discussed, are useful for displaying data. They also provide an easy way to distort the data and mislead the reader. This distortion occurs when the person drawing the graph or chart wishes to emphasise certain facts or misrepresent or hide the data. It is important that we take account of this when we interpret or draw bar charts.

The most common misuses of bar charts are:

- not labelling the axes. Any frequency axis without a scale is meaningless, but bar charts are often drawn without them in an attempt to mislead;
- making one bar wider than others in order to emphasise its importance.

The bar chart below illustrates these two points:

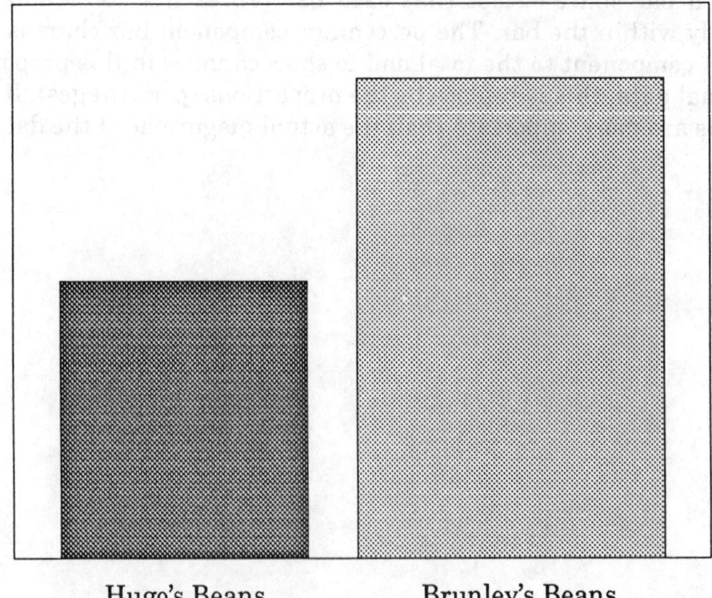

This bar chart actually means nothing but gives the impression that Brunley's Beans are somehow better.

- altering the scale of the vertical axis to exaggerate the differences between the bars. The two bar charts below show the same information:

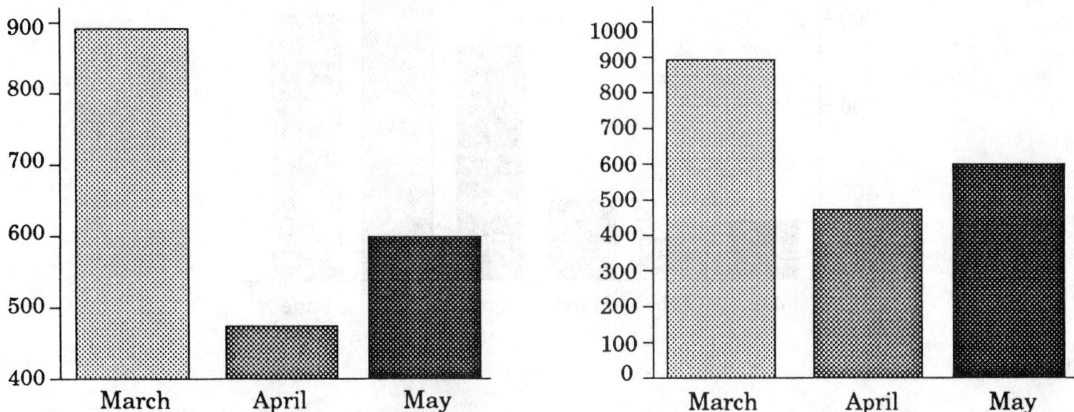

From the bar chart on the left it appears that sales in March were more than double sales in May but the true picture is given on the chart on the right. The vertical scale should always start at zero and where there is a break in scale this should be represented by a zig-zag line (unlike above). The inclusion of a zig-zag line may not be possible when using some computer spreadsheets to draw charts.

- comparison of similar bar charts with different scales should always be undertaken with great care. The two bar charts below do not appear vastly different:

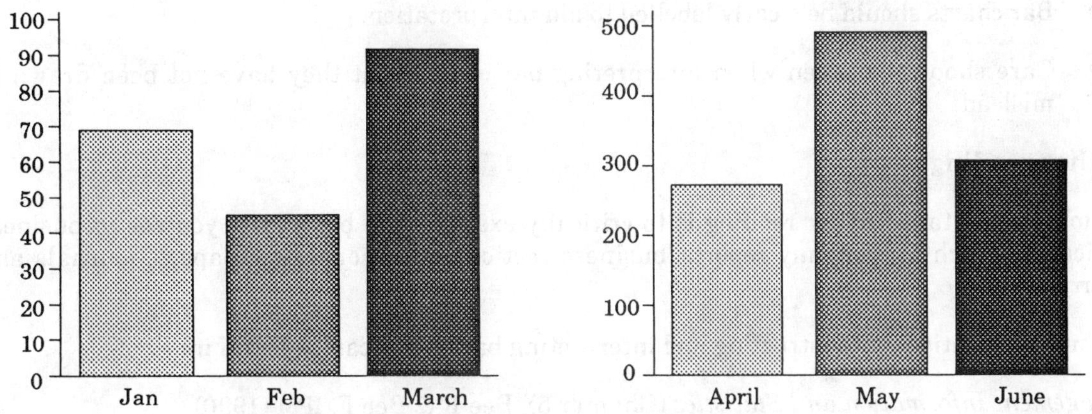

But when plotted on a common scale the difference is very evident:

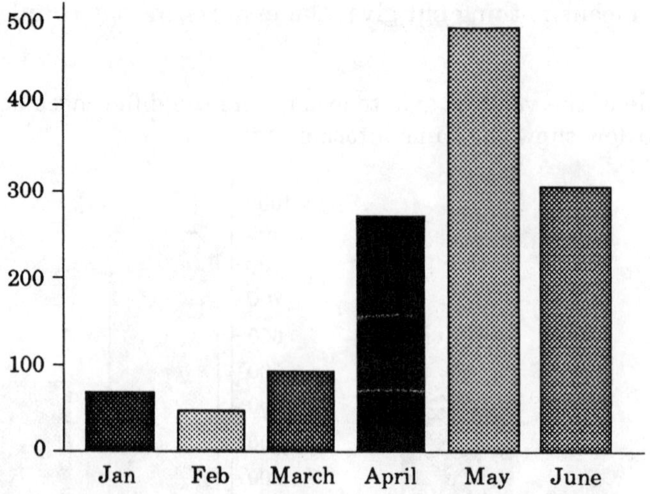

8.7 Summary

- Bar charts are used to illustrate categorical and discrete data graphically.
- There are four main types of bar chart:
  - simple bar charts to display frequencies for the components of one variable
  - multiple bar charts to display frequencies for the components of two or more variables
  - stacked bar charts to display frequencies and totals for the components of two or more variables
  - percentage component bar charts to display relative proportions (but not frequencies or totals) for the components of two or more variables.
- Bar charts should be clearly labelled to aid interpretation.
- Care should be taken when interpreting bar charts that they have not been drawn to mislead.

Further reading:

The most important further reading is to critically examine the bar charts you see in business publications such as company reports, business sections of national newspapers, journals and advertisements.

Further information on constructing and interpreting bar charts can be found in:

Management Information and Statistics (Chapter 5), Bee R & Bee F, IPM (1990)
Quantitative Approaches in Business Studies (Chapter 4), Morris C, PITMAN (1989)
A First Course in Business Mathematics and Statistics (Chapter 5), Rowe RN, DP PUBLICATIONS (1991)

Unit 9: Diagrams for categorical and discrete data: pie charts and pictograms

9.1 Pie charts

Bar charts are very good for illustrating which component of a variable is the most or least frequent. They are less good for displaying the share that each component has of a particular variable or making comparisons. In these instances a *pie chart* is much better. It is a blank circle divided into segments according to the share each component has of the variable. Each segment represents one component. Comparisons are made between the area of each segment rather than the length of each bar.

The table below gives the annual turnover of the brewing industry for a country during 1991-2:

Annual Turnover of the Brewing Industry 1991 – 2

Company	Annual turnover in £,000s
Metropolitans PLC	60,000
Lions PLC	36,000
Thornhill PLC	30,000
Greens PLC	24,000
Others[1]	50,000
Total	**200,000**

1 Others refers to all remaining Brewers

Source: Market Intelligence Report

The angle representing each component is determined by its share of the total frequency, translated into degrees. As the full circle is represented by 360°, the angle for each component is calculated by:

$$\text{angle of segement} = \frac{\text{frequency for component}}{\text{Total frequency for the variable}} \times 360$$

The frequency of each component divided by the total frequency for the variable equals the proportion of the whole circle taken up by the component. This is known as the relative frequency or f'. Each angle is the relative frequency multiplied by 360.

Thus Metropolitans PLC's angle is:

$$\frac{60{,}000}{200{,}000} \times 360 = 108^\circ$$

and Lions PLC's angle is:

$$\frac{36{,}000}{200{,}000} \times 360 = 64.8^\circ$$

The angles for the remaining slices can be calculated in the same way. They are: Thornhill PLC 54°, Greens PLC 43.2°, and Others 90°. The pie chart can be drawn using a compass and protractor or a computer spreadsheet. When drawing a pie chart it is good practice to include the value that the area of the pie represents as a note on the chart, in our case the note would be 'Total Annual Sales = £200,000,000'.

Annual Turnover of the Brewing Industry 1991 – 2

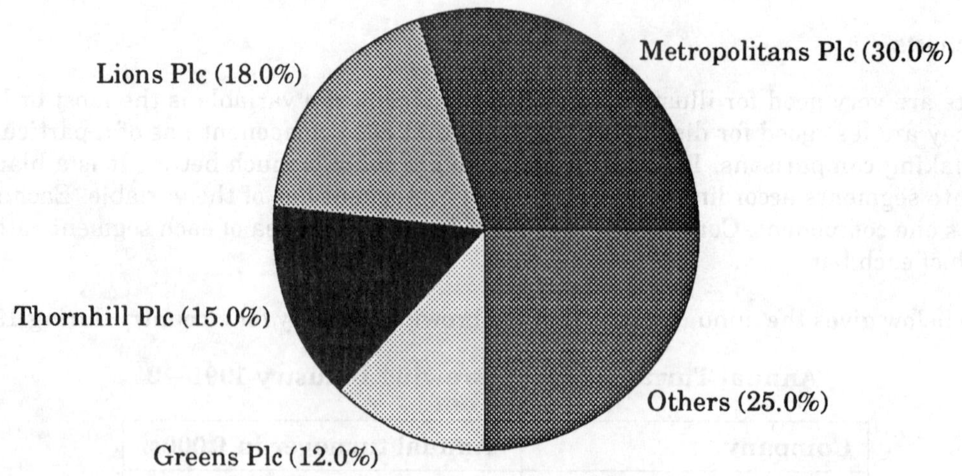

'Total Annual Sales = £200,000,000.'

Source: Market Intelligence Report

Pie charts are therefore useful when the proportions are more important than the original figures. Often the original figures are inserted in each segment to provide the user with additional data. Pie charts can provide a strong visual impact but the number of components we include must be kept low (usually less than ten) in order that they can be easily interpreted.

9.2 Comparative pie charts

We can also use pie charts to compare data about two or more variables. It is important to remember that it is the relative frequency (proportion) that is represented by the angle of the segment on a single pie chart and not the frequency.

If we want to compare sales by country for two footwear companies then we could construct two pie charts one for each company. However as the total sales differ then so should the total area of the two pie charts. The sales data of the two companies is given in the table below:

Sales of two Footwear Companies by Country 1993

Country	Sales by Runners' footwear (£,000)	Sales by Sprinters' footwear (£,000)
United Kingdom	350	250
France	450	200
Germany	400	150
Spain	200	100
Totals	1400	700

Source: Internal Company Reports

The pie charts below have been draw to enable comparison of proportion of sales by country between the two companies. The charts have also been drawn so that the area of each pie is proportional to the total sales. This means that the Sprinters' footwear pie chart is half the area of that for Runners' footwear:

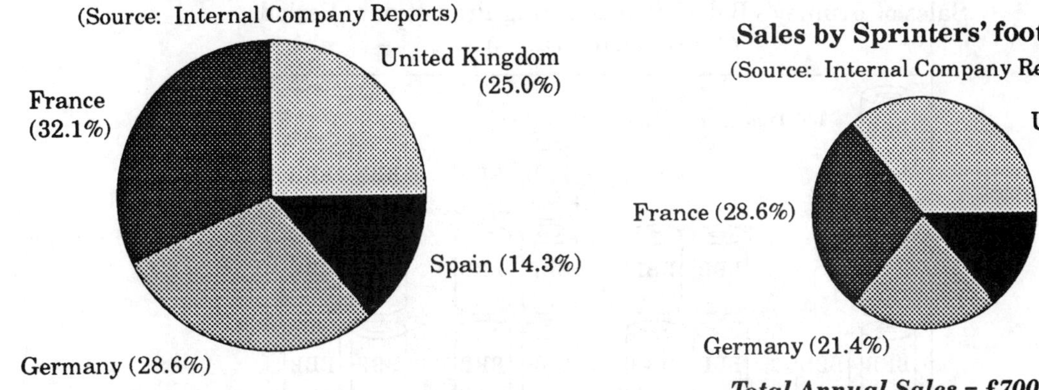

The area of the circle (or pie!) is based upon the square of its radius. Thus to find the radii when drawing proportional pie charts we need to find the square root of the total frequencies. We can then draw circles for each pie using the square root of the total frequencies for the radii.

For Runners' footwear the square root of 1400 is 37.42, whilst for Sprinters' footwear the square root of 700 is 26.45. If we were using a compass we could draw circles of radius 3.742 centimetres and 2.645 centimetres. We have divided both radii by the same number, ten, to fit both circles on the same page. As we have divided them by the same number the relationship between the areas of the two circles will remain the same.

Many computer spreadsheets are unable to make the necessary adjustments to the radii (and hence the relative areas). These spreadsheets should not be used for drawing comparative pie charts if the comparison of the total frequencies (represented by the area) is important.

9.3 Pictograms

One of the most eye-catching ways of presenting statistical information is the use of *pictograms.* We choose a symbol or picture to represent a specific quantity and this becomes our unit of measure. Using this method we can produce pictures to represent the figures. In the pictogram below we have used a baked bean tin to represent the sales of Brunley's own label baked beans. Each tin represents the sale of 100 tins of beans achieved during a four week promotion period of Brunley's beans. It is unusual to use less than half symbols so our data has been rounded to the nearest 50 tins of beans. Thus in the first week approximately 550 tins of Brunley's baked beans were sold.

BRUNLEY'S SUPERMARKETS

Sales of Brunley's Baked Beans during Promotional Period

(Source: Stores returns)

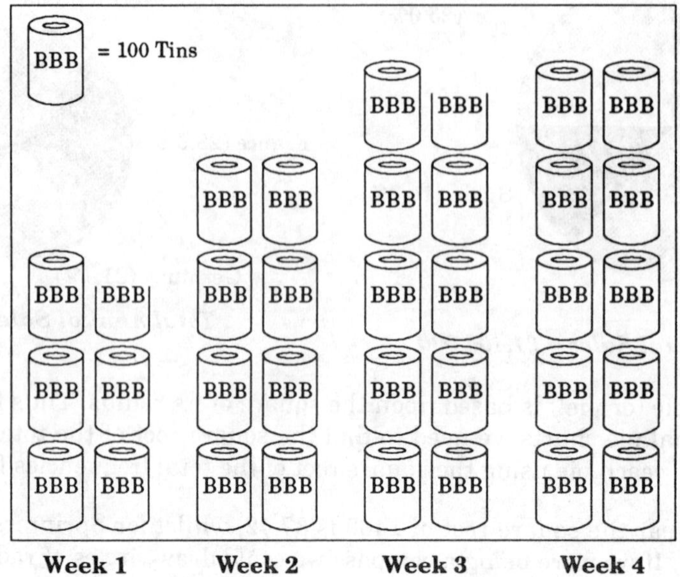

9.4 Misuse of pie charts and pictograms

The most common misuse of pie charts has already been alluded to: using pie charts to compare total frequencies which are of different magnitudes. Often this problem is compounded by there being no mention of the total frequencies that each pie represents. This means the reader has no idea that they are being misled. The pie charts below illustrate the impact of not taking the total frequencies into account when constructing comparative pie charts for the Runners' and Sprinters' footwear sales data.

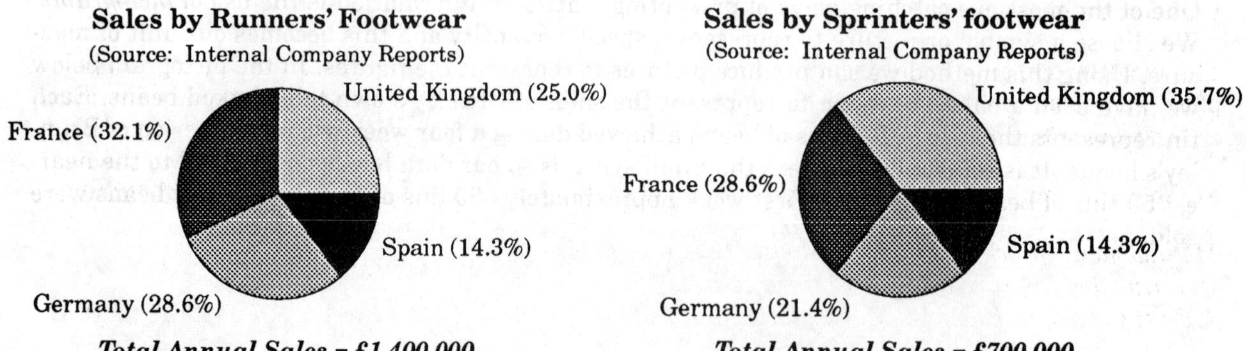

Total Annual Sales = £1,400,000 ***Total Annual Sales = £700,000***

It is very easy to mislead people with pictograms, especially if the images used are three dimensional. For example, if a beans company is selling twice as many tins of beans as a competitor it might use the following pictogram to illustrate this data:

This pictogram is misleading because the right-hand can is not twice the size of the left-hand one. It is twice as high, but also twice as wide and twice as deep. This means that it is actually distorting the data by a factor of eight!

It is therefore important to ensure that, if pictograms are used, they are drawn in proportion to area (2 dimensional) or volume (three dimensional) not just height, length or depth.

9.5 Summary

- Pie charts and pictograms are used to represent categorical and discrete data when the proportions are more important than the original figures.
- For comparative pie charts it is important that the area of the circles are proportional to the total frequencies.
- Care must be taken when drawing pictograms, especially 3 dimensional ones, as it is easy to distort the data.

Further reading:

The most important further reading is to critically examine the pie charts you see in business publications such as company reports, business sections of national newspapers, journals, and advertisements.

Further information on constructing and interpreting pie charts and pictograms can be found in:

Management Information and Statistics (Chapter 5), Bee R & Bee F, IPM (1990)
Quantitative Approaches in Business Studies (Chapter 4), Morris C, PITMAN (1989)
A First Course in Business Mathematics and Statistics (Chapter 5), Rowe RN, DP PUBLICATIONS (1991)

Unit 10: Diagrams for continuous and grouped discrete data: histograms and frequency polygons

10.1 The impact of data type

Although a table is one way of presenting continuous and grouped discrete data, we can create greater visual impact and make it easier to interpret by presenting it graphically. To do this we either use a histogram or a frequency polygon. Our choice of histogram rather than a bar chart is dependent upon the data:

- with categorical or discrete data there are a known finite number of values that our data could take. We therefore use a bar chart;
- with continuous or discrete data that has already been grouped we do not know the values that the data could take, only the class interval within which the data values fall. We therefore use a histogram.

10.2 Histograms for data with equal class widths

In unit 7 we created a table of the life expectancy of long life batteries which had been selected from a production line and tested to destruction.

Life expectancy in hours of Batteries tested to destruction (1993)

Class Interval (life expectancy)	LCB[1]	UCB[2]	Group Frequency (f) (number of batteries tested)
49.5 – < 59.5	49.5	59.5	2
59.5 – < 69.5	59.5	69.5	6
69.5 – < 79.5	69.5	79.5	6
79.5 – < 89.5	79.5	89.5	13
89.5 – < 99.5	89.5	99.5	26
99.5 – < 109.5	99.5	109.5	18
109.5 – < 119.5	109.5	119.5	13
119.5 – < 129.5	119.5	129.5	10
129.5 – < 139.5	129.5	139.5	3
139.5 – < 149.5	139.5	149.5	3

1 = Lower Class Boundary, 2 = Upper Class Boundary

Source: Quality Control Department

To construct a *histogram* we need to draw two axes. The vertical (y) axis represents frequency and the horizontal (x) axis represents the variable under investigation – in this case life expectancy of the battery in hours.

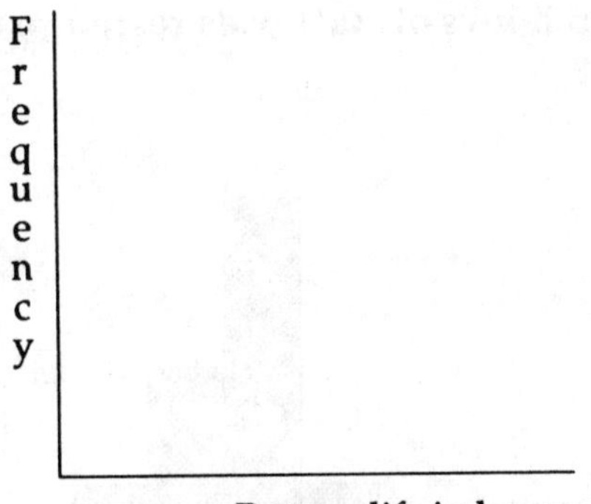

Next, we choose a scale for each axis. A zero point should appear on both axes. However because the first 'life' class interval starts at 49.5 hours the values between zero and just below this can be replaced with a zig-zag line (see unit 8.2). This indicates a break in the scale. (For yearly based data the convention is not to start the scale at zero; zig-zag lines are not used.) In our data the highest frequency value is 26 and the highest class interval ends 149.5 hours so we can label the scales accordingly.

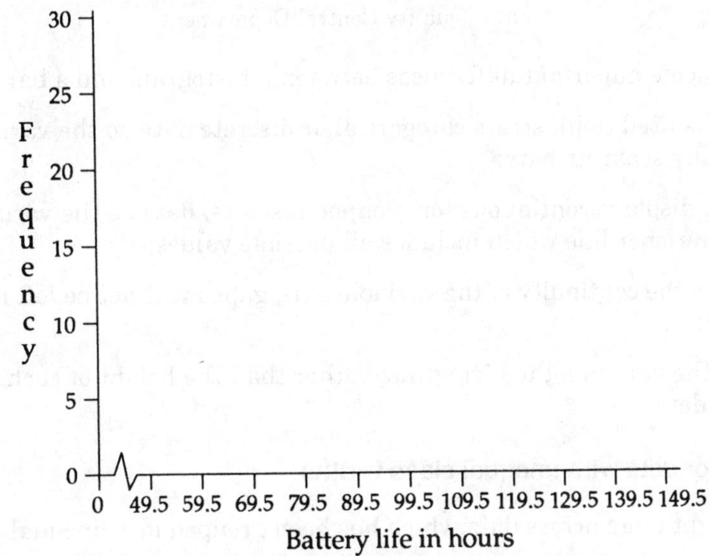

Once the axes have been drawn and labelled the data can simply be transferred to the histogram.

As we can see below, if all the class intervals are equal then the histogram is drawn in virtually the same way as a bar chart – the height of each bar represents the frequency. However no gaps should be left between the bars.

Life expectancy in hours of Batteries tested to destruction (1993)

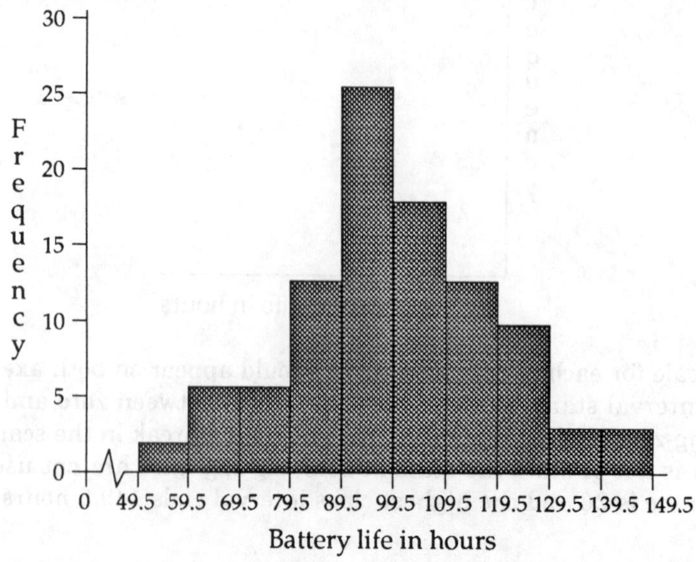

Source: Quality Control Department

However there are some important differences between a histogram and a bar chart:

- a bar chart is used to illustrate categorical or discrete data so the variable axis is divided into physically separate bars;
- a histogram displays continuous (or grouped discrete) data so the variable axis must be a continuous number line which includes all possible values;
- to emphasise the continuity of the variable axis, gaps must not be left between the bars in a histogram;
- the area of the bars in a the histogram, rather than the height of each individual bar represents the data.

10.3 Histograms for data with unequal class widths

Occasionally we might come across data which has been grouped into unequal width classes:

Length of Service of Leavers from Lewis's Research Ltd 1981 – 1990

Length of Service	Number of employees
< 6 months	2
6 months – < 1 year	4
1 – < 2 years	9
2 – < 3 years	9
3 – < 4 years	12
4 – < 5 years	14
5 – < 7 years	14
7 – < 10 years	6
Total	**70**

Source: Personnel Department

We can see the variable (length of service) has been grouped into classes in the normal way. However, the class intervals are not all the same size, for example:

6 months – < 1 year	=	0.5 years
1 – < 2 years	=	1 year
5 – < 7 years	=	2 years
7 – < 10 years	=	3 years

As the area of each bar should represent the proportion of the total frequency special measures must be taken to avoid distorting the data. Without doing this the height of the bar would still represent the frequency, not the area. Our histogram would be incorrect and would look like this:

Length of Service of Leavers from Lewis's Research Ltd 1981 – 1990 (Incorrectly drawn)

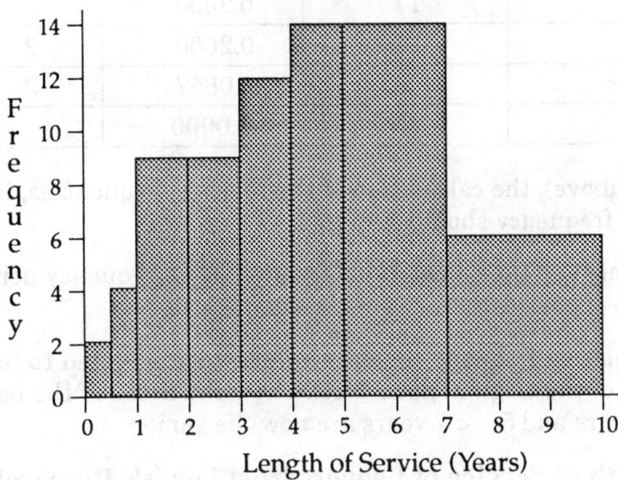

Source: Personnel Department

Our incorrectly drawn histogram (above) is very misleading because the height of each bar rather than the area represents the frequency. For example, the two class intervals with a frequency of 14 (4 – < 5 years and 5 – < 7 years) are shown with bars which are the same height. This is incorrect because although they both have the same frequency of leavers the class width is different and this needs to be reflected.

To overcome this distortion the area of each bar is used to represent that class interval's proportion of the total frequency (f). This is termed the *relative frequency (f')*. We can establish each bar's height in relation to class interval by undertaking the following calculations:

1. Calculate the relative frequency (f') for each class interval by dividing the frequency for that class interval by the total frequency:

$$\text{relative frequency} = \frac{\text{frequency for class interval}}{\text{total frequency}}$$

2. Calculate the height for each bar by dividing the relative frequency by the class interval:

$$\text{height} = \frac{\text{relative frequency}}{\text{class interval}}$$

The height of the bar is termed the *relative frequency density* abbreviated to *rfd*.

These calculations are easier to follow if we set them out as a table. Although we may be unable to plot a histogram of unequal class widths using some computer spreadsheets we can still use the spreadsheet to calculate the relative frequency and the relative frequency density (height of the bars) if we set out our working as below. (For ease of understanding spreadsheet row and column headings have been added.)

	A	B	C	D	E
1	Length of Service	Number of employees	Relative frequency	Class Width	Relative frequency density
2	< 6 months	2	0.0286	0.5	0.0572
3	6 months – < 1 year	4	0.0571	0.5	0.1142
4	1 – < 2 years	9	0.1286	1	0.1286
5	2 – < 3 years	9	0.1286	1	0.1286
6	3 – < 4 years	12	0.1714	1	0.1714
7	4 – < 5 years	14	0.2000	1	0.2000
8	5 – < 7 years	14	0.2000	2	0.1000
9	7 – < 10 years	6	0.0857	3	0.0286
10	Total	70	1.0000		

The answer to step 1 (above), the calculation of the relative frequencies, is recorded in column C. As a check the relative frequency should sum to 1.

The answer to step 2 (above), the calculation of the relative frequency density, is recorded in column E.

We can now use the relative frequency density values we calculated to produce an accurate and undistorted histogram of the original data. Notice how the areas of the bars which represent the class intervals 4- < 5 years and 5 – < 7 years are now the same:

Length of Service of Leavers from Lewis's Research Ltd
1981 – 1990 (Correctly drawn)

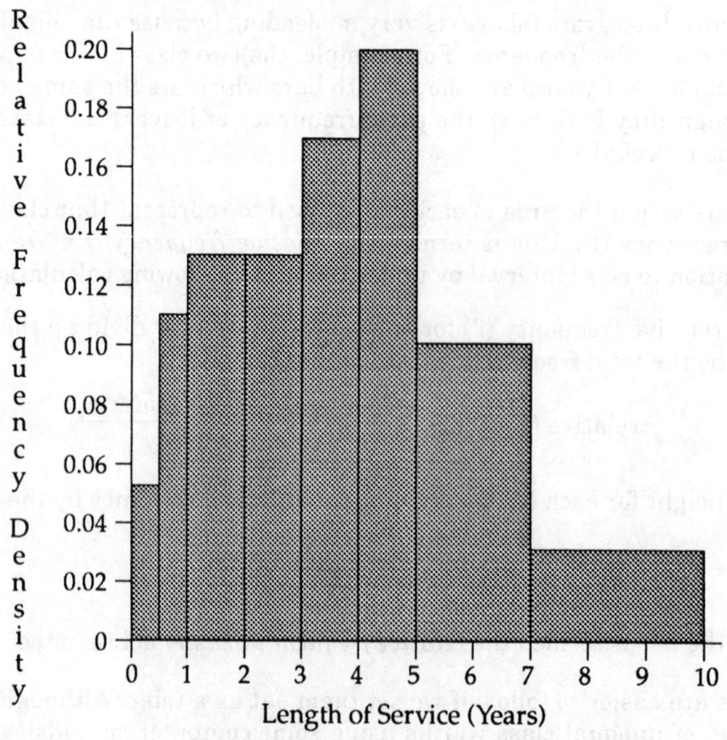

Source: Personnel Department

10.4 Frequency polygons (line graphs)

A *frequency polygon* is the name we give to the line which joins the centre of the tops of each bar in a histogram. It is often called a *line graph*. The frequency polygon has the same property as the histogram in that it is the area under the line that represents the data. Frequency polygons are often used in business to show trends over time such as sales, prices or the value of indices such as the Financial Times Share Index (FT-SE) 100.

A frequency polygon is often used as an alternative to a histogram. We use exactly the same axes but instead of drawing bars, a single point is plotted at the *mid-point* of the class interval. These points are then joined together with a line. If we want the frequency polygon to touch the variable axis, we add class intervals of zero frequency at both ends of the graph. In the case of equal class widths we simply extend the line down to the axis at the midpoints of these new class intervals. In the case of unequal class widths this is not so straight forward as we have to make sure the area under the line is correct.

Before drawing our frequency polygon we therefore need to calculate the 'mid point' for each class interval. This is simply the:

$$\frac{\text{Upper Class Boundary} + \text{Lower Class Boundary}}{2}$$

We can add this to our data on life expectancy of batteries tested.

Life expectancy in hours of Batteries tested to destruction (1993)

Class Interval (life expectancy)	LCB[1]	UCB[2]	Midpoint	Group Frequency (f) (number of batteries tested)
49.5 – < 59.5	49.5	59.5	54.5	2
59.5 – < 69.5	59.5	69.5	64.5	6
69.5 – < 79.5	69.5	79.5	74.5	6
79.5 – < 89.5	79.5	89.5	84.5	13
89.5 – < 99.5	89.5	99.5	94.5	26
99.5 – < 109.5	99.5	109.5	104.5	18
109.5 – < 119.5	109.5	119.5	114.5	13
119.5 – < 129.5	119.5	129.5	124.5	10
129.5 – < 139.5	129.5	139.5	134.5	3
139.5 – < 149.5	139.5	149.5	144.5	3

1 = Lower Class Boundary, 2 = Upper Class Boundary

Source: Quality Control Department

and plot the frequency polygon of the life expectancy of the batteries:

Life expectancy in hours of Batteries tested to destruction (1993)

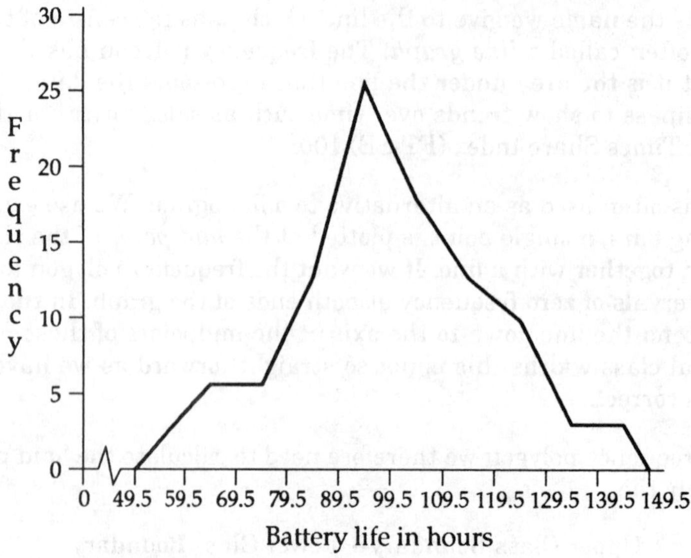

Source: Quality Control Department

10.5 Summary

- Histograms are used to represent continuous and grouped discrete data. This means that their should be no gaps between the bars on the variable axis.
- Unlike a bar chart the area of each bar represents the frequency, not the height.
- If the histogram has unequal class widths then the data may be misrepresented if the actual frequency has been plotted on the frequency axis rather than the relative frequency density.
- Frequency polygons (also called line graphs) are useful for showing trends over time for continuous and grouped discrete data. They are drawn by joining up the centre of the tops of each bar in a histogram.

Further reading:

The most important further reading is, as for units 8 and 9, to critically examine the histograms and frequency polygons you see in business publications such as company reports, business sections of national newspapers, journals, and advertisements.

Further information on constructing and interpreting histograms and frequency polygons can be found in:

Statistics (Chapter 2), Owen F & Jones R, PITMAN (1990)
A first course in Business Mathematics and Statistics (Chapter 5), Rowe RN, DP PUBLICATIONS (1991)

Unit 11: Measures of central tendency – means

11.1 Introduction to measures of central tendency

Various numerical techniques have been developed to summarise statistical data. The two most commonly used are:

- measures of central tendency or averages
- measures of dispersion

Measures of *central tendency* or averages seek to find values that indicate the centre of a distribution. These are also called measures of *location*. The purpose of calculating an average is to find a figure that represents the data. An average therefore gives an indication of the data values of a variable.

It is important to remember that any average is just a single figure and if not used correctly, can be just as misleading as it is informative. Taken by itself an average may not mean a great deal as the figure will not tell us how the data is dispersed around the average. It is here that measures of dispersion are helpful (units 13 and 14).

The validity of any measure of central tendency depends on the type of data, be it either categorical or quantitative, that we collect. Certain measures are more suited to categorical data and others more suited to quantitative. In addition the more data we collect the more certain we can be that the analysis is accurate. It is very dangerous to try to draw general conclusions if we only have a small sample of data. For example, we could not confidently say anything about the average salary in a large company if we only collected data from head office employees.

The term 'average' is regularly misused. Most people think there is only one average but in fact there are many, these include:

- arithmetic mean
- geometric mean
- harmonic mean
- median
- mode

We shall be concentrating on the first three in this unit, and will look at the median and mode in unit 12.

11.2 The arithmetic mean from raw data

The arithmetic mean, often just called the *mean,* is what most people call the average and can be calculated for all types of quantitative data. Care must however be taken that the resulting value makes sense; a mean family size of 1.84 children although statistically correct is unlikely to be of use to a family who want to have the 'average' number of children!

Calculating the mean for a set of data values is a simple procedure; we total the values in the distribution and divide this by the number of values in the distribution.

For example we wish to calculate the mean annual salary of employees working in the Administration Department of a medium sized company. We have obtained the following data from the computerised payroll:

Salaries In Administration Department 1992-3

Name	Annual Salary £'s
Jemma	6,963
Anthony	9,516
Douglas	11,652
Gregory	8,340
Michael	8,340
Jacob	11,652
Stacey	9,516
Anne	8,340
Jane	6,963
Elizabeth	7,359
Katie	8,340
Keith	17,841
Sue	6,963
Pamela	7,359
Sally	8,340
Stevie	14,071
Sean	8,340
Muriel	9,516
Kylie	6,963
Sharon	6,963
Total	**183,337**

Source: Company Payroll

The sum of the values is £183,337 and there are 20 values in the distribution. The mean is therefore:

$$\frac{183337}{20} = £9166.85$$

Like most statistical techniques, the calculation for mean can be expressed as a formula:

$$\bar{x} = \frac{\Sigma x}{n}$$

where x is each value in the distribution
$\bar{x}$ is the mean (called 'x-bar')
Σ is the sum of (called sigma)
n is the number of values

So, the formula simply says that the mean is equal to the sum of the values divided by the number of values.

The mean has a number of advantages:

- it takes all values into account;
- it forms part of the calculation for other statistics;
- it can be calculated without knowing all the data values.

For example, if we wanted to know the mean salary in the Administration Department, we could still calculate it if we knew that the total salary bill was £183,337 and there were 20 members of staff. There is no need to know the salary of every individual.

However, because it includes all the values in the distribution, one or two extreme values can distort the answer and make it appear not representative.

If, in our example, Stevie had a salary of £32,000 then the total salary bill would rise to £201,266 and the mean would rise to £10,063.30. Changing one person's salary has caused the mean salary to rise by nearly £900, a large impact!

As a general rule we quote the mean to one or more decimal places than the data that was provided, where this makes sense. Thus data for whole numbers are quoted to one or two decimal places. The most common exception to this rule is for age data. As this is usually recorded as 'age last birthday' we normally truncate the mean value. Thus a mean age of 33.1 years becomes 33 years. A mean age of 33.9 years will also be truncated to 33 years.

11.3 The mean from a discrete frequency distribution

Often when we are analysing data we are presented with discrete data which has already been summarised in a frequency distribution. This may be because we have collected the data in this way, or because we are analysing secondary data which is already in tabular form.

A personnel manager in a small company might have produced the following table in a monthly report relating to staff illness:

Number of Days Absence by Employees in February 1993

Number of Days absence	Number of Employees
0	20
1	3
2	5
3	7
4	8
5	2
14	1
Total	**46**

Source: Company Sickness Returns

The company manager wishes to know the mean number of absences per employee.

Taking the formula we used in section 11.2 to calculate the mean we could calculate all 46 values and then sum them to find the total. However, a quicker way is to add an extra column to the table. This column (C) calculates the value of the variable (x) multiplied by the frequency (f) and can easily be done using a computer spreadsheet (see below). If we use a computer spreadsheet it is advisable to label our columns to indicate the part of the calculation they contain.

	A	B	C
1	Number of Days absence x	Number of Employees f	fx
2	0	20	0
3	1	3	3
4	2	5	10
5	3	7	21
6	4	8	32
7	5	2	10
8	14	1	14
9	Total	46	90

We can then sum the column containing the frequency (B9) and the column containing the frequency multiplied by the value of the variable (C9) and calculate the mean using the formula for the mean of a discrete frequency distribution:

$$\bar{x} = \frac{\Sigma fx}{\Sigma f}$$

where x is the value of the variable
f is the frequency for the component
Σ means 'sum of'

So the mean number of days absence per employee in February is:

$$\frac{90}{46} = 1.96 \text{ days (to 2 decimal places)}$$

11.4 The mean from a grouped frequency distribution

We use a slightly different technique to calculate the mean from a frequency distribution using grouped data. If our data about the salaries of people in the Administration Department had been presented as a grouped frequency distribution (table) it would have looked like this:

Salaries In Administration Department 1992-3

Salary in £'s	Number of Employees
6,000 – < 8,000	7
8,000 – < 10,000	9
10,000 – < 12,000	2
12,000 – < 14,000	0
14,000 – < 16,000	1
16,000 – < 18,000	1
Total	20

Source: Company Payroll

We cannot multiply the class interval (in this case for salary) by the frequency (number of employees), so first we need to find the mid-point of each class interval. To find this mid-point we have to sum the upper class boundary and the lower class boundary and then divide by two.

For example, the mid-point of the 6,000 – < 8,000 class interval is

$$\frac{6{,}000 + 8{,}000}{2} = 7000$$

If we are using a computer spreadsheet to calculate the mid point it is useful to add three extra columns to our table (see below). The first two (B and C) record the lower and upper class boundaries for each class interval. The third (D) records the result of adding the lower class boundary to the upper class boundary and dividing by two, in other words the mid point. Once we have calculated the mid points, calculating the mean follows the same process as for grouped discrete data.

	A	B	C	D	E	F
1	**Salary in £'s (Class interval)**	**Lower Class Boundary**	**Upper Class Boundary**	**Mid point** x	**Number of Employees** f	**Frequency × Mid point** fx
2	6000 – < 8000	6000	8000	7000	7	49000
3	8000 – < 10000	8000	10000	9000	9	81000
4	10000 – < 12000	10000	12000	11000	2	22000
5	12000 – < 14000	12000	14000	13000	0	0
6	14000 – < 16000	14000	16000	15000	1	15000
7	16000 – < 18000	16000	18000	17000	1	17000
8	**Total**				**20**	**184000**

So, the mean is:

$$\frac{184000}{20} = £9{,}200$$

As we can see the answer is similar but not the same as the mean calculated in section 11.2 (£9,166.85). This is because by grouping the data we have lost some of the detail. For this reason it is important, whenever possible, to use the raw data when accuracy is required.

11.5 The mean of rates – the harmonic mean

Occasionally the arithmetic mean would not provide us with a sensible average. One such case might occur when we are calculating the average of rates such as speed (for example miles per hour) or prices (for example pounds per kilogram). In this case we may sometimes need to use the harmonic mean.

If a salesman has to travel between two towns which are 20 miles apart he might wish to calculate his average speed. He knows that the journey one way will be in the rush hour and he will only be able to travel at a steady 30 m.p.h. On the return journey he will be able to drive outside the rush hour and can travel at a steady 60 m.p.h.

If we were to calculate the arithmetic mean the average speed would be:

$$\frac{30 + 60}{2} = \frac{90}{2} = 45 \text{ m.p.h.}$$

However, this is wrong. If our salesman travels 20 miles at 30 m.p.h. it will take him 40 minutes, if he travels 20 miles at 60 m.p.h. it will take him 20 minutes. The total distance will therefore be 40 miles and it will have taken him 60 minutes. His average speed will therefore have been 40 m.p.h., not 45 m.p.h.

The formula for the harmonic mean overcomes this:

$$\text{Harmonic mean} = \frac{n}{\Sigma\left(\frac{1}{x}\right)}$$

where n is the number of observations (in this case journeys)
Σ means sum of
x is the actual value of the rate (in this case the m.p.h.)

We can substitute our estimated journey speed data from the salesman into the formula to calculate the harmonic mean:

$$\text{Harmonic mean} = \frac{2}{\left(\frac{1}{30}+\frac{1}{60}\right)}$$

$$= \frac{2}{\frac{3}{60}}$$

$$= \frac{2}{0.05}$$

$$= 40 \text{ m.p.h.}$$

However care must be taken when using the harmonic mean for rates. A rate is always expressed as a ratio. An example of such a ratio is:

- hours worked per employee.

If the rate is being averaged over a constant numerator unit, in our example – hours worked, then the harmonic mean should be used. In this case the hours worked remains constant.

If the rate is being averaged over a constant denominator unit, in our example – per employee, then the arithmetic mean should be used. In this case the number of employees (one) is constant.

11.6 The mean of proportional changes – the geometric mean

The other situation where the arithmetic mean is unlikely to provide us with a sensible average is when we need to calculate the average of a series of proportional increases (or decreases!) In this and similar situations we need to use the geometric mean. Within business a common use is calculating the average interest rate over a period when interest rates have fluctuated. Other examples would be if we needed to know the average rate of growth of a company from the annual growth rates.

As an example let us suppose we work for a company which has achieved an average annual growth rate in profits of 5% per annum over the past 3 years. Our competitor has published their percentage growth in profits on an annual basis for the same 3 years: 7%, 2%, 4%. We wish to compare our company' performance over this three year period with the competitor. To do this we need to calculate the geometric mean.

The formula we use for the geometric mean is:

$$\text{geometric mean} = \sqrt[n]{(x_1)\,(x_2)\,\ldots\,(x_n)}$$

where n is the number of observations made of the variable(in our case 3)
(x_1) is the first value (in our case the first percentage, 7%)
(x_2) is the second value (in our case the second percentage, 2%)
... refers to the intervening values (in our case none)
(x_n) is the n th value (in our case the third percentage, 4%)
$\sqrt[n]{\ }$ means take the nth root (in our case 3; the cubed root as we have 3 values)

We can the substitute our percentages into this formula:

$$\text{geometric mean} = \sqrt[3]{(7)(2)(4)}$$
$$= \sqrt[3]{7 \times 2 \times 4}$$
$$= \sqrt[3]{(56)}$$
$$= 3.83\% \text{ (to 2 decimal places)}$$

Therefore our company's average annual growth rate is higher than that of our competitors over the past three years.

Helpful hints when calculating the geometric mean:

Obviously undertaking calculations such as cubed roots is very complicated without using a calculator or a computer spreadsheet.

To be able to do this calculation on a calculator you will need to have a special x^y key.

For spreadsheet programs instead of taking the nth root of the rates multiplied together you will need to raise the rates by the reciprocal the nth root. In our example the reciprocal of the cube root would be $^1/_3$ and the full spreadsheet formula would be similar to:

= (7*2*4)^(1/3)

11.7 Summary

- The calculation of the arithmetic mean takes into account all the data values in a distribution.
- The arithmetic mean is the most commonly used measure of central tendency but is only one of a number of possible methods of calculating the 'average'.
- The arithmetic mean can be calculated if the total value and the number of observations are both known.
- The arithmetic mean is influenced by exceptional high or low values in the data.
- The harmonic mean is a specialised measure of central tendency normally used to calculate the average of rates or ratios. Care must be taken in its use.
- The geometric mean is a specialised measure of central tendency normally used to calculate the average of proportions.

Further reading:

Business Mathematics and Statistics (Chapters 7 & 9), Francis A, DP PUBLICATIONS (1993)
Quantitative Approaches in Business Studies (Chapter 5), Morris C, PITMAN (1989)
A first course in Business Mathematics and Statistics (Chapter 7), Rowe RN, DP PUBLICATIONS (1991)

Unit 12: Measures of central tendency – medians and modes

12.1 The median from raw data

The median means 'middle value,' so in a distribution half the values will be above the median and half below it. The first stage in calculating the median for any set of quantitative data is to rank the values in ascending order, the simplest way of doing this is to use the 'sort' feature of a computer spreadsheet. The frequency distribution below shows sorted staff salary data for a small office services business:

Salaries for Major's Office Services' Staff 1991-92 (ranked in ascending order)

Name	Annual Salary £'s	Rank
Fred	6,963	1
Norman	6,963	2
Mia	6,963	3
Jason	6,963	4
Tracy	6,963	5
Elspeth	7,359	6
Jasmine	7,359	7
Veronica	7,359	8
Alice	7,359	9
Joan	7,359	10
Richard	8,340	11
Sally	8,340	12
Simon	8,340	13
Tony	9,516	14
Jayne	9,516	15
Bruce	9,516	16
David	11,652	17
George	11,652	18
Maureen	14,071	19
Grenville	17,841	20
Total	**180,394**	

Source: Company Payroll

The next stage is to select the 'middle value'. We use a simple formula to locate the middle position, this is normally termed the *median pointer* as it points to the position in rank order that the median occupies:

$$\frac{n+1}{2}$$

where n is the number of values in the distribution.

In the our small office services business there are 20 values so the middle position is 10.5. This means that the middle value lies half way between the tenth (Joan) and eleventh (Richard) values. To calculate the median we therefore add together the tenth and eleventh values and divide by two:

$$\frac{7359 + 8340}{2}$$

$$= \frac{15699}{2} = £7,849.50$$

The median salary is therefore £7,849.50

It is important to remember that the median does not take the actual values into account, only their position. As a result, extreme values do not distort the median. If Grenville's salary was £25,000, the median would *not* change but the mean would increase from £9019.70 to £9377.65. It is therefore important to specify which average we have calculated.

12.2 The median from a discrete frequency distribution

To find the median from discrete data which has been summarised into a frequency distribution we need, as before, to locate the middle point of the distribution. In order to do this we need to add an extra column to the table (see below), called *cumulative frequency (F)*. This column records the values of the distribution that are included up to that point in the table. Thus for 0 days absence the cumulative frequency is 20, for 1 day of absence it is 20 + 3 = 23, for 2 days absence it is 20 + 3 + 5 and so on. The table below contains the absence data for a small company which we examined in unit 11.3.

Number of Days Absence by Employees in February 1993

Number of Days absence x	Number of Employees f	Cumulative frequency F
0	20	20
1	3	23
2	5	28
3	7	35
4	8	43
5	2	45
14	1	46
Total	**46**	

Source: Company Sickness Returns

As before we calculate the median pointer using the following formula:

$$\text{Median pointer} = \frac{46 + 1}{2} = 23.5$$

This tells us that the median lies halfway between the 23rd and the 24th value. Looking at the table we can see that 23 employees had up to 1 day of absence (which is the portion shaded) this means that the 24th employee must have had two days absence. As the median pointer is half way between these two employees then the median number of absences must also lie half way in-between, in this case 1.5 days absence.

12.3 The median from a grouped frequency distribution

When business data is presented as a grouped frequency distribution we can only estimate the median. Two methods of estimating the median are possible, by using a formula and by drawing a graph.

The easiest method of estimating to understand, and arguably the most accurate, is drawing a graph. This graph is called a *cumulative frequency curve* or *ogive.*

The table below contains the Administration Department salaries data we examined in unit 11.4:

	A	B	C	D	E
1	Salary in £'s (Class interval)	Number of Employees *f*	Cumulative frequency *F*	*F%*	Upper Class Boundary
2	6000 – < 8000	7	7	35	8000
3	8000 – < 10000	9	16	80	10000
4	10000 – < 12000	2	18	90	12000
5	12000 – < 14000	0	18	90	14000
6	14000 – < 16000	1	19	95	16000
7	16000 – < 18000	1	20	100	18000
8	Total	20			

The only extra data we need to calculate is the cumulative frequency, the percentage cumulative frequency, and the upper class boundary. To do this three extra columns have been added to the table:

1. cumulative frequency (C) which is calculated as described in section 12.2;
2. the percentage cumulative frequency (D) which expresses the cumulative frequency as a percentage of the total frequency (see unit 7.7 for percentage calculation);
3. the upper class boundary (E).

Once this is done we can draw a graph plotting each cumulative frequency against the upper class boundary of the appropriate class interval. The cumulative frequency should always be plotted against the upper boundary of the class interval and not the lower.

Cumulative frequency curve showing distribution of salaries in the Administration Department

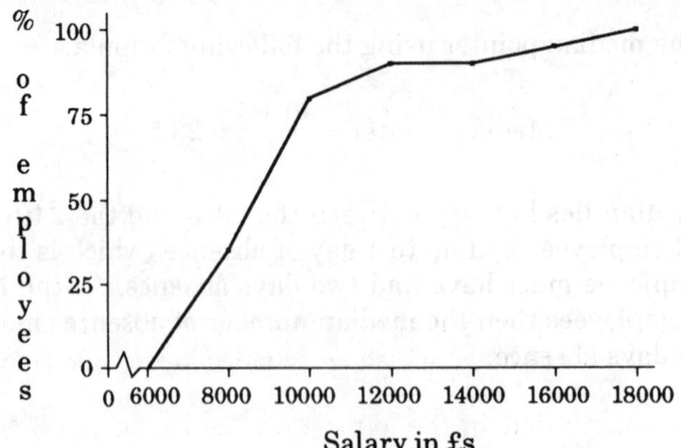

Source: Company Payroll

The position of the median is at the 50% position on the cumulative frequency (vertical) axis. A horizontal line is drawn from this point to see where it crosses the curve. A second line is then drawn down to the value axis and the appropriate value is read off.

Cumulative frequency curve showing distribution of salaries in the Administration Department

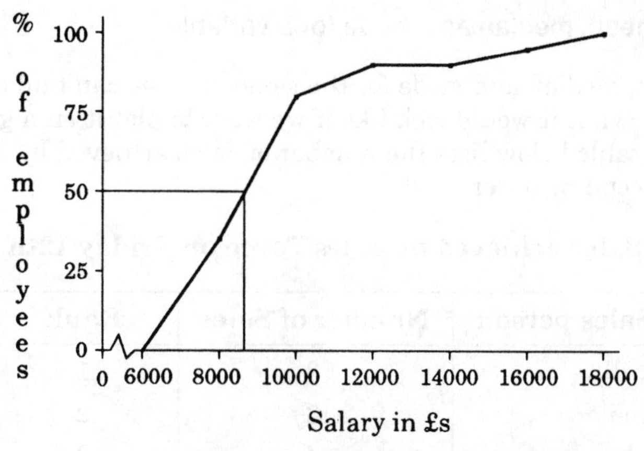

Source: Company Payroll

The median salary in the Administration Department is therefore approximately £8,600.

12.4 The mode

The *mode* is the most commonly occurring value or category. It is the only average that can be calculated for categorical data. It can also be calculated for quantitative data although it is rarely used for continuous data, other than when it has been grouped.

A Sandwich Bar keeps a record of all the sandwiches it sells over a week by type of filling. This data is illustrated in the table below:

Sandwich Sales by Filling – First week in July

Filling	Number of Sales
Cheese	188
Cheese and Tomato	43
Ham	79
Salad	32
Egg	68
Pork Luncheon Meat	12
Prawn	130
Crab	90

Source: Weekly Returns by Staff

The category with the highest frequency is cheese and this represents the mode. On a bar chart, the mode would be the highest bar and on a frequency polygon it would be the highest point.

If two sandwich fillings had both tied for the highest frequency, for example if sales of ham sandwiches had also been 188 then the mode would have been both ham and cheese. We call this *bi-modal.* Occasionally distributions are *tri-modal!*

On a continuous frequency distribution, the mode becomes the modal group – the group with the highest frequency.

Statistically, the mode is not used very often as it is not a particularly precise measurement of location. However, it is useful when you are using data that cannot be sensibly divided – the mean number of cars per household is 1.4, but have you ever seen 0.4 of a car?

12.5 Interpreting the mean, median and mode for a variable

By calculating the mean, median and mode for the same data we can find out how the data is distributed, in other words what it would look like if we were to plot it on a graph. This can be very useful in business. The table below lists the number of sales achieved by a company's sales force on one day ranked in ascending order:

Sales achieved by Sales Force on Friday 12th

Sales person	Number of Sales	Rank
Philip	3	1
Sheila	3	2
John	4	3
Adrian	4	4
Derek	4	5
Charles	5	6
Jonti	5	7
Susan	6	8
Graham	6	9
Peter	7	10
Sue	8	11
Pat	8	12
Edward	9	13
Jenny	10	14
Phil	11	15
Total	**93**	

Source: Telesales Ltd.

We can calculate the mean number of sales:

$$= \frac{93}{15} = 6.2 \text{ sales}$$

The median number of sales:

$$\text{median pointer} = \frac{15 + 1}{2} = 8$$

Therefore median = 6 sales

And if we construct a frequency distribution of the data we can see 'by eye' the modal number of sales:

Sales achieved by Sales Force on Friday 12th

Number of Sales achieved	Number of Sales Force
3	2
4	3
5	2
6	2
7	1
8	2
9	1
10	1
11	1

Source: Telesales Ltd

Therefore the mode = 4 sales.

Because the mean is greater than the median which is greater than the mode this tells us that our sales are *positively skewed*. In other words more members of our sales force will achieve sales below the mean than above it. We can illustrate this by assuming the number of sales are continuous and plotting a histogram of the tabulated data:

Sales achieved by Sales Force on Friday 12th

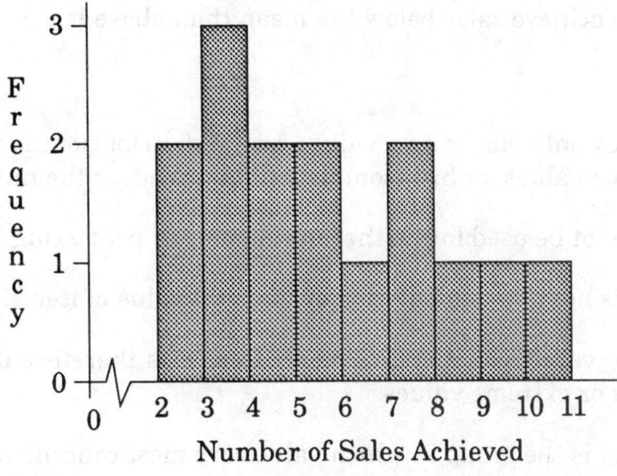

Source: Telesales Ltd

Often the frequency distribution is drawn as a frequency polygon.

If our mode, median and mean all have the same value then the frequency polygon looks like this:

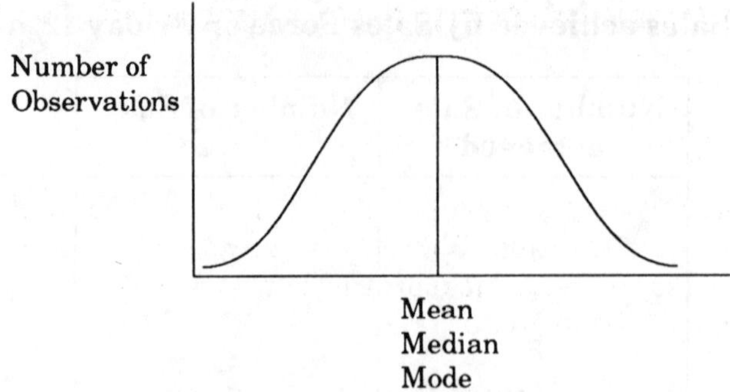

In this case we say that sales are *normally distributed.* Therefore we would expect the same proportion of our sales force to achieve sales above the mean as below it.

If the mean of our data is smaller than our median which is smaller than our mode then the frequency polygon would look like this:

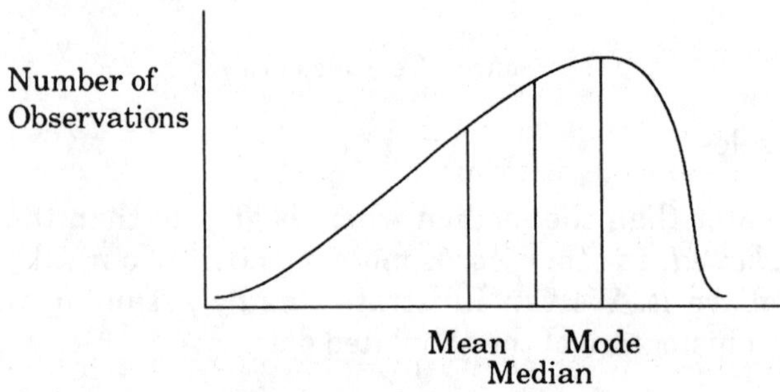

In this case we say that sales are *negatively skewed.* Therefore we would expect a smaller proportion of our sales force to achieve sales below the mean than above it.

12.6 Summary

- The median uses only one or two values in the distribution, it is therefore often not affected by extreme values, or by incomplete data providing the number of values is known.
- The median cannot be used for further mathematical processing.
- The median does not allow calculation of the total value of items.
- The mode is the value which occurs most often, it is therefore unlikely to be affected by incomplete data or extreme values.
- The modal group is the group in which values are most concentrated.
- The mode is not suitable for further mathematical processing.
- The mode does not allow calculation of the total value of items.
- By interpreting the mean, median and mode together we can reveal how our data is distributed.

Further reading:

Business Mathematics and Statistics (Chapters 8 & 9), Francis A, DP PUBLICATIONS (1993)
Quantitative Approaches in Business Studies (Chapter 5), Morris C, PITMAN (1989)
A First Course in Business Mathematics and Statistics (Chapter 7), Rowe RN, DP PUBLICATIONS (1991)

Unit 13: Measures of dispersion: ranges, quartiles, deciles and percentiles

13.1 Introduction to measures of dispersion

Any measurement that enables us to describe the spread of values in a distribution (set of data values) is called a measure of dispersion. We can also use these measures to compare distributions from different data sets. As with measures of location there are a number of techniques available. The more common of these are:

- range, quartiles, inter-quartile range, deciles and percentiles;
- variance, standard deviation and coefficient of variation.

We will be looking at the former of these in this unit, and the variance, standard deviation and coefficient of variation in unit 14.

13.2 The range from raw data

The range of a distribution is simply the difference between the highest and lowest values of the variable. Although the range gives us a quick idea of the variability in our data without having to do any calculations it ignores all the data but the two extremes. This means that the data values in the middle of the distribution have no influence at all.

The table below lists the ages of the eighteen employees in a small printing company. These have been ranked (sorted) into ascending order.

Ages of employees at Speedyprint Printers 1993

Name	Age	Rank
Sarah	16	1
Megan	19	2
Philip	19	3
Katie	20	4
Claire	22	5
James	23	6
Jeremy	24	7
Liam	24	8
Alistair	26	9
Peter	27	10
Jemma	29	11
Emma	30	12
Mark	33	13
Jonathan	38	14
Eileen	39	15
Kenneth	40	16
Benjamin	49	17
Alison	56	18

Source: Interview with Employees

The range in this example is the difference between Alison's and Sarah's ages:

$$56 - 16 = 40$$

It is easy to see how the range can be affected by extreme values; if Alison's age was 64 the range would increase to 48. Although we would know the difference between the extreme values, it tells us nothing about the data values in between.

13.3 The upper and lower quartiles and the inter-quartile range from raw data

Quartiles

The way round this is to divide the range into sections. The median divided the range into two, with 50% of data values below the median and 50% above it. We can further sub-divide the range to give four equal sections called *quartiles*.

The *lower quartile* (or first quartile) is the value below which 25% of all data values fall. The *upper quartile* (or third quartile) is the value above which 25% of the data values fall. Obviously, 50% of all values fall between the upper and lower quartiles.

The lower and upper quartile pointers are identified in much the same way as the median pointer. Here are the formulae:

Lower quartile pointer:

$$\frac{n+1}{4}$$

Upper quartile pointer:

$$\frac{3 \times (n+1)}{4}$$

where n is number of values in the distribution.

Let us reconsider the dispersion of the ages of Speedyprint employees (unit 13.2). There are eighteen values so the lower quartile pointer is:

$$\frac{18+1}{4} = 4.75$$

and the upper quartile pointer is:

$$\frac{3 \times (18+1)}{4} = 14.25$$

To calculate the lower quartile we will need to work out the value corresponding to the lower quartile pointer, 4.75. This value lies three quarters of the way between the fourth and fifth positions – Katie and Claire. To calculate the upper quartile we will need to work out the value one quarter of the way between the fourteenth and fifteenth positions – Jonathan and Eileen.

The median pointer is 9.5, this is half way between Alistair and Peter. The following table illustrates these pointers.

Ages of employees of Speedyprint Printers 1992

Name	Age	Rank	
Sarah	16	1	
Megan	19	2	
Philip	19	3	
Katie	20	4	← Lower Quartile pointer 4.75
Claire	22	5	
James	23	6	
Jeremy	24	7	
Liam	24	8	
Alistair	26	9	← Median pointer 9.5
Peter	27	10	
Jemma	29	11	
Emma	30	12	
Mark	33	13	
Jonathan	38	14	← Upper Quartile pointer 14.25
Eileen	39	15	
Kenneth	40	16	
Benjamin	49	17	
Alison	56	18	

Source: Interview with Employees

To find the actual value at the lower quartile pointer, first calculate the difference between the values at the fifth and fourth positions:

$$22 - 20 = 2$$

The next step is to calculate three-quarters (0.75) of the difference as the pointer lies three quarters of the way between the fourth and the fifth positions:

$$2 \times 0.75 = 1.5$$

The final step is to add this value to the value corresponding to the fourth position:

$$20 + 1.5 = 21.5 \text{ years}$$

This is the value at the 4.75th pointer. A similar calculation is required to find the value at the upper quartile pointer, 14.25, which lies one quarter (0.25) of the way between the 14th and 15th positions.

The difference between the values at the 15th and 14th positions is:

$$39 - 38 = 1$$

One quarter of this difference is:

$$1 \times 0.25 = 0.25$$

So, the value at the 14.25th pointer is:

$$38 + 0.25 = 38.25 \text{ years}$$

Inter-quartile range

The inter-quartile range or *quartile deviation* is the difference between the upper and lower quartiles. It is the range within which the middle 50% of values fall. This is represented by the formula:

$$IQR = UQ - LQ$$

where IQR is the inter-quartile range
UQ is the upper quartile
LQ is the lower quartile

The inter-quartile range is therefore:

$$38.25 - 21.5 = 16.75 \text{ years}$$

This tells us that the ages of half the staff are within a range of 16.75 years. This figure is far more meaningful than the total range figure between the highest and lowest ages because it is not distorted by the extreme data values of the distribution. It tells us the range of variability into which 50% of the data values fall.

Sometimes we see the *semi inter-quartile range* quoted in business publications. This as its name suggests is simply half the inter-quartile range, in this case 8.375.

13.4 Percentiles and deciles

Instead of dividing the data distribution into four equal parts to give us quartiles, we can divide it into 100 equal parts. Each of these parts is termed a *percentile*. This allows us to calculate values at any given percentage using a similar method to the calculation for quartile pointers. Thus the pointer for the 40 percentile would be found using the formula:

$$40\text{th percentile} = \frac{40 \times (n + 1)}{100}$$

where n is the number of values.

In addition we can calculate any percentile range, e.g. the 80 percentile range would lie between the 10th percentile and the 90th percentile and give the range into which that 80% of data values would fall.

The median is the 50th percentile and the upper and lower quartiles are the 75th and 25th percentiles respectively.

Deciles refers to when we divide a distribution up into 10 equal parts. Therefore the 10th percentile is the 1st decile.

13.5 Quartiles and the inter-quartile range from a discrete frequency distribution

As with raw data we calculate the quartiles by finding the quartile pointers and then locate the value at each pointer. If we consider our employee absence data from unit 12.2:

Number of Days Absence by Employees in February 1993

Number of Days absence x	Number of Employees f	Cumulative frequency F
0	20	20
1	3	23
2	5	28
3	7	35
4	8	43
5	2	45
14	1	46
Total	**46**	

Source: Company Sickness Returns

The lower quartile pointer is:

$$\frac{46 + 1}{4} = 11.75$$

This tells us that the lower quartile lies three quarters of the way between the 11th and the 12th values. Looking at the table we can see that the first 20 employees had no days absence which means that the 11.75th employee position would have had no days absence.

The upper quartile pointer is:

$$\frac{3 \times (46 + 1)}{4} = \frac{141}{4}$$

$$= 35.25$$

This tells us that the upper quartile lies a quarter of the way between the 35th and the 36th values. Looking at the table we can see that the first 35 employees had up to 3 days absence and the 36th had four days absence. As the quartile pointer is a quarter of the way between these two employees then the upper quartile number of absences must also a quarter of the way in-between, in this case 3.25 days absence.

The inter-quartile range is calculated the same way as before:

upper quartile – lower quartile = inter-quartile range

3.25 – 0 = 3.25 days absence.

13.6 The quartile and inter-quartile range from a grouped frequency distribution

To discover the upper and lower quartiles for a continuous frequency distribution we can use the same method as we did for the median (unit 12.3): draw a cumulative frequency curve (ogive). In this case we would draw lines at the 25% and 75% positions on the cumulative frequency (vertical) axis then read off the appropriate values. This is illustrated using our Administration Department salary data from unit 12.3:

Cumulative frequency curve showing distribution of salaries in the Administration Department

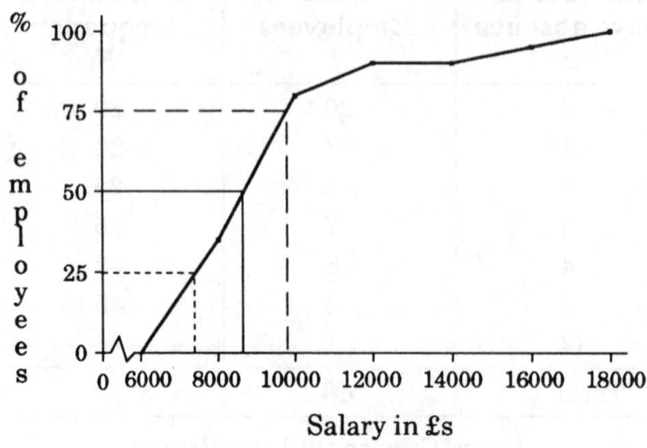

Source: Company Payroll

The lower quartile salary is approximately £7,400 and the upper quartile salary is approximately £9,800. The inter-quartile range is therefore £2,400.

13.7 Interpreting the quartiles and median for a variable

Although the quartiles, range and median of a variable are useful statistics on their own they can tell us more when considered together.

We have received job offers from two life assurance companies and have been given the following statistics about their salaries:

Salary Statistics of two Life Assurance Companies (199-)

Statistics	Oxstalls Life Salaries	Park Life Salaries
Median	£16,700	£17,800
Upper Quartile	£21,980	£19,430
Lower Quartile	£13,480	£14,390
Inter-quartile Range	£8,500	£5,040

Source: Oxstalls Life & Park Life

The decision we need to make is which job offer to accept. If we look at the statistics individually we can see that Park Life has the higher median salary and Oxstalls Life has the larger inter-quartile range.

We also need to know how these salaries are distributed in order to make our decision. To find this out we need to look at the quartiles in conjunction with the median. The general rules are:

- if the lower quartile is closer to the median than the upper quartile this suggests the data is positively skewed;
- if the upper quartile is closer to the median than the lower quartile this suggests the data is negatively skewed;
- if the upper and lower quartiles are equal distance from the mean this suggests the data is normally distributed.

Looking at our salary statistics we can see that:

For Oxstalls life salaries the lower quartile is closer to the median than the upper quartile. This suggests that salaries are positively skewed, so the 50% of employees on below median salaries are likely to have less variation in their earnings than the 50% earning above the median salaries.

For Park Life salaries the upper quartile is closer to the median than the lower quartile. This suggests that salaries are negatively skewed, so the 50% of employees on above median salaries are likely to have less variation in their earnings than the 50% earning below median salaries.

To return to our decision about which job offer to take; this will depend upon a variety of factors. However we now know that although the median salary for Park Life is the higher, employees earning above the median salary have less variation in their salaries than those earning below the median salary. By contrast, although the median salary is lower for Oxstalls life, employees earning above the median have more variation in their salaries than those earning below the median salary. Thus if we wanted a job that afforded us the maximum earnings potential we would probably take the offer from Oxstalls Life.

13.8 Summary

- The range provides a measure of spread of the entire data distribution.
- The lower and upper quartiles represent points which are one quarter and three quarters through a ranked (sorted) data distribution.
- The inter-quartile range provides a measure of spread of the middle 50% of the data distribution.
- Percentiles and deciles provide alternative methods of dividing the data distribution.
- Using the median, upper and lower quartiles and inter-quartile range statistics in conjunction with each other can convey information about the skewness of the data distribution.

Further reading:

Business Mathematics and Statistics (Chapters 10 & 12), Francis A, DP PUBLICATIONS (1993)
Quantitative Approaches in Business Studies (Chapter 5), Morris C, PITMAN (1989)

Unit 14: Measures of dispersion: variance, standard deviation and coefficient of variation

14.1 Introduction

The measures of dispersion associated with quartiles and the range are relatively easy to understand. Unfortunately they are not suitable for further statistical processing. Conceptually, and statistically, in business it is often better to look at the extent to which a set of values differ from their mean; as this is what we need to know to assess the usefulness of the mean as a typical value for the distribution. If the data values are all close to the mean then the mean is much more representative than if they are not close to the mean.

The statistics that enables us to do this are the variance, standard deviation and the coefficient of variation. Of these the variance is used least often as we shall see.

14.2 The standard deviation from raw data

The standard deviation is a more complicated measure of dispersion than the inter-quartile range. It has the same advantages and disadvantages as the mean and is commonly used in more advanced statistical work.

The *standard deviation* tells us how far the data values in a distribution vary from the distribution's mean for data which is normally distributed (see units 12.5 and 14.5). Probably the best way to understand this is to use an example. We can calculate the standard deviation setting out our working in tabular form as below, either by using a calculator or a computer spreadsheet. (As in earlier sections we have added row and column headings to show how the data would look on a computer spreadsheet.) Alternatively we can use the statistical function key labelled σ which is on some calculators; or the statistical function 'standard deviation' contained in many computer spreadsheets.

Suppose we have a factory which builds motor cars 'by hand'. We know that the mean number of cars built each week is 7, but we want to know how much this varies from week to week. The table below shows the total number of cars built each week over an eight week period.

Number of Cars built per week in 1st 8 weeks of 1993

Week	Cars Built
One	7
Two	8
Three	5
Four	9
Five	5
Six	8
Seven	6
Eight	8
Total	56

Source: Production Controller

The first stage in calculating the standard deviation is to calculate the mean, we already know this is 7, however we shall check it!:

The formula for the mean from raw data (see unit 11.2) is:

$$\bar{x} = \frac{\Sigma x}{n}$$

$$= \frac{56}{8} = 7$$

The next stage is to calculate how far each of the data values (in this case weekly number of cars built) deviates from the mean. To do this we take the mean away from each value and place the answer in a new column (C) in our table, $x - \bar{x}$:

	A	B	C
1	Week	Cars Built x	Deviation $x - \bar{x}$
2	1	7	0
3	2	8	1
4	3	5	-2
5	4	9	2
6	5	5	-2
7	6	8	1
8	7	6	-1
9	8	8	1
10	Total	56	0

We can make sure that we have got our calculations right by checking that the total of the deviations from the mean is zero (cell C10). This is always the case as the mean is the arithmetic centre of the distribution of values.

However, because the total of the mean deviations is 0, it is not much use to make comparisons. As we are only interested in the size of the deviation not the direction, we next calculate the square of the deviations and place the answer in a new column (D) $(x - \bar{x})^2$.

	A	B	C	D
1	Week	Cars Built x	Deviation $x - \bar{x}$	(Deviation)^2 $(x - \bar{x})^2$
2	1	7	0	0
3	2	8	1	1
4	3	5	-2	4
5	4	9	2	4
6	5	5	-2	4
7	6	8	1	1
8	7	6	-1	1
9	8	8	1	1
10	Total	56	0	16

We can now sum our eight values to give a *total squared deviation of* 16 from the mean (cell D10).

The next step is to calculate the mean of these squared deviations. This value is called the *variance* and is calculated using the formula:

$$\text{Variance} = \frac{\Sigma(x - \bar{x})^2}{n}$$

where Σ means sum of
$x - \bar{x}$ is the deviation from the mean squared (in our case 16 when summed)
n is the number of data values (in our case 8)

$$\text{Variance} = \frac{16}{8} = 2$$

The problem with the variance is that it is expressed in terms of the square of the data values and not the data values themselves. This makes any interpretation very difficult as the mean is expressed as, in our case, cars; and the variance is expressed in square cars! However it is worth remembering as the variance is used in a number of other statistical calculations.

The final stage is to calculate the *standard deviation* which is the square root of the variance.

$$\text{Standard deviation} = \sqrt{\frac{\Sigma(x - \bar{x})^2}{n}}$$

As we have already calculated the variance this is simply:

$$\text{Standard deviation} = \sqrt{2} = 1.41 \text{ cars (to 2 decimal places)}$$

Thus the mean (average) production of cars each week is 7 and the standard deviation from this is 1.41 cars each week.

A distribution in which the values are widely spread will produce a high standard of deviation and one in which the values are close to the mean will produce a low standard deviation.

Note: If the data we are using is from a sample – and not a population as in our example (see unit 5.1) – then a slightly different formula is used to calculate the standard deviation is:

$$\text{Standard deviation} = \sqrt{\frac{\Sigma(x - \bar{x})^2}{n - 1}}$$

The only difference is that we divide the squared deviation by the number of data values – 1, rather than the number of data values. Most computer spreadsheet formulas distinguish between the standard deviation of a sample and that of a population.

The computational formula for standard deviation

Sometimes we see a different formula for the standard deviation known as the *computational formula*. This gives exactly the same results, however it is preferred by some as it is arguably easier to calculate. The computational formula for the standard deviation for a population is:

$$\sqrt{\frac{\Sigma x^2}{n} - \bar{x}^2}$$

and the computational formula for the standard deviation of a sample is:

$$\sqrt{\frac{\Sigma x^2}{n - 1} - \bar{x}^2}$$

14.3 Standard deviation from a discrete frequency distribution

Calculating the standard deviation of a discrete frequency distribution requires a different formula:

$$\text{Standard deviation} = \sqrt{\frac{\Sigma fx^2}{\Sigma f} - \left(\frac{\Sigma fx}{\Sigma f}\right)^2}$$

where f is the frequency
fx is the frequency × value
Σ means sum of

Although this formula looks quite different from the formula in section 14.2 , it has been derived in much the same way. However the key point, as far as we are concerned, is that we can set out the calculation as a table in a similar way to the standard deviation for raw data. We can therefore calculate it by first working out each of the components of the formula and then substituting these values into the formula. This can be done using either a calculator or a computer spreadsheet.

Suppose we work for a leisure centre and have recorded the number of children in each family group visiting our centre on a Saturday morning. We want to know how much variation there is in the number of children per family. Our raw data looks like this:

Number of Children in Family Groups visiting Centre on 6.2.93

No. of children in group x	No. of family groups f
0	8
1	15
2	23
3	16
4	7
5	3
Total	**72**

Source: Survey by Centre Manager

The first step is to construct a new table of the data with three extra columns as below. These columns will enable us to calculate fx, fx^2, Σf, Σfx and Σfx^2 to input into the formula:

	A	B	C	D	E
1	x	f	fx	x^2	fx^2
2	0	8	0	0	0
3	1	15	15	1	15
4	2	23	46	4	92
5	3	16	48	9	144
6	4	7	28	16	112
7	5	3	15	25	75
8	Total	72	152		438

Column A contains the number of children in each family group (x).

Column B contains the frequency of family groups (f), the total of this column gives us the value for Σf (in this case 72).

Column C contains the result of multiplying each frequency (f) by the number of children (x). The total of this column gives us the value for Σfx (in this case 152).

Column D contains the values of x^2.

Column E contains the result of multiplying each frequency (f) by x^2, the total of this column gives us the value of Σfx^2 (in this case 438).

These values can be substituted into the equation for the standard deviation which can then be calculated. (N.B. in the calculation below all figures have been rounded to 2 decimal places).

$$\text{Standard deviation} = \sqrt{\frac{\Sigma fx^2}{\Sigma f} - \left(\frac{\Sigma fx}{\Sigma f}\right)^2}$$

$$\text{Standard deviation} = \sqrt{\frac{438}{72} - \left(\frac{152}{72}\right)^2}$$

$$= \sqrt{\frac{438}{72} - 2.11^2}$$

$$= \sqrt{6.08 - 4.45}$$

$$= \sqrt{1.63}$$

$$= 1.28$$

The mean is simply the total of column C (Σfx) divided by the total of column B (Σf):

$$\text{Mean} = \frac{152}{72} = 2.11 \text{ (to 2 decimal places)}$$

From this we can see that the mean number of children with each family group is 2.11 and the standard deviation is 1.28 children; a large variation given the mean number of children.

14.4 Standard deviation from a grouped frequency distribution

To calculate the standard deviation for a grouped frequency distribution we use the same formula as for a discrete frequency distribution (see above). The only difference is that we need to use the midpoint to represent each class interval (x) rather than the class value. Once again we can set out the calculation as a table and work out the components of the formula first of all. The table below records salary data for a small computer company.

Salaries of Employees of the Small Computer Company 1993

Salary in £'s (Class interval)	Frequency f
6000 – < 8000	2
8000 – < 10000	3
10000 – < 12000	3
12000 – < 14000	4
14000 – < 16000	3
16000 – < 18000	2
18000 – < 20000	1
Total	**18**

Source: Company Payroll

The first stage is to construct a new table of data with six extra columns! These columns will enable us to calculate the midpoint of each class interval x, fx, fx^2, Σf, Σfx and Σfx^2 to input into the formula:

	A	B	C	D	E	F	G	H
1	Salary in £'s (Class interval)	Freq-uency f	LCB	UCB	Mid point x	Frequency × Midpoint fx	x^2	fx^2
2	6000 – < 8000	2	6000	8000	7000	14000	49000000	98000000
3	8000 – < 10000	3	8000	10000	9000	27000	81000000	243000000
4	10000 – < 12000	3	10000	12000	11000	33000	121000000	363000000
5	12000 – < 14000	4	12000	14000	13000	52000	169000000	676000000
6	14000 – < 16000	3	14000	16000	15000	45000	225000000	675000000
7	16000 – < 18000	2	16000	18000	17000	34000	289000000	578000000
8	18000 – < 20000	1	18000	20000	19000	19000	361000000	361000000
9	Total	18				224000		2994000000

Columns A and B contain the data from our table. Column B is summed to give the value for Σf (in this case 18).

Columns C, D and E are used to calculate the mid point of each class interval by adding the lower class boundary (LCB) to the upper class boundary (UCB) and dividing by two. The midpoint (x) is recorded in column E.

Column F contains the result of multiplying each frequency (f) by the midpoint of the class interval (x). The total for this column gives us the value for Σfx (in this case 224000).

Column G contains the values of x^2.

Column H contains the result of multiplying each frequency (f) by x^2, the total of this column gives us the value of Σfx^2 (in this case 2994000000).

These figures can then be substituted into the equation for the standard deviation which can then be calculated. (In this equation we have calculated the answer to 10 significant figures in order to fit it on the page!).

$$\text{Standard deviation} = \sqrt{\frac{\Sigma fx^2}{\Sigma f} - \left(\frac{\Sigma fx}{\Sigma f}\right)^2}$$

$$= \sqrt{\frac{2994000000}{18} - \left(\frac{224000}{18}\right)^2}$$

$$= \sqrt{166333333.3 - 12444.44444^2}$$

$$= \sqrt{11469135.80}$$

$$= 3{,}386.61 \text{ (to 2 decimal places)}$$

The mean salary is simply the total of column F (Σfx) divided by the total of column B (Σf):

$$\text{Mean} = \frac{224000}{18} = £12{,}444.44$$

From this we can say that the mean salary is £12,444.44 with a standard deviation of £3,386.61. As we are using monetary values there is no point in being more accurate than two decimal places.

14.5 Problems when calculating the standard deviation for large numbers

As can be seen above the numbers involved in the calculation of the standard deviation start off as tens of thousands and end up as numbers in the billions! Whilst such large numbers are usually no problem if we are using a computer spreadsheet they are impossible to handle on many calculators!

To overcome this problem, the large numbers can be substituted with smaller ones by using a formula involving an assumed mean and the class intervals.

The central mid-point (the *assumed mean*) of the Small Computer Company's salary data is calculated using the formula:

$$\text{Smallest Lower Class Boundary} + \frac{\text{Largest Upper Class Boundary} - \text{Smallest Lower Class Boundary}}{2}$$

$$= 6000 + \frac{20000 - 6000}{2} = 13{,}000$$

The class interval for all classes is 2,000.

Using the assumed mean, we can calculate the value for the deviation from the mean (d) using the following formula:

$$d = \frac{x - x_0}{c}$$

where x_0 assumed mean (in this case 13,000),
x mid point of the class,
c class width (in this case 2,000)

Calculating d for each frequency group makes the values used in the calculation of the mean and standard deviation much easier to work with.

As before it helps if we set our calculation out as a table, even though we are not using a spreadsheet.

The table below shows how the deviation (d) is calculated:

Salary in £'s (Class interval)	Frequency f	LCB	UCB	Mid point x	Assumed mean x_0	Class width c	Deviation d
6000 – < 8000	2	6000	8000	7000	13000	2000	-3
8000 – < 10000	3	8000	10000	9000	13000	2000	-2
10000 – < 12000	3	10000	12000	11000	13000	2000	-1
12000 – < 14000	4	12000	14000	13000	13000	2000	0
14000 – < 16000	3	14000	16000	15000	13000	2000	1
16000 – < 18000	2	16000	18000	17000	13000	2000	2
18000 – < 20000	1	18000	20000	19000	13000	2000	3
Total	**18**						**0**

The midpoint (x) for each class interval is calculated by adding the lower class boundary to the upper class boundary and dividing by 2.

The assumed mean (x_0) has already been calculated (see above).

The class width (c) is calculated by subtracting the lower class boundary from the upper class boundary.

The formula above can then be used to calculate each deviation from the mean (d).

As we can see this makes the numbers far more manageable when using a calculator.

We can now use the following formula to calculate the standard deviation:

$$\text{Standard deviation} = c \times \sqrt{\frac{\Sigma fd^2}{\Sigma f} - \left(\frac{\Sigma fd}{\Sigma f}\right)^2}$$

To work out the various components of the formula it is easiest to set out our calculation as a table:

Salary in £'s (Class interval)	f	**Mid point** x	d	fd	d^2	fd^2
6000 – < 8000	2	7000	-3	-6	9	18
8000 – < 10000	3	9000	-2	-4	4	12
10000 – < 12000	3	11000	-1	-3	1	3
12000 – < 14000	4	13000	0	0	0	0
14000 – < 16000	3	15000	1	1	1	3
16000 – < 18000	2	17000	2	4	4	8
18000 – < 20000	1	19000	3	3	9	9
	18		**0**	**-5**		**53**

These values can be substituted into the equation for the standard deviation and the answer worked out using a calculator or by hand. In this case it is important not to round numbers until the final part of the calculation as early rounding could have a large impact on the final figure:

$$\text{Standard deviation} = c \times \sqrt{\frac{\Sigma fd^2}{\Sigma f} - \left(\frac{\Sigma fd}{\Sigma f}\right)^2}$$

$$\text{Standard deviation} = 2000 \times \sqrt{\frac{53}{18} - \left(\frac{-5}{18}\right)^2}$$

$$= 2000 \times \sqrt{2.944444 - (-0.277777)^2}$$

$$= 2000 \times \sqrt{2.944444 - 0.07716}$$

$$= 2000 \times \sqrt{2.867284}$$

$$= 2000 \times 1.693306$$

$$= 3{,}386.61$$

As before we can say that the mean salary is £12,444.44 with a standard deviation of £3,386.61

Do not worry if you do not understand how these formulae are derived. It is more important that we can complete the calculations and interpret the resultant standard deviation. This is covered in detail in the next section.

14.6 Interpreting the standard deviation for normally distributed data

There are a number of ways we can interpret the standard deviation for normally distributed data. To illustrate some of these we will compare data on the time it takes two garages to complete a major car service. We obtain the times it took for the last 100 occasions they did these services. Using this data we have calculated the mean and the standard deviation for each garage's repair times.

Mean and Standard Deviation of Time to Complete a Major Service

Garage	Mean time (hours)	Standard deviation (hours)
Railway Arch Garage	4	0.5
Joe's Auto Repairs	4	1

Source: Analysis of last 100 Services, June 1991

The means tell us that both garages complete the jobs in the same average time, but the standard deviations tell us that the times for the Railway Arch Garage vary considerably less than for Joe's Auto Repairs.

We can take this analysis a stage further if the shape of the distribution is approximately symmetrical about the mean. This type of distribution is called a *normal distribution* (see unit 12.5). The further away a distribution is from the 'normal curve', the more difficult it becomes to interpret the standard deviation accurately. To recap the key characteristics of any normal distribution are:

- it is symmetrical about the mean;
- the majority of values tend to cluster about the mean;
- the frequencies of values tend to taper away symmetrically either side of the mean, this means it is a 'bell shaped curve'.

If we draw the frequency curves for the two garages and they look like this:

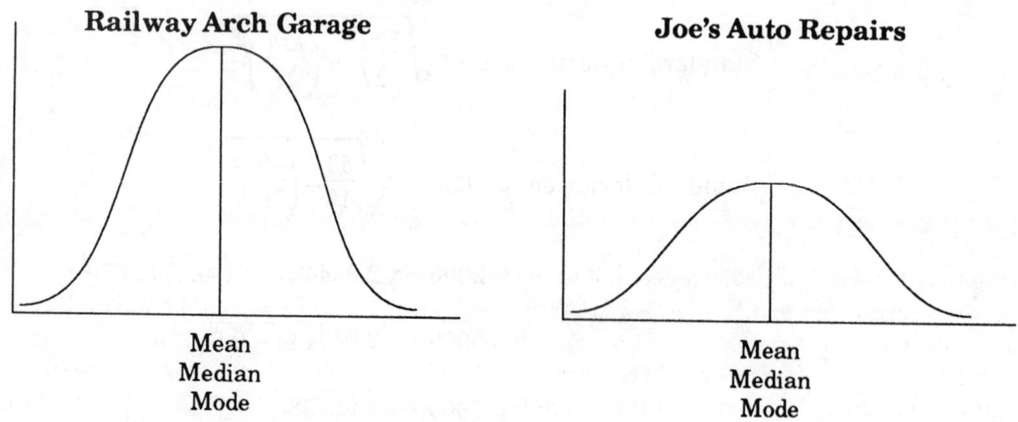

As we can see the data (repair times) is normally distributed.

Statisticians have found the following properties for data which is normally distributed:

- 68% of values lie within plus or minus 1 standard deviation from the mean;
- 95% of values lie within plus or minus 1.96 standard deviations from the mean;
- 99% of values lie within plus or minus 2.57 standard deviations from the mean;
- virtually 100% of values lie within plus or minus 4 standard deviations from the mean.

On a normal distribution curve, this information looks like this:

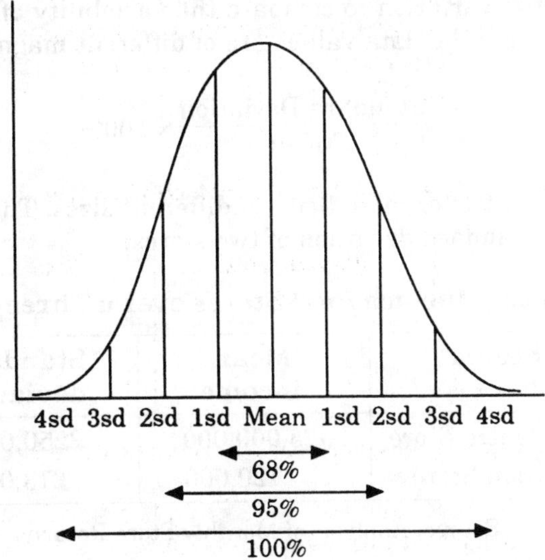

We can use this information to assess the likely variation in repair time for each of the two garages. The mean plus or minus 1 standard deviation will tell us the repair times that both garages should be within 68% of the time. The mean plus or minus 1.96 standard deviations will tell us the repair times that both garages should be within 95% of the time and so on. This information has been tabulated below:

Likely Major Service Times for Railway Arch Garage and Joe's Auto Repairs

Garage	Mean service time	Standard deviation	68% of services completed between....	95% of services completed between....	99% of services completed between....
Railway Arch	4 hrs	0.5 hrs	3.5 and 4.5 hrs	3.02 and 4.98 hrs	2.715 and 5.285 hrs
Joe's Auto Repairs	4 hrs	1 hour	3 and 5 hrs	2.04 and 5.96 hrs	1.43 and 6.57 hrs

Source: Analysis of last 100 Services, June 1991

Using this information we can now draw the following conclusions about the two garages:

The time taken by Railway Arch Garage to complete a major service is less variable than that of Joe's Auto Repairs. For example Railway Arch Garages will take between 3 and 5 hours (3.02 and 4.98 to be precise) to complete a major service 95% of the time. By contrast Joe's Auto Repairs will take somewhere between 2 and 6 hours (2.04 and 5.96 to be precise) for a major service 95% of the time. Our conclusion should therefore be that Railway Arch Garage is much more consistent in the time they take to complete a major service.

However if we wanted a major service done quickly (in under two hours) we would be better going to Joe's Auto Repairs as there would be a greater chance of it being done in this time. This concept is developed further in unit 25.

14.7 The coefficient of variation

We can use the coefficient of variation to compare the variability of different data distributions. This is especially useful where the data values are of different magnitudes. It is calculated using the following formula:

$$\frac{\text{Standard Deviation}}{\text{Mean}} \times 100\%$$

For example we can compare two or more firms of different sizes. The table below gives the mean monthly sales income and standard deviation of two stores:

Mean Monthly Income for 2 Stores over a Three Year Period

Stores	Mean income	Standard deviation
City Centre Store	£3,000,000	£250,000
Suburban Store	£120,000	£13,000

Source: Analysis of Monthly Store Returns

We can calculate the coefficient of variation for each store (both answers rounded to 2 decimal places):

$$\text{City Centre Store Coefficient of Variation} = \frac{250000}{3000000} \times 100 = 8.33$$

$$\text{Suburban Store Coefficient of Variation} = \frac{13000}{120000} \times 100 = 10.83$$

From these calculations we can see that there is relatively more variation in the monthly income of the suburban store than the city centre store.

14.8 Summary

- The standard deviation is a measure of dispersion – it measures the extent to which data are spread around the mean and includes all data values in its calculation.
- The standard deviation can be calculated for quantitative data.
- The greater the dispersion, the larger the standard deviation.
- The further away a distribution is from the 'normal curve', the more difficult it becomes to interpret the standard deviation accurately.
- The coefficient of variation enables us to compare the variability of distributions of different magnitudes.

Further reading:

Business Mathematics and Statistics (Chapters 11 & 42), Francis A, DP PUBLICATIONS (1993)
Quantitative Approaches in Business Studies (Chapter 5), Morris C, PITMAN (1989)
Statistics (Chapter 9), Owen F & Jones R, PITMAN (1990)

Unit 15: Time series: variations and moving averages

15.1 Introduction to time series

A vast amount of business data comes in the form of a time series; such as weekly sales, monthly absences, annual turnover. Time series data is therefore data that is collected over a period of time, usually at even time intervals. Within business we need to understand this data, and in particular the way in which it varies over time. Time series analysis enables this data to be understood, trends to be identified and forecasts or projections to be made.

In this unit we will be looking at the simpler methods of analysing and understanding time series data and in unit 16 using time series to forecast future trends.

15.2 Simple time series

A *time series* is a set of numerical data collected at various points through time. The data is usually recorded at regular intervals, such as weekly, monthly, quarterly or annually, and most often presented in the form of a line graph (unit 10.4). The data in the table below is a time series of the number of tonnes of sweets produced by a sweet factory:

Number of Tonnes of Sweets produced Quarterly by Factory 1988-1992

Year	Quarter 1 Jan.-March	Quarter 2 April-June	Quarter 3 July-Sept.	Quarter 4 Oct.-Dec.
1988	636	680	704	744
1989	700	756	784	828
1990	800	840	880	936
1991	860	944	972	1014
1992	920	1034	1083	1186

Source: Factory Production Department

The first thing we usually do when examining time series data is to draw a line graph. It is customary to plot time against the x (horizontal) axis and the variable against the y (vertical) axis:

Number of Tonnes of Sweets produced Quarterly by Factory 1988-1992

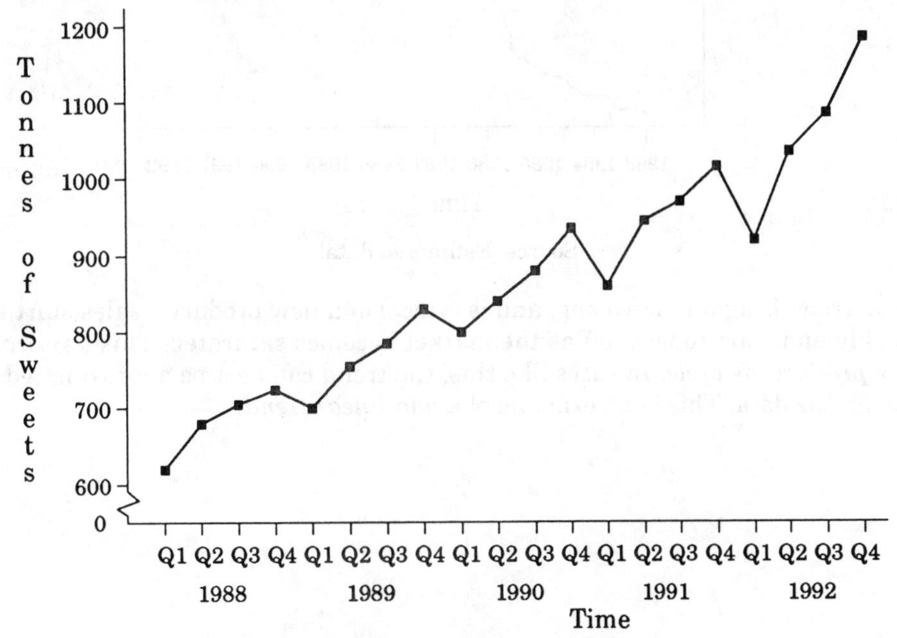

Source: Factory Production Department

The time series illustrated above, like all time series, exhibits a number of features. The main ones are:

- long-term trend;
- seasonal variations;
- cyclical fluctuations (not illustrated above);
- residual influences.

Long-term trend

The *long-term*, or *secular,* trend of a time series is the underlying movement of the series over time. The trend may be upward or downward or there may be no definable trend. The long-term trend shows the overall and consistent pattern of change affecting the data over time. If we look at unemployment figures then the majority of people hope that the long term trend will be downwards. However this reduction is unlikely to be steady as there are other factors which will cause variations.

Looking at the time series graph of our sweet factory's production, a gradual upward trend can be seen. To help identify the long-term trend, we can draw a straight line on the graph to approximate the overall trend. This is an example of an *increasing linear* trend. If the sales had been falling the line would be sloping downwards and the time series would show a *decreasing linear* trend.

However, not all time series trends can be represented by a straight line. Here is a graph of the sales of Personal Computers over the past ten years:

Sales of Personal Computers 1983-1992

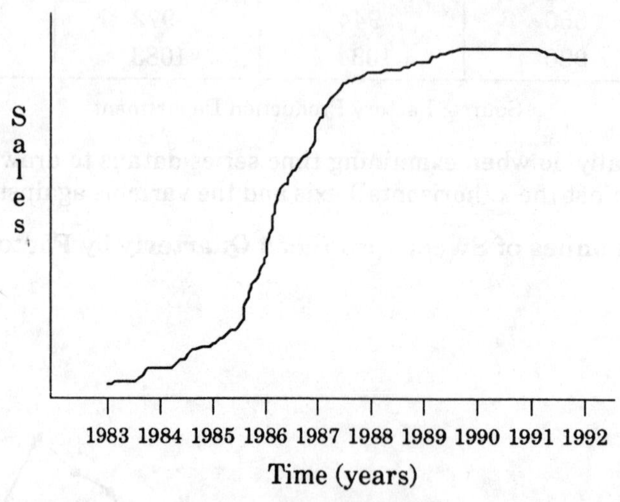

Source: Estimated data!

The long-term trend is again increasing, and is typical of a new product – sales start slowly, then increase quickly and start to level off as the market becomes saturated. This pattern is often referred to as a *product life cycle.* In cases like this, the trend can best be approximated by drawing a curve through the data. This is an example of a *non-linear trend.*

Sales of Personal Computers 1983-1992

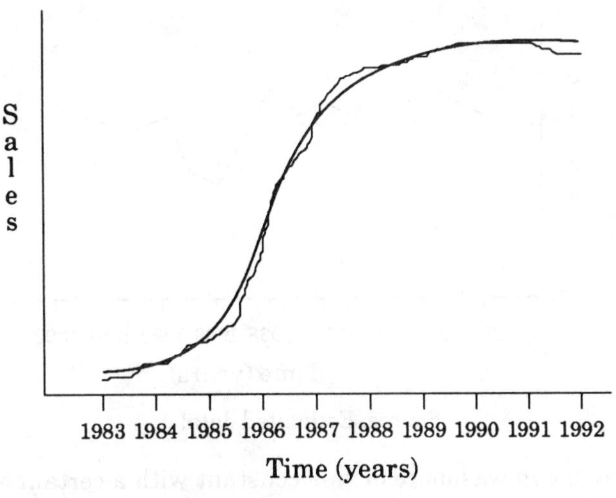

Source: Estimated data!

Seasonal variations

One factor influencing data is the time of year. Economic activity varies during the year because of the climate and cultural events. Building and construction work slows down in the winter months when the weather is poor, and consumer spending is usually much higher in the weeks leading up to Christmas. *Seasonal variations* are movements in a time series that recur year after year in the same months (or quarters) with more or less the same degree of variation. Our time series showing the sales of sweets has a regular peak in the last quarter (October to December), and a regular trough in the first quarter (January to March) of each year.

We can therefore explain these variations by purely seasonal factors. Regular variations on a weekly basis are also sometimes called *seasonal,* although the name is perhaps unfortunate, as the pattern repeats itself over a period much shorter than a year.

Cyclical fluctuations

In addition to seasonal variations business activity follows a pattern of booms and slumps. This cycle is usually about 7 years long, but can vary between 4 and 15 years. Our time series showing the sales of sweets therefore does not include cyclical fluctuations. *Cyclical fluctuations* are therefore similar to a seasonal variation but the pattern of fluctuation lasts longer than a year. In order to detect a cyclical variation in a time series data often has to be collected and analysed over many years. Economists have noted that over a series of cycles an overall trend is observable with each successive boom being greater than its predecessor.

Residual influences

Residual influences are unforeseen or random events which also affect the figures in our time series. These are either caused by easily-identifiable events such as elections, wars or earthquakes, or have no apparent cause. The latter are known as *random variations.* The time series of egg sales over the last ten years illustrates both types of residual influences.

Time series of egg sales

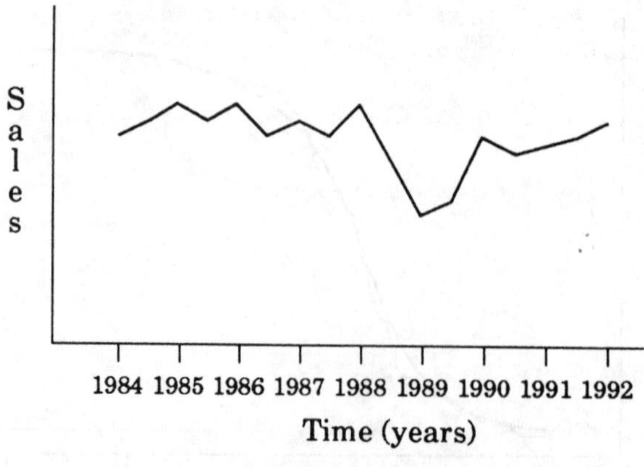

Source: Estimated data!

Until 1988, the long-term trend was more or less constant with a certain amount of random variation. There are no specific reasons for these variations they simply reflect random consumer behaviour. However, in 1988 sales plummeted due to the salmonella scare – an unforeseen variation from the long-term trend but with a clearly identifiable cause.

It is relatively easy for us to identify the factors which cause fluctuations in data collected over time. Unfortunately it is often far more difficult to disentangle them and estimate the future trend.

15.3 Determining the trend: moving averages

As we have seen, trends can be estimated by drawing a freehand line through the data on a time series graph, but this is not a very accurate method on which to base future decisions. The most straightforward method is using *moving averages*. This involves calculating the arithmetic mean for successive groups of data within the time series.

The table below records the quarterly sales for a multi-national company over four years:

Sales in £ million for Mega Trading Company 1989-1992

Year	Quarter	Sales
1989	1	114
	2	142
	3	155
	4	136
1990	1	116
	2	150
	3	153
	4	140
1991	1	128
	2	158
	3	169
	4	159
1992	1	137
	2	180
	3	192
	4	172

Source: Audited Company Annual Accounts

The line graph of the time series data (below) suggests that there is a trend, but there is also variation. The moving average provides us with a method of smoothing out the variation in the data to provide a more accurate estimate of the trend.

Sales in £ million for Mega Trading Company 1989-1992

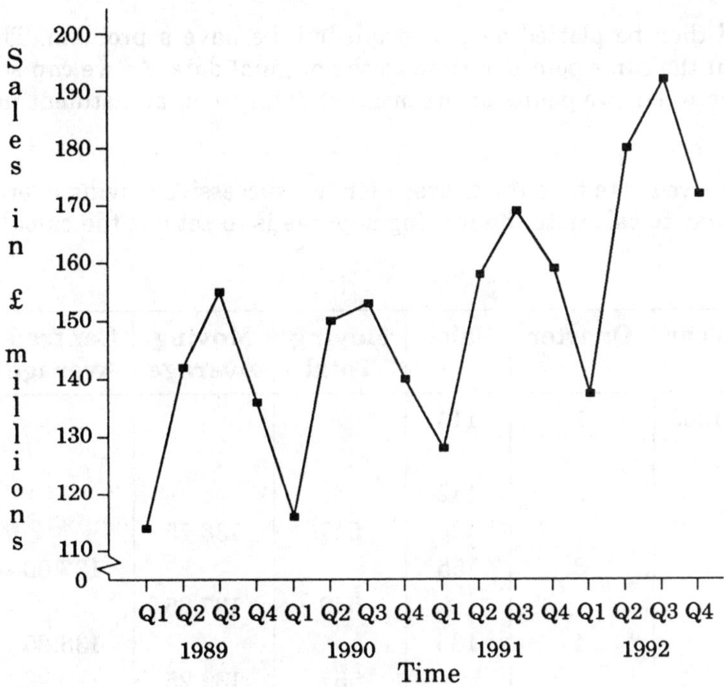

Source: Audited Company Annual Accounts

A moving average is calculated by replacing each value in a time series with an average of that value and those values directly preceding and following it. The first step is to select an appropriate number of data values for the average.

As our data shows a seasonal variation that is repeated annually and our data is recorded quarterly, a four *period* moving average should be used to smooth out the fluctuations. However, if appropriate, we could use a three period or five period moving average.

The moving average (mean) is calculated by finding the total value of sales in the first four periods (547) and then dividing this figure by the number of periods (4):

Year	Quarter (period)	Sales	Four period total	Four period average
1989	1	114		
	2	142		
			547	136.75
	3	155		
	4	136		

So, the average for the first four periods is:

$$\frac{547}{4} = 136.75$$

In other words, the moving average is simply the mean of the four periods.

This figure should then be plotted on our graph but we have a problem. The moving average should be plotted at the same points in time as the original data. As we can see above each moving average falls between two points of the original data, so an adjustment needs to be made to overcome this.

The way this is achieved is to take the average for two successive moving averages and *centre* the data. The easiest way to calculate the moving average is to set out the calculation as a table as illustrated below:

Year	Quarter	Sales	Moving Total	Moving Average	Centred Average
1989	1	114			
	2	142			
			547	136.75	
	3	155			137.00
			549	137.25	
	4	136			138.25
			557	139.25	
1990	1	116			
	2	150			

The **sales** column records the value of sales in £ million.

The **moving total** column records the result of calculating the moving total of successive four periods as described above. Because each moving total falls half way between two points in the original data we put the moving totals half way between the sales values.

The first moving total is the total sales from Quarter 1 1989 to Quarter 4 1989, the second is the total from Quarter 2 1989 to Quarter 1 1990 and so on.

The next column, **moving average**, records the result of calculating the moving average by dividing the total by the number of periods, in this case four.

The final column, **centred average**, records the result of averaging each successive pair of moving averages to provide a centred average. The first centred average is calculated by adding together the first two moving averages and dividing by two:

$$\frac{136.75 + 137.75}{2} = 137.00$$

The second centred average is calculated by adding together the second and third moving averages and dividing by two:

$$\frac{137.25 + 139.25}{2} = 138.25$$

and so on.

The figures of 137.00 and 138.25 now correspond to Quarter 3 and Quarter 4 1989, and can be plotted on a graph.

There is a quicker way we can calculate the centred average that involves calculating just one mean. This time we have set out the calculation as a table as you would see it on a spreadsheet. This means it is not possible to place the moving totals (and the centred totals) half way between the sales values. We have therefore placed them in the cell below. Thus the first moving total instead of being half way between cells D3 and D4 is placed in cell D4 (see below):

	A	B	C	D	E	F
1	Year	Quarter	Sales	Moving Total	Centred Total	Centred Average
2	1989	1	114			
3		2	142			
4		3	155	547	1096	137.000
5		4	136	549	1106	138.250
6	1990	1	116	557	1112	139.000
7		2	150	555	1114	139.250
8		3	153	559	1130	141.250
9		4	140	571	1150	143.750
10	1991	1	128	579	1174	146.750
11		2	158	595	1209	151.125
12		3	169	614	1237	154.625
13		4	159	623	1268	158.500
14	1992	1	137	645	1313	164.125
15		2	180	668	1349	168.625
16		3	192	681		
17		4	172			

A centred total is calculated (Column E). This is simply the total of each successive pair of moving four period totals. The first centred total is:

$$547 + 549 = 1096$$

The second centred total is:

$$549 + 557 = 1106$$

and so on.

We then calculate the centred average, (Column F), by dividing the centred total by eight. The total is divided by eight and not four because the centred total is the sum of two sets of four periods – a total of eight periods. This centred average is sometimes referred to as the centred moving average.

If we plot our time series and moving average on the same line graph, we can see that the moving average smoothes out the fluctuation from the original data. We can now see that the overall trend has been one of increasing sales over the period.

Sales in £ million for Mega Trading Company 1989-1992

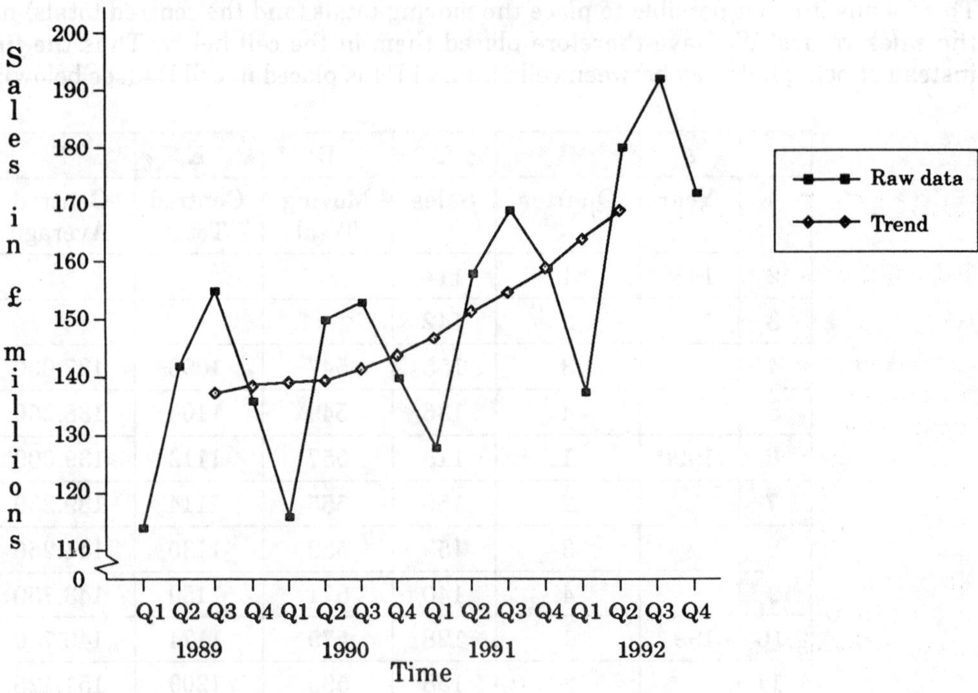

Source: Audited Company Annual Accounts

It is only necessary for us to centre the moving averages when it is calculated over an even number of time periods. If we are calculating a moving average over an odd number of periods there is no need to centre, each moving average is automatically positioned at a time corresponding to our original data. When dealing with data which has no obvious cycle we choose the moving average time period which gives the smoothest trend. A good guideline is usually to look at the patterns between the peaks or troughs in the raw data series and use these to determine the averaging period.

15.4 Summary

- Time series refers to data that is collected over a period of time, usually at regular intervals.
- Time series analysis breaks down time series data into trends that can be identified and enables forecasts to be made.

- The main features of a time series are the long term trend, seasonal variations, cyclical fluctuations and residual influences.
- One method of calculating a trend is to use a moving average. This involves calculating the arithmetic mean for successive overlapping values.
- When calculating moving averages with an even period the resulting average must subsequently be centred. This ensures that each trend value lines up with a point in time.

Further reading:

Management Information Systems and Statistics (Chapter 11), Bee R & Bee F, IPM (1990)
Business Mathematics and Statistics (Chapters 18 & 19), Francis A, DP PUBLICATIONS (1993)
Quantitative Approaches in Business Studies (Chapter 13), Morris C, PITMAN (1989)

Unit 16: Time series: forecasting and seasonal variation

16.1 Introduction

Forecasting trends is crucial for success in many businesses. Managers need sufficient information about the future to enable them to plan ahead and make decisions based upon what is likely to happen. Some of these predictions will be concerned with internal events; the personnel department of a large multinational company will be concerned with manpower planning, assessing the number of people required to ensure the continued success of the business. Other forecasts will be concerned with events external to the company such as changes in market size or interest rates.

Information is very important to this planning process but data about the current situation may not be that useful on its own when planing for the future. What we need is some method of projecting the existing figures into the future so decisions can be made on the basis of accurate information, rather than based on speculation. In other words, we need to make *forecasts* based on the data already available. Forecasting can involve a number of statistical methods including regression analysis (unit 18.3) and time series. This unit is concerned with *time series forecasting.*

16.2 Forecasting from the (centred) moving average

In unit 15 we looked at the trend in sales for the Mega Trading Company between 1989 and 1992. As part of this we calculated the moving average as a line on a line graph. We now wish to forecast future sales.

Calculating the average variation

To make this forecast we could extend the moving average line on our graph 'by eye' into the future. As this is not very accurate one solution involves calculating the average variation in sales for each quarter using the previous quarter's moving average as our base. This is called forecasting from the moving average. Once again we can set this out as a table and use either a calculator or a computer spreadsheet:

	A	B	F	G
1	Year	Quarter	Centred Moving Average	Variation from previous quarter
2	1989	1		
3		2		
4		3	137.000	
5		4	138.250	1.250
6	1990	1	139.000	0.750
7		2	139.250	0.250
8		3	141.250	2.000
9		4	143.750	2.500
10	1991	1	146.750	3.000
11		2	151.125	4.375
12		3	154.625	3.500
13		4	158.500	3.875
14	1992	1	164.125	5.625
15		2	168.625	4.500
16		3		
17		4		

The way we do this is to take the centred moving average (column F) and calculate the variation from one quarter to the next (column G). For example, the first figure in cell G5 is the difference between the second and first figures in cells F5 and F4.

$$138.250 - 137.000 = 1.250$$

This represents the variation from one quarter to the next. The calculation is repeated for each quarter and then the average variation is calculated by summing the all variations from the previous quarters and dividing the total by the number of observations.

$$\text{Average variation} = \frac{\text{total of variations}}{\text{no. of observations}}$$

$$= \frac{31.625}{11}$$

$$= 2.875 \text{ (to 3 decimal places)}$$

So, the average variation is 2.875 per quarter. This means that, on average, the value of sales by the Mega Trading Company is increasing by £2.875 million per quarter. This is the *long-term trend*.

Forecasting

Our average variation figure (the long term trend) can now be used to forecast future values of sales as shown in the table below:

	A	B	H	I	J
1	Year	Quarter	Previous quarter trend	Average variation	Basic trend forecast
16	1992	3	168.625	2.875	171.500
17		4	171.500	2.875	174.375
18	1993	1	174.375	2.875	177.250
19		2	177.250	2.875	180.125
20		3	180.125	2.875	183.000
21		4	183.000	2.875	185.875
22	1994	1	185.875	2.875	188.750
23		2	188.750	2.875	191.625

Taking the last figure from the moving average the next quarter's figure has been projected by adding the average variation to the existing trend. This new figure then becomes the base figure for the next quarter.

Cell H16 contains the last moving average which calculated for the second quarter of 1992 (168.625). This is the 'previous quarter's moving average' for the third quarter of 1992.

The average variation (2.875) is added to it from cell I16 and the answer, the basic trend forecast for the third quarter of 1992, recorded in cell J16.

This figure (in cell J16) is copied to cell H17 to become the 'previous quarter's moving average' for the 4th quarter of 1992.

In general terms each cell in:

column H records the trend for the previous quarter;

column I records the average variation;

and column J, the basic trend forecast, that is the trend for the previous quarter plus the average variation.

From this we can work out that the forecast for quarter 2 of 1994 is £191.625 million of sales.

We could continue this method of forecasting almost indefinitely but two things should be noted:

- this method does not take any seasonal variations into account but only smoothes them out by using the moving average, thus if there is any seasonality in our data this will not be included in the forecast;

- the forecast assumes that the factors affecting the trend will be the same in the future as they have been in the past and predicts the future trend using a straight line.

As with all forecasting the further we move from our real data and into the forecast, the more likely there are to be errors in our forecast.

16.3 Taking seasonal variation into account

So far, the methods we have looked at have not taken into account the effect of seasonal or cyclical variations. To clarify the long-term trend, seasonal variations are often removed from the data to produce *seasonally adjusted* data. Unemployment figures are usually quoted as being seasonally adjusted.

To produce a forecast that includes the seasonal variations, we need to examine the difference between the centred moving average in column F (sometimes called the trend) and the raw data (column C):

	A	B	C	F	G
1	Year	Quarter	Sales	Centred Moving Average (Trend)	Variation from trend (C – F)
2	1989	1	114		
3		2	142		
4		3	155	137.000	18.000
5		4	136	138.250	-2.250
6	1990	1	116	139.000	-23.000
7		2	150	139.250	10.750
8		3	153	141.250	11.750
9		4	140	143.750	-3.750
10	1991	1	128	146.750	-18.750
11		2	158	151.125	6.875
12		3	169	154.625	14.375
13		4	159	158.500	0.500
14	1992	1	137	164.125	-27.125
15		2	180	168.625	11.375
16		3	192		
17		4	172		

Column C records our original sales data.

Column F records the trend we calculated using the centred moving average (see unit 15.3).

Column G shows the variation from the trend. Each variation is calculated by subtracting the value in column F from the value in column C. The variation (answer) is positive when the actual value of sales is greater than the trend and negative when the actual value of sales is less than the trend.

We begin to calculate the seasonal variations by collecting together the variations for each quarter. The variations for each quarter are then summed:

Year	Quarter 1	Quarter 2	Quarter 3	Quarter 4
1989			18.000	-2.250
1990	-23.000	10.750	11.750	-3.750
1991	-18.750	6.875	14.375	0.500
1992	-27.125	11.375		
Total	**-68.875**	**29.000**	**-44.125**	**-5.500**

Taking each quarter in turn, we calculate the average (mean) variation from the trend by taking the total variation for each quarter and dividing this by the number of observations (in this case three). In this case there is no need to take these calculations to many decimal places as all that is required is an equitable allocation between the four seasons.

For example, the calculation for quarter 1 is:

$$\frac{-68.875}{3} = -22.958 \text{ (to 3 decimal places)}$$

The average seasonal variation for each quarter is given below:

	Quarter 1	Quarter 2	Quarter 3	Quarter 4
Average Seasonal variation	-22.958	9.667	14.708	-1.833

Technically, if we added all the average seasonal variations together the result should be zero. If all the variation from the trend was due to seasonal factors then this would be the case. But usually there are also cyclical and residual variations, so the average seasonal variation needs to be adjusted to take account of this. To do this, the sum of the average seasonal variations must be corrected to zero.

$$\text{Total average seasonal variation} = -22.958 + 9.667 + 14.708 - 1.833 = -0.416$$

This means that there is an excess variation of –0.416 to be corrected.

We divide this excess figure by the number of periods to give the average correction factor:

$$\text{average correction} = \frac{-0.416}{4} = -0.104$$

and then subtract the correction factor from each quarter to give a corrected seasonal variation. Therefore the:

$$\text{corrected value for quarter 1} = -22.958 - (-0.104) = -22.854$$

and so on as shown below:

	Quarter 1	Quarter 2	Quarter 3	Quarter 4
Average Seasonal variation	-22.958	9.667	14.708	-1.833
Average Correction	-0.104	-0.104	-0.104	-0.104
Corrected average seasonal variation	–22.854	9.771	14.812	–1.729

We can easily check that our calculations of the corrected seasonal variations are correct as they should always sum to zero:

$$-22.854 + 9.771 + 14.812 + (-1.729) = 0$$

Using these figures we can now say that on average, in every Quarter 1, the value of sales is £22.854 million below the trend line, in every Quarter 2, £9.771 million above the trend line, and so on.

The relative magnitude of the average correction when compared with the raw data gives us an idea of the accuracy of any forecast as it represents all the residual variations in our data. The larger the residual variation, the lower the accuracy of any forecast.

We can use the figures either to seasonally adjust the trend or to make more accurate forecasts.

16.4 Seasonally adjusting the trend

This process, sometimes called deseasonalising, is achieved by subtracting the average seasonal variations from the original data.

	A	B	C	L	M
1	Year	Quarter	Sales	Average seasonal variation	Seasonally adjusted Sales
2	1989	1	114	-22.854	136.854
3		2	142	9.771	132.229
4		3	155	14.812	140.188
5		4	136	-1.729	137.729
6	1990	1	116	-22.854	138.854
7		2	150	9.771	140.229
8		3	153	14.812	138.188
9		4	140	-1.729	141.729
10	1991	1	128	-22.854	150.854
11		2	158	9.771	148.229
12		3	169	14.812	154.188
13		4	159	-1.729	160.729
14	1992	1	137	-22.854	159.854
15		2	180	9.771	170.229
16		3	192	14.812	177.188
17		4	172	-1.729	173.729

We can use the resulting seasonally adjusted data for forecasting in the same way as the original data (section 16.2). The remaining fluctuations in the seasonally adjusted figures are due to cyclical fluctuations and random influences.

16.5 Forecasting using the seasonal variation

Using a moving average, we calculated in section 16.2 that on average the value of sales is increasing by £2.875 million per quarter. This is the overall change in the trend, not taking account of seasonal factors. Now that we have calculated the average seasonal variations we can incorporated these into our forecast and produce more accurate projections.

This relatively straight forward. All we need to do is add the average seasonal variation (column K) to the basic trend forecast (column J) produced towards the beginning of section 16.2, and record the answer in column L.

	A	B	H	I	J	K	L
1	Year	Quarter	Previous quarter trend	Average variation	Basic trend forecast	Average seasonal variation	This quarter trend
16	1992	3	168.625	2.875	171.500	14.812	186.312
17		4	171.500	2.875	174.375	-1.729	172.646
18	1993	1	174.375	2.875	177.250	-22.854	154.396
19		2	177.250	2.875	180.125	9.771	189.896
20		3	180.125	2.875	183.000	14.812	197.812
21		4	183.000	2.875	185.875	-1.729	184.146
22	1994	1	185.875	2.875	188.750	-22.854	165.896
23		2	188.750	2.875	191.625	9.771	201.396

So, the forecast value of sales for quarter 2, 1994 using seasonally adjusted figures is £201.396 million.

16.6 Summary

- The simplest method of forecasting the trend is using the moving average. This method does not take seasonal variations into account.
- The average variation per quarter is termed the long-term trend.
- Seasonal factors are often important in a time series when accounting for variations. Their impact can be calculated as deviations from the trend.
- Seasonally adjusting involves subtracting seasonal values from trend values. This is termed deseasonalising the trend.
- A forecast that is seasonally adjusted has taken account of the seasonal variation in the raw data.

Further reading:

Management Information Systems and Statistics (Chapter 11), Bee R & Bee F, IPM (1990)
Business Mathematics and Statistics (Chapter 20), Francis A, DP PUBLICATIONS (1993)
Quantitative Approaches in Business Studies (Chapter 13), Morris C, PITMAN (1989)

Unit 17: Relationships between variables: correlation

17.1 Introduction to relationships between variables

Within business we often need to establish if there is any relationship between two variables, such as between sales of a new product and sales of similar established product or between advertising costs and monthly sales. These two examples highlight the fact that we can have two sorts of relationship between variables:

- when a change in one variable is accompanied by a change in another variable, when they are *correlated*;
- when a change in one variable causes a change in another variable, when there is a *cause and effect* relationship.

Using statistics we can establish the strength (or amount) of a relationship that exists from data we have collected about the two variables. For relationships where we only know that a change in one variable is accompanied by a change in another we can use statistics such as:

- Pearson's Product Moment Correlation Coefficient (discussed in this unit) for quantitative data;
- Spearman's Rank Correlation Coefficient (discussed in this unit) for quantitative and categorical data which can be ranked in some natural way;
- Chi Square Test (discussed in unit 19) for categorical data which cannot be ranked but has been tabulated.

For cause and effect relationships we can calculate a correlation coefficient and a regression coefficient if we have quantitative data. Correlation will only tell us how strongly our two variables are related whilst regression will tell us the nature (cause and effect) of the relationship. In addition we can calculate a regression equation to predict data values. This is discussed in unit 18.

17.2 Types of relationship between two variables

When trying to establish if there is a relationship between two variables the first stage is to plot the points on a graph. This form of graph is called a *scatter graph*. On the scatter graph below each cross (point) represents one pair of data values. We can see that as the amount of petrol sold increases so does the amount of engine oil sold. This is termed a *positive* correlation, as one variable increases so does the other.

Scatter graph of Petrol Sales against Engine Oil Sales (Positive Correlation)

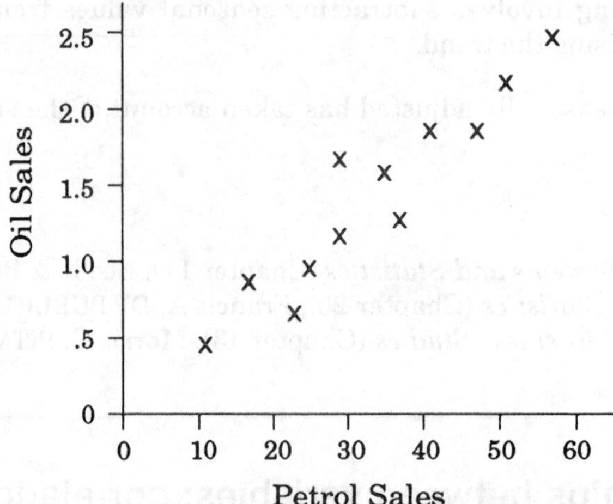

The strength of this correlation is indicated by the closeness of each point to an imaginary line. As we are looking for a *linear* relationship it will be a straight line. If all the points lie on our imaginary line we have *perfect correlation*. We can therefore see that the scatter graph drawn below illustrates a weaker correlation as the points are more dispersed. On this scatter graph the correlation is between the price of the product (in pounds) and the amount sold (in kilograms). This is termed a *negative* correlation, as one variable's values increase the other's decrease.

Scatter graph of Price against Amount Sold (Negative Correlation)

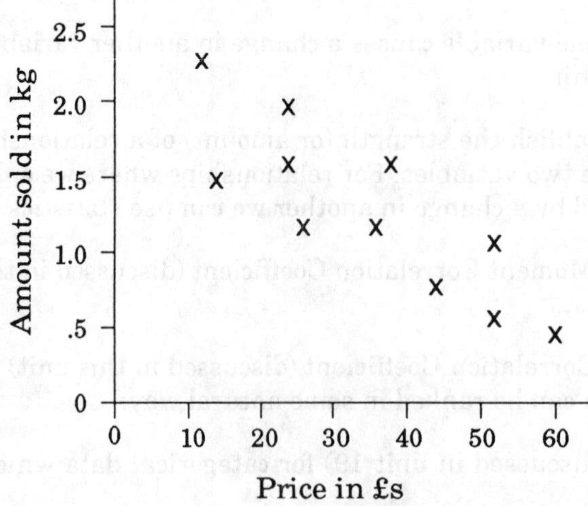

Scatter graphs can also indicate that there is no relationship between the two variables, in other words *no correlation* as shown below:

Scatter graph of Income against Cigars Smoked (No correlation)

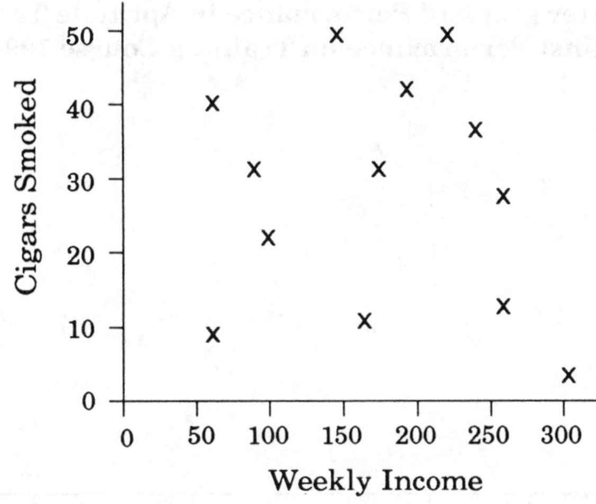

17.3 Spearman's rank correlation coefficient

The correlation statistic we calculate depends upon the type of business data we have. If our data is quantitative and we have actual measured values we can use Pearson's Product Moment Correlation Coefficient, often known as the *PMCC* or *Pearson's r* (see 17.4). Alternatively we can rank our data and use Spearman's Rank Correlation Coefficient. If we have less detailed data and only know the order or rank we can still use Spearman's Rank Correlation Coefficient. For instance we can rank by status or importance, and in competitions competitors are naturally ranked in order. Spearman's Rank Correlation Coefficient also has the added advantage that, although slightly less accurate, it is quicker to calculate and provides a good approximation when there is a linear relationship.

Let us suppose we work for the training department of a large company. We have been asked if there is a relationship between employees' aptitude test scores and how well they performed on a recent training course. Unfortunately, whilst we have the actual results of the aptitude test, the results of the performance on the training course were only recorded in rank order. This means we will have to use rank correlation. Our raw data is given in the table below:

Staff results in aptitude test and performance on training course 199-

Staff member	Aptitude Test	Training Course
Heather	70%	3
Eric	95%	4
Alice	46%	15
Anthony	42%	10
Sonia	71%	2
Linda	90%	1
Pamela	25%	13
Stephen	58%	9
David	48%	12
Jack	64%	5
Emily	67%	6
Andrew	38%	14
Sheila	50%	11
Katie	58%	8
Jenny	47%	7

Source: Training Department

The first stage is to plot a scatter graph of the two variables to see if there is any correlation:

Scatter graph of Performance in Aptitude Test against Performance on Training Course 199-

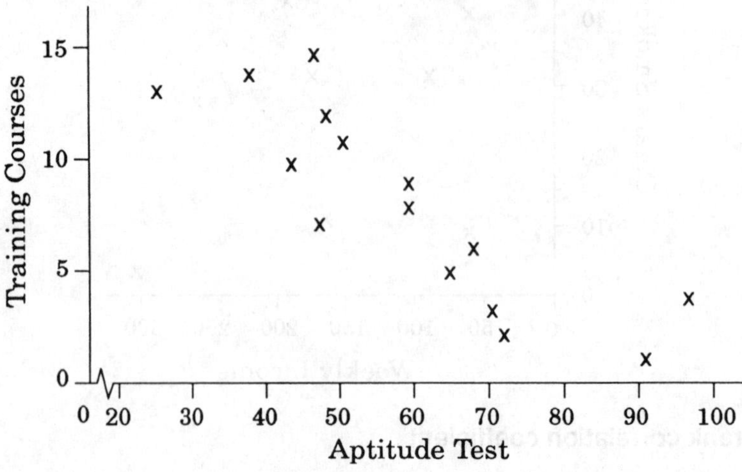

Source: Training Department

As we can see there is a strong negative correlation. This is because the best performer on the training course was ranked 1st, whilst the best performer in the aptitude test gets a score of 95%. Once we have ranked the aptitude test scores so that the highest score is ranked 1st the correlation will be positive.

The next stage is to rank the aptitude test scores (see table below). In the case of a tie, we give each tied item a rank equal to the mean of the ranks they jointly occupy. However care must be taken if there are a more than a few tied ranks as this affects the accuracy of the statistic. In our case we only have one tied rank, that of Stephen and Katie. The calculation is therefore:

$$\frac{7+8}{2} = 7.5$$

Once we have done this we can use Spearman's Rank Correlation Coefficient known by the symbol r^s.

The calculation for Spearman's rank correlation uses the formula:

$$r^s = 1 - \frac{6\Sigma d^2}{n(n^2 - 1)}$$

which can be translated as:

1. Take each pair of rankings and calculate the difference between them. This is d in the formula.
2. Calculate the square of each difference and afterwards add them all together. This is Σd^2.
3. Multiply the sum of the squares of the differences by six ($6\Sigma d^2$).
4. Divide the result by the result of multiplying the number of pairs involved (n) by the number of pairs squared less one (n^2-1).
5. Finally, we subtract the answer from 1.

As in previous units, it is easier to understand if we set the calculation out as a table. This also makes it easier to do using a computer spreadsheet!

	A	B	C	D	E	F
1	**Staff member**	**Aptitude Test**	**Aptitude Test (ranked)**	**Training Course**	*d*	d^2
2	Eric	95%	1	4	-3.0	9.00
3	Linda	90%	2	1	1.0	1.00
4	Sonia	71%	3	2	1.0	1.00
5	Heather	70%	4	3	1.0	1.00
6	Emily	67%	5	6	-1.0	1.00
7	Jack	64%	6	5	1.0	1.00
8	Stephen	58%	7.5	9	-1.5	2.25
9	Katie	58%	7.5	8	-0.5	0.25
10	Sheila	50%	9	11	-2.0	4.00
11	David	48%	10	12	-2.0	4.00
12	Jenny	47%	11	7	4.0	16.00
13	Alice	46%	12	15	-3.0	9.00
14	Anthony	42%	13	10	3.0	9.00
15	Andrew	38%	14	14	0.0	0.00
16	Pamela	25%	15	13	2.0	4.00
17	Total					62.50

Column E records the differences between each of the rankings (*d*).

Column F records the results of squaring each of these differences (d^2); by summing this column we get Σd^2, in our case 62.5.

There are 15 data pairs, therefore $n = 15$.

We can substitute these figures into the formula rounding our answers at each stage to 2 decimal places:

$$r^s = 1 - \frac{6 \times 62.5}{15(15^2 - 1)}$$

$$= 1 - \frac{375}{15 \times (225 - 1)}$$

$$= 1 - \frac{375}{3360}$$

$$= 1 - 0.12$$

$$= 0.88 \text{ (to 2 decimal places)}$$

The value we have calculated for Spearman's Rank Correlation Coefficient indicates the strength of the correlation between the two variables. The result is always a value between +1 and –1. If:

$r^s = 1$ we have a perfect positive correlation;
$r^s = -1$ we have a perfect negative correlation;
$r^s = 0$ we have no correlation;

r^s is close to 1 or –1 we have a strong positive or negative correlation;
r^s is close to zero we have little correlation.

From this we can see that there is a strong positive correlation between a staff member's results in the aptitude test and how well they performed on the training course. This means that in future we could use the aptitude test to help us select those members of staff most suitable for this training course.

17.4 Pearson's product moment correlation coefficient

If we have quantitative data then we can calculate *Pearson's Product Moment Correlation Coefficient*. As with rank correlation this only measures the strength of a relationship, it does not imply causality. Although the calculation is slightly more complicated than rank correlation it is more accurate. In addition it forms the basis of our calculation for the regression coefficient (unit 18.5).

We work for a pizza company that runs a home delivery service for short distances in the city. To cost and plan our service it is necessary to estimate the time for deliveries for any given distance. We believe that this is related to the actual distance from our pizza parlour and so have recorded the distance and time for the last 500 deliveries. Values for ten of these are given below to make the calculations quicker, although in real life we would use all of them and use a computer spreadsheet!

Distance and Delivery Time 199-

Distance (miles)	Time (minutes)
3.5	16
2.4	13
4.9	19
4.2	18
3.0	12
1.3	11
1.0	8
3.0	14
1.5	9
4.1	16

Source: Speedy Pizza Company

The first stage is to check that the two variables are correlated and that the relationship is linear by plotting a scatter graph. (We will eventually go on to calculate a regression equation (unit 18)). In this relationship we know that one of the variables, the *dependent variable,* changes in response to fluctuations in the other variable, the *independent variable*. In this case time is likely to change in response to distance. Convention says that we plot the dependent variable against the y (vertical) axis and the independent variable against the x (horizontal) axis:

Distance and Delivery Time 199-

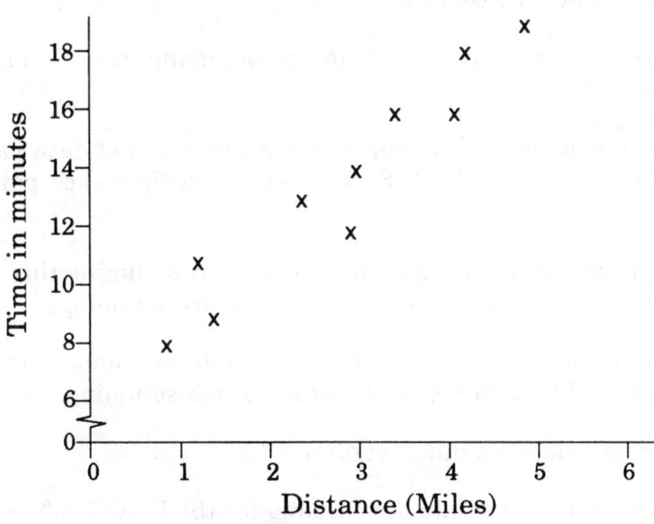

Source: Speedy Pizza Company

From this scatter graph we can see that there is a linear relationship and that the correlation is positive. We can now calculate the PMCC, known as r, to discover the strength of this relationship. The most widely used formula is the computational formula:

$$r = \frac{n\Sigma xy - \Sigma x \Sigma y}{\sqrt{(n\Sigma x^2 - (\Sigma x)^2)(n\Sigma y^2 - (\Sigma y)^2)}}$$

where n is number of pairs of data
x is independent variable
y is dependent variable
Σ means take the sum of

Although the formula for calculating the PMCC appears complicated it is relatively straight forward if we set it out as a table. This enables us to calculate the components of the formulae Σx, Σy, Σxy, Σx^2 and Σy^2. As we have discussed in previous units, this also makes the calculation easier to do using a computer spreadsheet.

	A	B	C	D	E	F
1		Distance x	Time y	xy	x^2	y^2
2		3.5	16	56.0	12.25	256
3		2.4	13	31.2	5.76	169
4		4.9	19	93.1	24.01	361
5		4.2	18	75.6	17.64	324
6		3.0	12	36.0	9.0	144
7		1.3	11	14.3	1.69	121
8		1.0	8	8.0	1.0	64
9		3.0	14	42.0	9.0	196
10		1.5	9	13.5	2.25	81
11		4.1	16	65.6	16.81	256
12	Total	28.9	136	435.3	99.41	1972

Column B records the independent variable (x) distance in miles; by summing this column we get Σx to put into the formula, in our case 28.9.

Column C records the dependent variable (y) time; by summing this column we get Σy to put into the formula, in our case 136.

Column D records the results of multiplying x by y for each of the data pairs; by summing this column we get Σxy, in our case 435.3. (N.B. we need to multiply each pair of data before summing).

Column E records the results of squaring each value of x; by summing this column we get Σx^2, in our case 99.41. (N.B. we need to square each value of x before summing).

Column F contains the results of squaring each value of y; by summing this column we get Σy^2, in our case 1972. (N.B. we need to square each value of y before summing).

There are 10 pairs of data values, on other words $n = 10$.

We can now substitute these values into our formula for the PMCC. Where ever necessary components' values have been rounded to 2 decimal places at each stage of the calculation. Note the extra brackets to ensure we do the calculation in the right order (N.B. work out what is inside the brackets first):

$$r = \frac{(10 \times 435.3) - (28.9 \times 136)}{\sqrt{(10 \times 99.41 - (28.9)^2)(10 \times 1972 - (136)^2)}}$$

$$= 0.96 \text{ (to 2 decimal places)}$$

The value we have calculated for the PMCC indicates the strength of the correlation between the two variables in the same way as Spearman's Rank Correlation Coefficient. A coefficient of 0.96 means that there is a very strong relationship between the distance travelled and the time taken. With such a strong correlation we would probably go on to calculate the regression equation (unit 18).

17.5 Summary

- Correlation measures the association between two variables, it does not imply causality.
- The correlation coefficient calculated will always lie between 1 and –1 including both extreme values.
- A value of 1 implies perfect positive correlation, –1 perfect negative correlation and 0 no correlation between the two variables.
- Spearman's Rank Correlation Coefficient (r^s) can be calculated using any data that can be normally ranked, care should be taken if there are a large number of tied values..
- Pearson's Product Moment Correlation Coefficient (r or PMCC) can be calculated using quantitative data; care should be taken when the scatter graph shows a non-linear relationship.

Further reading:

Business Mathematics and Statistics (Chapter 16), Francis A, DP PUBLICATIONS (1993)
Quantitative Approaches in Business Studies (Chapter 11), Morris C, PITMAN (1989)

Unit 18: Relationships between variables: regression

18.1 Introduction

In unit 17 we looked at cause and effect relationships between two variables and calculated Pearson's Product Moment Correlation Coefficient (PMCC). The correlation coefficient only told us how strongly our two variables were related, regression enables us to explore this relationship further.

Regression is used in business to explore the relationship between two or more data variables. It enables us to calculate the equation for the best fit straight line that will run through our data points when plotted on a scatter graph. Once calculated the *regression equation* can be used to predict values for the dependent variable given any value of the independent variable. In addition we can calculate a measure of how good a predictor our regression equation is likely to be, the *coefficient of determination*. For example, if we have collected data on amount of sales of ice cream and temperature each day for a year, we can calculate a regression equation to predict sales of ice cream (our dependent variable) for a range of temperatures (our independent variable). We can also calculate the coefficient of determination to give us a measure of how good a predictor our equation is likely to be.

18.2 Calculating the regression equation

As regression is often used once a relationship has been established through correlation, we will continue with our example of the Pizza Company. In this example we were investigating the relationship between distance travelled and time taken for a delivery (unit 17.4). We have already established a strong positive correlation between distance travelled and time taken, and that time is the dependent variable and distance the independent variable.

In order to be able to predict time taken we need to calculate the equation of the best fit line that runs through our data points, the regression equation. The diagram below is a stylised graph of this straight line:

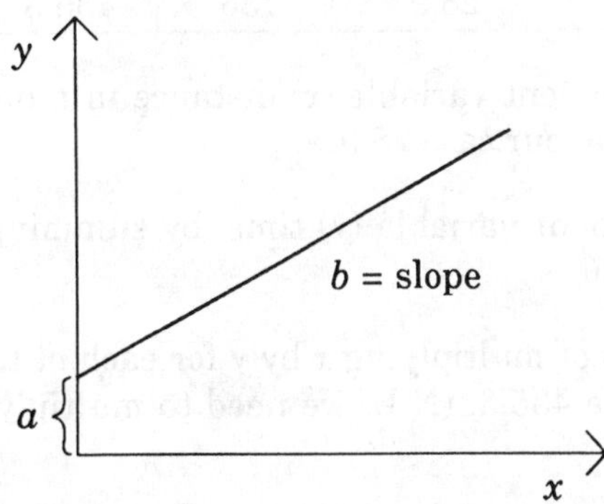

The straight line is represented by the regression equation of a general form:

$$y = a + bx$$

where y = dependent variable
a = the point of intercept on the y axis
b = the slope or gradient of the regression line
x = the independent variable

Once we have worked out the values of a and b for this equation we can, given any value of our independent variable y, calculate the value of our dependent variable x.

The key to be able to use this technique is therefore calculating the values of a and b.

Values of a and b are normally calculated using what is called the *least squares method*, using the following formulae:

$$\text{(Gradient) } b = \frac{n\Sigma xy - \Sigma x \Sigma y}{n\Sigma x^2 - (\Sigma x)^2}$$

$$\text{(intercept) } a = \frac{\Sigma y - b\Sigma x}{n}$$

Although these equations look complicated they are relatively straightforward if we set out our working as a table. The key point to remember is that the gradient b must be calculated first as the intercept a cannot be worked out until the value of b is known. The calculations for the components of these formulae are shown below. As usual row and column headings have been included to show how it could be set out on a computer spreadsheet:

	A	B	C	D	E
1		Distance x	Time y	xy	x^2
2		3.5	16	56.0	12.25
3		2.4	13	31.2	5.76
4		4.9	19	93.1	24.01
5		4.2	18	75.6	17.64
6		3.0	12	36.0	9.00
7		1.3	11	14.3	1.69
8		1.0	8	8.0	1.00
9		3.0	14	42.0	9.00
10		1.5	9	13.5	2.25
11		4.1	16	65.6	16.81
12	Total	28.9	136	435.3	99.41

Column B contains the independent variable (x) distance in miles; by summing this column we get Σx to put into the formula, in our case 28.9.

Column C contains the dependent variable (y) time; by summing this column we get Σy to put into the formula, in our case 136.

Column D contains the results of multiplying x by y for each of the data pairs; by summing this column we get Σxy, in our case 435.3. (N.B. we need to multiply each pair of data before summing).

Column E contains the results of squaring each value of x; by summing this column we get Σx^2, in our case 99.41. (N.B. we need to square each value of x before summing).

There are 10 pairs of data values, in other words $n = 10$.

As we can see this is almost the same as the table we set up to calculate Pearson's Product Moment Correlation Coefficient. We can now substitute these values into our formula for the Gradient b. Note the extra brackets to ensure we do the calculation in the right order. (N.B. work out what is inside the brackets first):

$$b = \frac{(10 \times 435.3) - (28.9 \times 136)}{(10 \times 99.41) - 28.9^2}$$

$$= \frac{4353 - 3930.4}{994.1 - 835.21}$$

$$= \frac{422.6}{158.89}$$

$$= 2.66 \text{ (to 2 decimal places)}$$

Once the gradient (b) is known, we can calculate a by substituting in the values to the equation:

$$a = \frac{136 - (2.66 \times 28.9)}{10}$$

$$= \frac{136 - 76.874}{10}$$

$$= \frac{59.126}{10}$$

$$= 5.91$$

The equation for our regression line is therefore:

$$y = 5.91 + 2.66\,x$$

time taken = 5.91 + 2.66 x delivery distance.

This might be made up of 5.91 minutes loading and unloading time plus an additional 2.66 minutes for each mile.

18.3 Interpreting the regression equation

We can use the regression equation to predict delivery times for other distances; for example 4 miles:

$$y = 5.91 + 2.66 \times 4$$

$$= 16.55 \text{ minutes}$$

As we predicted between known data points this is termed *interpolation*.

We can also use the regression equation to predict delivery times for distances outside the range of distances in our data set. This is known as *extrapolation*. Care must be taken when extrapolating values as the regression equation is only based upon values within the data range and is likely to be less accurate outside these values. Values outside this range may behave differently, for example longer distances are likely to include faster stretches of road.

However we must remember that if we 'plug' our raw data into any regression equation it will not give the true answer unless we have a perfect correlation between our two variables (–1 or +1).

18.4 Regression and time series data

A regression line equation can also be calculated for time series data (units 15 and 16) and used to determine the trend. In this situation the regression technique is exactly the same with time being the independent variable. The only change is that sometimes time is expressed as number of periods from the first data collection point as this makes the calculation easier. Thus if data were collected quarterly, the independent variable (time) would be converted as shown below:

Time Series	1991				1992		
	Quarter 1	Quarter 2	Quarter 3	Quarter 4	Quarter 1	Quarter 2	Quarter 3
Regression Independent variable	0	1	2	3	4	5	6

It should be remembered that regression is sometimes a poor predictor of future trends and methods, such as those discussed in unit 16, are normally used.

18.5 Calculating and interpreting the coefficient of determination

The *coefficient of determination* is very straight forward to calculate once we have calculated Pearson's Product Moment Correlation Coefficient. It is, in fact, the square of the PMCC, so all we need to do is to square the value we calculated earlier.

Thus for our pizza delivery example (unit 17.4) the coefficient of determination represented by r^2 is:

$$r^2 = 0.96^2 = 0.9216$$

$$= 0.92 \text{ (to 2 decimal places)}$$

This measure is usually expressed as a percentage and tells us the amount of variation in the dependent variable (y) which is explained by the linear relationship with the independent variable (x). Thus our r^2 value of 0.92 means that 92% of the variation in delivery time can be explained by the distance travelled. Distance travelled is therefore a good predictor. The remaining 8% of the variation is caused by other factors which have not been included in our regression equation.

If we have not calculated the PMCC we could calculate the coefficient of determination using the following formula:

$$r^2 = \frac{\text{Sum of squares explained by the regression}}{\text{Total sum of squares before regression}}$$

The sum of squares explained by the regression can be computed using the following formula:

$$\frac{\left(\Sigma xy - \dfrac{\Sigma x \Sigma y}{n}\right)^2}{\Sigma x^2 - \dfrac{(\Sigma x)^2}{n}}$$

The total sum of squares before the regression can be computed using the following formula:

$$\Sigma y^2 - \frac{(\Sigma y)^2}{n}$$

All of the components for these formulae apart from Σy^2 have already been computed for the regression equation, so it is simply a case calculating this by adding a y^2 column to our table and summing it. We have already calculated this figure, 1972, in unit 17.4. It can therefore be substituted into the equation with the others. In the equation all components have been rounded to 2 decimal places:

$$\text{Sum of Squares explained by the regression} = \frac{\left(435.3 - \dfrac{28.9 \times 136}{10}\right)^2}{99.41 - \dfrac{28.9^2}{10}}$$

$$= \frac{(435.3 - 393.04)^2}{99.41 - 83.53}$$

$$= \frac{1785.91}{15.89}$$

$$= 112.39$$

$$\text{Sum of Squares before the regression} = 1972 - \frac{136^2}{10}$$

$$= 1972 - 1849.6$$

$$= 122.4$$

$$\text{Therefore the coefficient of determination} = \frac{112.39}{122.4}$$

$$= 0.92 \text{ (to 2 decimal places)}$$

This is the same answer as that calculated by squaring the PMCC (r).

Within business additional predictive factors are often also included into the regression equation so that there are a number of independent variables. This technique is called *multiple regression* and is almost always undertaken using a specialist computer statistics package.

18.6 Summary

- Regression analysis is used to determine the relationship between a dependent and one or more independent variables.
- Regression analysis expresses this relationship as a regression equation in the form:

  $$y = a + bx$$

- The most common technique used to determine this relationship is called least squares.
- The regression equation can be used with confidence to interpolate values of the dependent variable within the range of the independent variable. However care must be taken with extrapolation.
- The coefficient of determination r^2, normally expressed as a percentage, tells us the amount of variation in the dependent variable that is explained by the independent variable.

Further reading:

Business Mathematics and Statistics (Chapter 15), Francis A, DP PUBLICATIONS (1993)
Quantitative Approaches in Business Studies (Chapter 12), Morris C, PITMAN (1989)
Statistics (Chapter 22), Owen F and Jones R, PITMAN (1990)

Unit 19: Testing for significance: the chi square test

19.1 Introduction

Often in business our data has been summarised and presented as a table. Whether the data is quantitative or categorical the fact that it is no longer raw data may mean that we cannot test for any relationships by calculating a correlation coefficient. The chi square test, represented by the Greek letter χ^2, enables us to see whether or not the observed values of data in our table differ significantly from that which we would expect if there were no underlying factors influencing the pattern of these values. In other words, we can compare our tabulated values (the observed values) with the values we would expect to have (the expected values) if there had been no underlying relationship.

We calculate the chi square statistic for tables of one and two variables using slightly different methods. In both cases we are using the statistic to answer the question: does the observed distribution in our table differ significantly from that which we would expect if there were no underlying factors influencing the pattern?

19.2 Chi square test for frequency distributions

We work for a market research department of a company that manufactures dog food and have been given the task of assessing whether consumers (the dogs) express a significant preference for certain brands. We have supplied 500 dog owners with four different brands in plain tins and asked them to find out which one of the brands their dog preferred. The results of this are shown in the frequency distribution below:

Results of Testing of Four Dog Food Brands

	Brand A	Brand B	Brand C	Brand D	Total
Number of Dogs	140	115	145	100	500

(Source: Degree Dog food Company, 199-)

By using the chi square test we can discover whether this pattern differs significantly from that which we would have expected to have seen if the dogs showed no preference; in other words, we want to compare the observed pattern with what we would expect.

Because we are using a statistical test (chi square) we need to phrase this as a hypothesis and a null hypothesis. The *hypothesis,* known as H_1, is simply the theory that we wish to test, in this case:

Dogs do express a significant preference for a brand of dog food.

The *null hypothesis,* known as H_0, is sometimes referred to as the hypothesis of no change or the hypothesis where nothing happens, in this case it is:

Dogs do not express a significant preference for a brand of dog food.

Before we can calculate the chi square statistic we need to work out our expected values. For a frequency distribution this is straightforward. If dogs did not show a significant preference for any one of the four brands we would expect an equal number of dogs to choose each brand. As there are four different brands in our table, we would expect the number of dogs preferring each to be:

$$\frac{500}{4} = 125$$

To calculate the chi square statistic we use the following formula:

$$\chi^2 = \Sigma \frac{(O - E)^2}{E}$$

where O is the observed value
E is the expected value

We can set out this calculation as a table which could also be entered into a computer spreadsheet. For each component of the calculation numbers are rounded to 2 decimal places where necessary as this is the accuracy required for the table 'Critical Values of Chi Square' (see later in this section):

	A	B	C	D	E	F
1	Brand	Observed O	Expected E	$O - E$	$(O - E)^2$	$\frac{(O - E)^2}{E}$
2	A	140	125	15	225	1.80
3	B	115	125	-10	100	0.80
4	C	145	125	20	400	3.20
5	D	100	125	-25	625	5.00
6	Total			0		10.80

Columns A and B record our data from the frequency distribution.

Column C records our expected values, E.

Column D records the result of subtracting the expected value from the observed value, $O - E$.

Column E records the result of squaring the values calculated in column D, $(O - E)^2$.

Column F records the result of dividing the values calculated in column E by the expected values. This values are summed to give the chi square statistic (cell F6).

From the table we can see that our value of chi square is 10.8.

Before we can look up our calculated chi square value in the 'Critical Values of Chi Square Table' to discover if there is a significant difference we need to calculate the *degrees of freedom*.

When we assigned the expected values to the number of dogs preferring each brand of dog food we were free to put in what values we wanted, providing the values summed to 500. In theory, once the first value had been assigned to brand A, we were still free to put in what values we wanted for the other brands. This is our first degree of freedom. Likewise for brands B and C our second and third degrees of freedom. However, once we had defined our values for brands A, B and C then we had already defined the value for brand D as we already knew the total, in this case 500.

The general formula we use to calculate degrees of freedom for any frequency distribution is:

number of values – 1

Remember that the number of values does not include the total.

Thus for our dog food example the degrees of freedom are:

$$4 - 1 = 3$$

We now know the chi square statistic (10.8) and the degrees of freedom (3) and can look the value up in the 'Critical Values of Chi Square Table' (Appendix 4). As our degrees of freedom are 3 we look down the d.f. column until we come to 3. We then read across this row which has been shaded on the extract of Appendix 4 below:

Extract from Critical Values of Chi Square Table

	Significance Level		
d.f.	.1	.05	.01
1	2.71	3.84	6.63
2	4.61	5.99	9.21
3	6.25	7.81	11.30
4	7.78	9.49	13.30

Source: Appendix 4

If the chi square value is greater than the value in the table, we can reject the null hypothesis and accept the hypothesis at that significance level. We can therefore reject our null hypothesis and accept our hypothesis at the 0.05 level but not the 0.01 level.

This means that dogs do show a significant preference for a brand of dog food at the 0.05 significance level. This level of significance is sometimes expressed as the 95% level, in other words we are 95% certain that dogs do show a significant preference for a brand of dog food.

Generally when using chi square the most commonly used significance levels are the 0.05 and the 0.01 levels (95% and 99%).

19.3 Problems with the chi square test (and Yate's Correction)

The chi square test makes a number of assumptions about the data we use. If these assumptions are not satisfied, then we should not use the statistic. If the expected frequency of any cell is small then the conclusions based on the statistic may well be wrong. One of the following two rules needs to be satisfied to prevent this:

1. For tables of two cells (excluding total) the expected frequencies in each cell must not be less than 5;

2. For tables of more than two cells (excluding totals) no more than 20% of the cells should have expected frequencies of less than 5.

If either of these is the case, the accepted solution is to combine rows or columns until all the expected frequencies are 5 or more.

For tables where there is only one degree of freedom we need to apply a correction to the chi square statistic. This is called *Yate's Correction* and involves subtracting half from the absolute difference between the observed and expected values. We can see how this works for the following example. In this case we want to see if there is a significant difference in the gender of our customers from that which we would expect. Our null hypothesis is 'There is no significant difference in gender of our customers from that which we would expect' and our hypothesis is 'There is a significant difference in gender of our customers from that which we would expect'.

Gender	Observed	Expected	$O - E$	$\lvert O - E\rvert - 0.5$	$(\lvert O - E\rvert - 0.5)^2$	$\frac{(\lvert O - E\rvert - 0.5)^2}{E}$
Male	140	150	-10	9.5	90.25	0.60
Female	160	150	10	9.5	90.25	0.60
Total	300	300	0			1.20

The first two columns of our calculation table represent our actual data. We have subsequently calculated the expected values based on the assumption that we will have an equal number of male and female customers. The only change to the actual chi square calculation is the addition of an extra column $\lvert O - E\rvert - 0.5$. The two vertical lines mean take the absolute value; this means the answer to the calculation $O - E$ will always be positive. We then have to subtract 0.5 from this figure to apply Yate's correction.

Our chi square value is 1.2 with 1 degree of freedom. If we look this up in the 'Critical Values of Chi Square Table' (Appendix 4) we can see that chi square is smaller than the tabulated values. We must therefore accept our null hypothesis: 'there is no significant difference in gender of our customers from that which we would expect.'

19.4 Chi square test for two variable tables

We can use chi square to test for significant differences between observed and expected values for two variable tables. Chi square is extremely useful if we want to test whether the observed pattern of data in our table differs significantly from that which we would expect if there were no pattern. These tables are often called *contingency tables* to indicate dependence between the variables.

We have been given the following table of data on the amount of money spent by the customers of a jewellery shop on a visit, as well as their social class, and asked if there is a significant difference in amount spent between social classes:

Amount of Money Spent per Visit by Social Class of Customers

Social Class	Under £10	£10 to under £20	£20 and over	Total
Upper	10	20	70	**100**
Middle	20	40	60	**120**
Lower	60	10	10	**800**
Total	**90**	**70**	**140**	**300**

Source: Jewellery Shop Till Receipts (199-)

We can use chi square to help us answer this question. The first thing we need to do is to state our hypothesis: 'There is a significant relationship between the amount of money spent by customers and their social class', and our null hypothesis: 'There is no significant relationship between the amount of money spent by customers and their social class.'

Next we need to work out the expected values. To do this we need to calculate what each of our cell values would be if we only knew the row and column totals:

Social Class	Under £10	£10 to under £20	£20 and over	Total
Upper	A	B	C	**100**
Middle	D	E	F	**120**
Lower	G	H	I	**80**
Total	**90**	**70**	**140**	**300**

To calculate the expected value for each cell we use the following formula:

$$\frac{\text{Column total for column containing cell} \times \text{Row total for row containing cell}}{\text{Grand Total}}$$

Thus for cell A the expected value is: $\frac{90 \times 100}{300} = 30$

and for cell B the expected value is: $\frac{70 \times 100}{300} = 23.33$ (to 2 decimal places)

Our completed table of expected values is shown below; all expected values have been calculated to 2 decimal places as this is sufficient accuracy:

Social Class	Under £10	£10 to under £20	£20 and over	Total
Upper	30.00	23.33	46.67	**100**
Middle	36.00	28.00	56.00	**120**
Lower	24.00	18.67	37.33	**80**
Total	**90**	**70**	**140**	**300**

Now we have calculated all the expected values we can calculate the chi square statistic using the same formula as for a one dimensional table:

$$\chi^2 = \Sigma\frac{(O-E)^2}{E}$$

As before it is easiest if we set out our calculations as a table. As before all figures have been rounded to 2 decimal places, and row and column headings added to show how it would look on a computer spreadsheet:

	A	B	C	D	E	F	G
1	Class	Amount	Observed	Expected	$O-E$	$(O-E)^2$	$\frac{(O-E)^2}{E}$
2	Upper	< £10	10	30.00	-20.00	400.00	13.33
3		£10 – < £20	20	23.33	-3.33	11.09	0.48
4		£20 plus	70	46.67	23.33	544.29	11.66
5	Middle	< £10	20	36.00	-16.00	256.00	7.11
6		£10 – < £20	40	28.00	12.00	144.00	5.14
7		£20 plus	60	56.00	4.00	16.00	0.29
8	Lower	< £10	60	24.00	36.00	1296.00	54.00
9		£10 – < £20	10	18.67	-8.67	75.17	4.03
10		£20 plus	10	37.33	-27.33	746.93	20.01
11	Total		300	300.00	0		116.05

This gives us a chi square statistic of 116.05.

To calculate the degrees of freedom we use a different formula to that for a single variable table:

$$\text{degrees of freedom} = (\text{rows} - 1) \times (\text{columns} - 1)$$

for our original data table. As we had a table of three rows and three columns (excluding totals) the degrees of freedom are:

$$\begin{aligned} \text{d.f.} &= (3-1) \times (3-1) \\ &= 2 \times 2 \\ &= 4 \end{aligned}$$

If we look up the value of chi square in the 'Critical Values of Chi Square Table' (Appendix 4) we can see that our calculated value of chi square (116.05) is greater than the tabulated value for 4 d.f. at the 0.01 level. This means we can reject our null hypothesis and accept our hypothesis:

there is a significant relationship between the amount of money spent by customers and their social class at the 0.01 level.

19.5 Summary

- The chi square statistic (χ^2) is used to compare an actual distribution with an expected distribution to see if there is a significant difference.
- The chi square statistic should not be used where the expected cell frequency is unusually small.
- For tables with 1 degree of freedom Yate's correction should be applied to the chi square statistic.
- Degrees of freedom are calculated differently for one variable and two variable tables; in both cases row and column total cells are excluded from the calculation.
- If the calculated value for chi square is greater than the tabulated value for the appropriate degrees of freedom then we can reject the null hypothesis and accept the hypothesis.
- The Null Hypothesis (H_0) states that there is no significant difference between the observed and the expected values.
- The Hypothesis (H_1) states that there is a significant difference between the observed and the expected values.

Further reading:

Quantitative Techniques (Chapter 6), Lucey T, DP PUBLICATIONS (1988)
Quantitative Approaches in Business Studies (Chapter 10), Morris C, PITMAN (1989)
Statistics (Chapter 21), Owen F and Jones R, PITMAN (1990)

Unit 20: Index numbers using one item: quantity and price indices, value indices

20.1 Index numbers in business

An index number is a measure designed to show relative changes in the quantity, value or price of one variable or a number of variables over time. Not surprisingly the principal use of index numbers in business is to make comparisons over time. Many companies use index numbers to measure changes through time of factors such as:

- raw material consumption;
- sales income;
- employee turnover;
- transportation costs.

Index numbers are widely used in business publications and by businesses. The Financial Times share indices such as the FT-SE 100 and the All Share Index track share prices, building societies such as the Nationwide and the Halifax regularly publish house price indices, and perhaps the most widely known the Retail Price Index is used to measure the rate of inflation. These, and index numbers calculated for specific purposes within a business, allow managers to look at and compare relative changes as opposed to actual figures.

20.2 Simple quantity index

If we know that our company has produced 280,000 cars in 1988 and 220,000 in 1993 we can compare the relation between the two years by calculating a simple index number. As we are looking at quantities or volumes we call this a *quantity index* or a *volume index*:

$$1988 \qquad \frac{280000}{280000} \times 100 = 100$$

$$1993 \qquad \frac{220000}{280000} \times 100 = 78.6$$

This is usually expressed by the formula:

$$\text{Quantity index} = \frac{q_n}{q_o} \times 100$$

where q_n is quantity in period of interest
q_o is quantity in base period

We call the period with which we are making our comparisons the *base period*. In this case it is fixed at one year so it is termed a *fixed base*. This is expressed as:

$$1988 = 100$$

The base index number is nearly always 100, the most notable exception being the FT-SE 100 whose base is 1000. In our example we can see that by 1993 the index number has decreased to 78.6. Because the index number is below 100 we know that the quantity of cars produced has decreased. Subtracting from the base number of 100 we can see that the difference between the years is 21.4, a fall of 21.4%.

20.3 Simple price index

Index numbers are especially useful when making comparisons between numbers of different magnitudes. The table below shows the price of individual items produced at three factories over a six year period:

Price of Items Produced at 3 factories in £

Factory	1987	1988	1989	1990	1991	1992
Northton	21.00	23.00	24.50	26.00	27.00	27.50
Ketting	410.00	550.00	690.00	700.00	700.00	690.00
Lester	18.00	22.00	24.00	25.80	26.00	27.20

Source: Factories

The Managing Director of the Group owning these factories has asked us two questions:

1. Which factory's item has had the greatest increase in price since 1987?
2. How did the price of the item from the Northton factory change relative to the Lester factory between 1987 and 1992?

These questions are easy to answer once the data is expressed as index numbers, using a *price index* and 1987 as the base year (100).

To calculate a price index we use the formula:

$$\text{Price index} = \frac{p_n}{p_o} \times 100$$

where p_n is price in period of interest
p_o is price in base period

For the Northton Branch the price indices are calculated as follows:

$$\text{Price index 1987} = \frac{21}{21} \times 100 = 100$$

$$\text{Price index 1988} = \frac{23}{21} \times 100 = 109.52 \text{ (to 2 decimal places)}$$

$$\text{Price index 1989} = \frac{24.5}{21} \times 100 = 116.67 \text{ (to 2 decimal places)}$$

$$\text{Price index 1990} = \frac{26}{21} \times 100 = 123.81 \text{ (to 2 decimal places)}$$

and so on.....

We can put the index numbers in one table, remembering to add notes about which is the base period (e.g. 1987 = 100) and its magnitude (e.g. 1987 = £21). In the table below all index numbers have been calculated to 2 decimal places.

Index of Price of Items produced at Factories (1987 = 100)

Factory	1987	1988	1989	1990	1991	1992
Northton	100[1]	119.52	116.67	123.81	128.57	130.95
Ketting	100[2]	134.15	168.29	170.73	170.73	168.29
Lester	100[3]	122.22	133.33	143.33	144.44	151.11

[1] 1987 = £21 [2] 1987 = £410 [3] 1987 = £18

Source: Factories

Interpretation of these numbers is relatively straight forward. However we must remember that the price index is always comparing back to the base period, in this case 1987. We could also plot these index numbers on a multiple line graph (see unit 10.4) to aid interpretation:

Index of Price of Goods produced at Factories (1987 = 100)

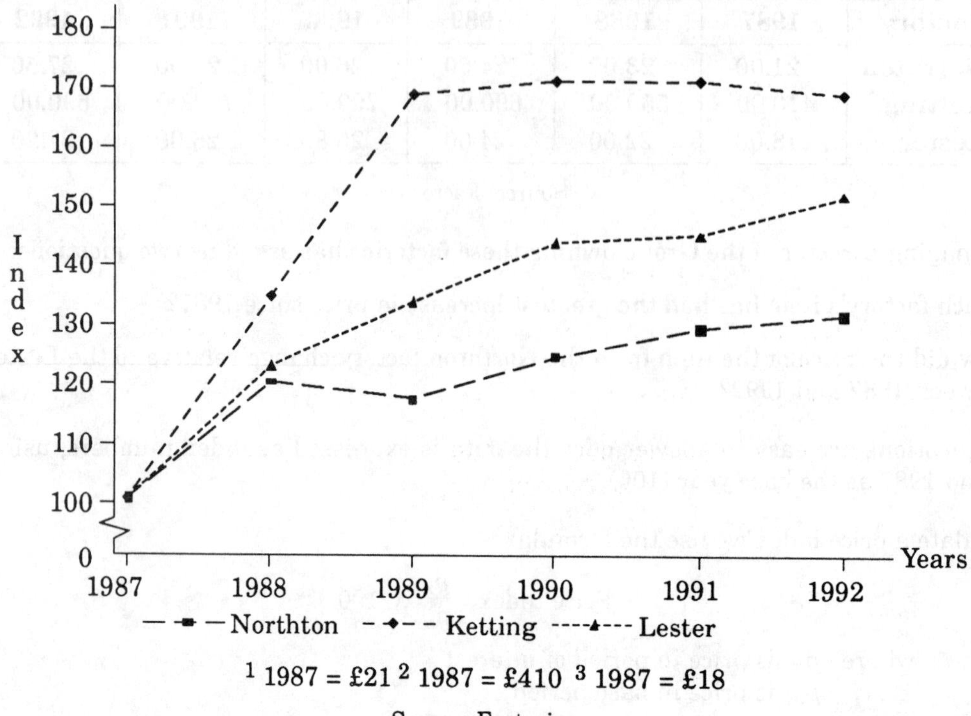

[1] 1987 = £21 [2] 1987 = £410 [3] 1987 = £18

Source: Factories

From the index numbers we can see that the price of the item produced at the Ketting Factory has increased most since 1987. In answer to our Manager's second question we can say that the price of the item from the Northton Factory has increased less than that from the Lester factory, although both have followed a similar trend over the past six years.

We could have easily calculated the price index using a different base period. If we choose 1990 as our base period the index numbers for the factories (again calculated to 2 decimal places) are:

Index of Price of Items produced at Factories (1987 = 100)

Factory	1987	1988	1989	1990	1991	1992
Northton	80.77	88.46	94.23	100[1]	103.85	105.77
Ketting	58.57	78.57	98.57	100[2]	100.00	98.57
Lester	69.77	85.27	93.02	100[3]	100.78	105.43

[1] 1990 = £26 [2] 1990 = £700 [3] 1990 = £25.80

Source: Factories

As we can see this provides a very different set of values for the same data. In this case the most striking fact is that the product manufactured at the Ketting Factory has reduced in price since 1990.

20.4 Value or expenditure index

The *value*, or *expenditure index* takes into account the quantity of a product as well as its price. This is very useful in business as, for example, consumption patterns often alter with price. The formula is:

$$\text{Value index} = \frac{p_n q_n}{p_o q_o} \times 100$$

Where p_n is the price of the product in the period of interest
q_n is the quantity of the product in the period of interest
p_o is the price of the product in the base period
q_o is the quantity of the product in the base period

So, if the price of a gallon of petrol was £1.80 in July 1990 and a customer bought 5 gallons a week, while in September 1992 the price was £2.30 and the quantity bought was still 5 gallons a week, the value index using 1990 as the base year would be:

$$\frac{2.30 \times 5}{1.80 \times 5} \times 100 = 127.78 \text{ (to 2 decimal places)}$$

This indicates that expenditure on petrol has increased by 27.8%. Of course, we could have worked this out by taking a simple percentage increase of £2.30 on £1.80. However, things are more complicated if the quantities purchased differ.

If the price of petrol had increased to £2.30 and the customer was buying only 4 gallons per week then the value index using 1990 as the base year would be:

$$\frac{2.30 \times 4}{1.80 \times 5} \times 100$$

$$= \frac{9.2}{9.0} \times 100 = 102.22 \text{ (to 2 decimal places)}$$

This would indicate that expenditure had increased by only 2.22%.

The value or expenditure index can also be used to calculate changes in value. For example a firm produced 5,000 pairs of shoes a month which were sold for £8.00 a pair in 1986 and produced 4,000 pairs which were sold for £11.00 a pair in 1992. From this data it is unclear whether the value of production has increase or fallen.

The value index for 1992 using 1986 as a base is:

$$\text{Value Index} = \frac{4000 \times 11}{5000 \times 8} \times 100$$

$$= \frac{44000}{40000} \times 100 = 110$$

From this we can see that the value of shoes produced has risen by 10% since 1986 despite a decline in the quantity produced.

20.5 Summary

- Index numbers are used to measure relative changes over time.
- These changes are measured against a base period usually expressed as 100.
- A price index takes the price for a given item and measures the change in price of that item against the price in the base period.
- A quantity index takes the amount of an item consumed and measures the change in quantity of that item consumed against the quantity consumed in the base period.
- A value or expenditure index takes into account the quantity as well as the price when measuring relative change.

Further reading:

Business Mathematics and Statistics (Chapter 22), Francis A, DP PUBLICATIONS (1993)

Other useful further reading at this stage is to look at examples of current uses of index numbers in business. These can be found in many journals and newspaper articles including:

Employment Gazette look for Retail Price Index
Financial Times look for the various Share Price Indices

Unit 21: Index numbers using more than one item: average index, Laspeyre's index and Paasche's index

21.1 Introduction

In unit 20 we considered indices using only one item. In this unit we are going to look at indices using more than one item. Within business such indices include the Retail Price Index and the Financial Times Share Indices such as the FT-SE 100.

Indices using more than one item are important in business as they enable us to reflect the change in overall prices paid or quantities consumed over a period of time. For example we may wish to see how the price of a weekly 'shopping basket' of goods and services has changed over time.

21.2 Average indices

The *average price index* and the *average quantity index* as their names suggest are calculated by taking an average (arithmetic mean) of a number of individual price or quantity indices (see unit 20). These indices can be very useful when we have a number of items, all of equal importance, and we want to see how the overall price of these items has changed over time.

We work for a company that offers training courses for computer software and have been asked by one of our customers to work out what the average change in prices for our courses has been over the period 1989 – 1993. We have been given the following data by our company's managing director:

Cost of Computer Courses 1989 – 1993

Course	1989 Price	1993 Price
Spreadsheets (1 day)	£250	£350
Spreadsheets (3 day)	£700	£900
Word processing (1 day)	£200	£280
Word processing (3 day)	£600	£780
Databases (2 day)	£480	£620

Source: The Computer Training Company

To calculate the average price index we use the formula:

$$\text{Average price index} = \frac{\Sigma\left(\dfrac{p_n}{p_o} \times 100\right)}{N}$$

where p_n is price in the period of interest (in this case 1993)
p_o is price in the base period (in this case 1989)
N is the number of items (in this case 5)

As we mentioned earlier, this formula simply tells us to take the average of the price indices for each item.

To do this it helps to set out the calculation as a table; in the table below all figures have been rounded to 2 decimal places:

	A	B	C	D
1	Course	1989 Price p_o	1993 Price p_n	Price Index $\frac{p_n}{p_o} \times 100$
2	Spreadsheets (1 day)	£250	£350	140.00
3	Spreadsheets (3 day)	£700	£900	128.57
4	Word processing (1 day)	£200	£280	140.00
5	Word processing (3 day)	£600	£780	130.00
6	Databases (2 day)	£480	£620	129.17
7	Total			667.74
8				
9	Average Price Index	(Total / N)		133.55

Columns A to C record our raw data.

Column D records the result of calculating the price index for each of the five courses $\left(\frac{p_n}{p_o} \times 100\right)$. This is the result of dividing the value in column C by the value in column B and multiplying by 100.

When we sum column D (cell D7) we get the sum of the price indices for all the items, in this case 667.74.

We then divide this by the total number of items (5) to get the average price index (133.55).

Alternatively we could have calculated each of our price indices and then substituted them into the formula:

$$\text{Average price index} = \frac{140.00 + 128.57 + 140.00 + 130.00 + 129.17}{5}$$

$$= \frac{667.74}{5}$$

$$= 133.55 \text{ (to 2 decimal places)}$$

We can see that prices of our courses have increased on average by 33.55%.

We can calculate the average quantity index in exactly the same way except quantities are used rather than prices. The formula is:

$$\text{Average quantity index} = \frac{\Sigma\left(\frac{q_n}{q_o} \times 100\right)}{N}$$

21.3 Weighted average indices

When we calculated the average price index for the computer courses run by our company we did not need to take into account the relative importance of the courses to us as a company. In some cases it is necessary to give greater importance to those items which are of a greater consequence to us when calculating the average price or volume indices. The *weighted average price index* (or weighted price relative index) takes account of changes in price and reflects the importance of each item by including a weighting. This weighting is often the amount of money we spend on it. Providing we know how much money we spend on each item we can use these amounts to weight each item accordingly.

If we are interested in, say, our rising cost of living, it is important that we weight our weekly shopping basket to reflect the relative importance of the items we buy. The table below shows a somewhat unusual, but simple, weekly shopping basket!

Simple Weekly Shopping Basket 1983 and 1993

Purchase	Unit Price 1983	Unit Price 1993	Weighting
Wine (litre)	£1.00	£2.50	40%
Bread (loaf)	£0.25	£0.75	40%
Cheese (kg)	£1.50	£3.00	20%

Source: Interview

The weightings show that the majority of the money is spent on wine and bread – 40% of our income on each (as opposed to 20% on cheese). To reflect this particular (and peculiar!) situation we use *weighted index numbers.*

To calculate the weighted average price index we use the following formula:

$$\text{Weighted average price index} = \frac{\Sigma\left(w \times \frac{p_n}{p_o} \times 100\right)}{\Sigma w}$$

where w is the weight;
p_n is the price in the period of interest (in this case 1993)
p_o is the price in the base period (in this case 1983)

As we can see this is similar to the formula for the average price index with a weighting added to the individual price indices.

To do this it is easier to set out the calculation as a table; this can also be done using a computer spreadsheet:

	A	B	C	D	E	F
1	Purchase	Unit Price 1983 (p_o)	Unit Price 1993 (p_n)	Weighting w	$\frac{p_n}{p_o} \times 100$	$\frac{p_n}{p_o} \times 100 \times w$
2	Wine (litre)	£1.00	£2.50	40	250	10000
3	Bread (loaf)	£0.25	£0.75	40	300	12000
4	Cheese (kg)	£1.50	£3.00	20	200	4000
5	Total			100		26000
6						
7	Weighted	Index	26000/100	=	260	

Columns A to C record the raw data.

Column D records the weightings for each of the three items.

Column E records the result of calculating the price index for each of the three items $\left(\frac{p_n}{p_o} \times 100\right)$.

Column F records the result of multiplying each price index by its weighting (w).

When we sum column F (cell F5) we get the sum of the weighted price indices for all the items, in this case 26000.

We then divide this by the total weightings 100 (cell D5) to get the weighted average price index (260).

Alternatively we could have calculated each of the weighted price indices and then substituted them into the formula:

$$\text{Weighted average price index} = \frac{10000 + 12000 + 4000}{100}$$

$$= \frac{26000}{100}$$

$$= 260$$

The price of the weekly shopping basket, once the items have been weighted in terms of importance, has increased by 160%. This is due to the relative weightings put on the items, as wine has increased in price by 150%, Bread 200% and Cheese 100%. If we had calculated the average price index (without weights) the price of the weekly shopping basket would have increased by only 150%. The new weighted average price index is higher than the average price index. It is 260 as opposed to 250. In the case of this example the price increase is highest on the item that is joint most important (bread) and this is why the final index is higher. The increase reflects the fact that the items are not of equal importance to the purchaser – some are more important than others.

We can also calculate the weighted average quantity index in exactly the same way except quantities are used rather than prices. The formula is:

$$\text{Weighted average quantity index} = \frac{\Sigma\left(w \times \frac{q_n}{q_o} \times 100\right)}{\Sigma w}$$

21.4 Laspeyre's price index

The purpose of 'weighting' the numbers is simply to obtain an overall average which correctly reflects the relative importance of the constituent items. In reality, if we were seeking to measure changes in food prices, we would have to decide the consumption pattern we were going to use as a basis for our calculations. There are a number of different types of index numbers that can be calculated to show this, of which the two most common are Laspeyre's price index and Paasche's price index.

Laspeyre's price index is used to calculate a *base weighted* aggregate price index, in other words when the consumption in the base period is typical. For this reason it is also known as the *base weighted aggregate price index.* To work out Laspeyre's price index we:

Calculate total expenditure on items in the base period using the quantities that were consumed. This is represented in the formula by:

$$\Sigma p_o q_o$$

Calculate total expenditure on items in the period of interest given that the same quantities were consumed as in the base period. This is represented in the formula by:

$$\Sigma p_n q_o$$

We then calculate expenditure in the period of interest as a proportion of expenditure in the base period. This gives the complete formula:

$$\text{Laspeyre's price index} = \frac{\Sigma p_n q_o}{\Sigma p_o q_o} \times 100$$

If we look at the simple weekly shopping basket we can see how the calculation works. Once again figures have been rounded to 2 decimal places where necessary in the table:

	A	B	C	D	E	F
1	Purchase	Unit Price 1983 (p_o)	Quantity 1983 (q_o)	Unit Price 1993 (p_n)	Expenditure 1983 ($p_o q_o$)	Expenditure 1993 ($p_n q_o$)
2	Wine (litre)	£1.00	3 bottles	£2.50	3.00	7.50
3	Bread (loaf)	£0.25	4 loafs	£0.75	1.00	3.00
4	Cheese (kg)	£1.50	1 pack	£3.00	1.50	3.00
5	Total				5.50	13.50
6						
7	Laspeyre's	Price Index	=	245.45		

Columns A to D record raw data, including the quantity consumed in the base period (column C).

Column E records the results of the calculation of the expenditure in the base period for each item ($p_o q_o$). These are then summed in cell E5 to give $\Sigma p_o q_o$ (5.50).

Column F records the results of the calculation of the expenditure in the period of interest for each item ($p_n q_o$). These are then summed cell F5 to give $\Sigma p_n q_o$ (13.50).

The result of the final part of the calculation is recorded in cell D7. Here the total expenditure for the current period ($\Sigma p_n q_o$) has been divided by the total expenditure for the base period ($\Sigma p_o q_o$) and multiplied by 100.

Alternatively we could have calculated the expenditure on each item and then substituted into the formula:

$$\text{Laspeyre's price index} = \frac{(7.50 + 3.00 + 3.00)}{(3.00 + 1.00 + 1.50)} \times 100$$

$$= \frac{13.50}{5.50} \times 100$$

$$= 245.45 \text{ (to 2 decimal places)}$$

Therefore we can say that the price of the weekly shopping basket increased by 145.45% between 1983 and 1993 using 1983 consumption patterns.

There are a number of factors that should be born in mind when using Laspeyre's price index:

- the use of base period quantities (weights) implies that consumption does not vary over time and that consumer tastes do not change;
- normally if the price of a commodity rises people will buy less, perhaps finding substitutes. As Laspeyre's price index assumes quantities are stable, if they fall it tends to overstate increases in price.

21.5 Paasche's price index

An alternative approach is to take current consumption pattern as typical and calculate a *current weighted price aggregate index* or *Paasche's price index*. To do this we:

Calculate total expenditure on items in base period using the quantities that were consumed in the period of interest. This is represented by the formula:

$$\Sigma p_o q_n$$

Calculate total expenditure on items in the period of interest for the quantities consumed in the period of interest. This is represented by the formula:

$$\Sigma p_n q_n$$

We then express expenditure in the period of interest as a proportion of expenditure in the base period. This gives the complete formula:

$$\frac{\Sigma p_n q_n}{\Sigma p_o q_n} \times 100$$

Using the shopping basket example we can set out the calculation as a table as shown below. As before figures have been rounded to 2 decimal places were necessary:

	A	B	C	D	E	F
1	Purchase	Unit Price 1983 (p_o)	Quantity 1993 (q_n)	Unit Price 1993 (p_n)	Expenditure 1983 ($p_o q_n$)	Expenditure 1993 ($p_n q_n$)
2	Wine (litre)	£1.00	4 bottles	£2.50	4.00	10.00
3	Bread (loaf)	£0.25	3 loafs	£0.75	0.75	2.25
4	Cheese (kg)	£1.50	2 pack	£3.00	3.00	6.00
5	Total				7.75	18.25
6						
7	Paasche's	Price Index	=	235.48		

Columns A to D record the raw data, including the quantity consumed in the period of interest (column C).

Column E records the result of the calculation of the expenditure in the base period for each item ($p_o q_n$). These are then summed in cell E5 to give $\Sigma p_o q_n$ (7.75).

Column F records the result of the calculation of the expenditure in the period of interest for each item ($p_n q_n$). These are then summed in cell F5 to give $\Sigma p_n q_n$ (18.25).

The result of the final part of the calculation is recorded in cell D7. The total expenditure for the current period ($\Sigma p_n q_n$) is divided by the total expenditure for the base period ($\Sigma p_o q_n$) and multiplied by 100.

Alternatively we could have calculated the expenditure on each item and then substituted into the formula:

$$\text{Paasche's price index} = \frac{(10.00 + 2.25 + 6.00)}{(4.00 + 0.75 + 3.00)} \times 100$$

$$= \frac{18.25}{7.75} \times 100$$

$$= 235.48$$

Thus we can say that the price of the weekly shopping basket increased by 135.48% between 1983 and 1993 using 1993 consumption patterns.

The Paasche price index overcomes the problems that were present with Laspeyre's price index, but there are a number of factors that need to be borne in mind when using it:

- It assumes that we would have bought the same quantities in the base period as the period of interest, even if base period prices were relatively lower. This means that it tends to understate increases in price.
- It may take a long time to collect the necessary data to determine period of interest quantities, resulting in delays in calculating the index.
- Because the quantities (weights) change every new period, it is difficult to make comparisons between time periods as changes in the indices reflect both price and quantity changes.

21.6 Laspeyre's volume index

So far we have only considered changes in price. However, changes in volume or quantity are often of interest. A good example of this is the index of production which measures changes in volume of output over a period of time. To do this we must fix the prices and allow the quantities to vary. This means that any variation will be due to the changes in quantities bought.

If we take the base prices as typical we can calculate a *base weighted aggregate volume index* or *Laspeyre's volume index*. To calculate Laspeyre's volume index we:

Calculate the total quantity of items consumed in the base period assuming the base period prices. This is represented by the formula:

$$\Sigma p_o q_o$$

Calculate the value of the total quantity of items consumed in the period of interest assuming the base period prices. This is represented by the formula:

$$\Sigma p_o q_n$$

We then express consumption in the period of interest as a proportion of consumption in the base period. This gives a complete formula:

$$\frac{\Sigma p_o q_n}{\Sigma p_o q_o} \times 100$$

Using our shopping basket example the calculation can be set out as a table; once again the figures have been rounded to 2 decimal places where necessary:

	A	B	C	D	E	F
1	Purchase	Unit Price 1983 (p_o)	Quantity 1983 (q_o)	Quantity 1993 (q_n)	Consumption 1983 ($p_o q_o$)	Consumption 1993 ($p_o q_n$)
2	Wine (litre)	£1.00	3 bottles	4 bottles	3.00	4.00
3	Bread (loaf)	£0.25	4 loaves	3 loaves	1.00	0.75
4	Cheese (kg)	£1.50	1 pack	2 packs	1.50	3.00
5	Total				5.50	7.75
6						
7	Laspeyre's	Vol. Index	=	140.91		

Columns A to D record raw data, including the prices in the base period (column B).

Column E records the result of calculating the consumption in the base period for each item (p_oq_o). These are summed in cell E5 to give Σp_oq_o (5.50).

Column F records the result of calculating the consumption in the period of interest for each item (p_oq_n). These are summed in cell F5 to give Σp_oq_n (7.75).

The result of final part of the calculation is recorded in cell D7. The total consumption for the period of interest (Σp_oq_n) is divided by the total consumption for the base period (Σp_oq_o) and multiplied by 100.

Alternatively we could have calculated the consumption of each item and then substituted into the formula:

$$\text{Laspeyre's volume index} = \frac{(4.00 + 0.75 + 3.00)}{(3.00 + 1.00 + 1.50)} \times 100$$

$$= \frac{7.75}{5.50} \times 100$$

$$= 140.91 \text{ (to 2 decimal places)}$$

Thus we can say that the volume of the weekly shopping basket increased by 40.91% in terms of its value between 1983 and 1993 using 1983 prices. It should be noted that the disadvantages discussed earlier (21.4) still apply.

21.7 Paasche's volume index

Paasche's volume index is, like Paasche's price index, weighted to the current period. It is calculated in a similar way using the formula:

$$\frac{\Sigma p_nq_n}{\Sigma p_nq_o} \times 100$$

This is set out as a table below:

	A	B	C	D	E	F
1	Purchase	Unit Price 1993 (p_n)	Quantity 1983 (q_o)	Quantity 1993 (q_n)	Consumption 1983 (p_nq_o)	Consumption 1993 (p_nq_n)
2	Wine (litre)	£2.50	3 bottles	4 bottles	7.50	10.00
3	Bread (loaf)	£0.75	4 loafs	3 loaves	3.00	2.25
4	Cheese (kg)	£3.50	1 pack	2 packs	3.50	7.00
5	Total				14.00	19.25
6						
7	Paasche's	Vol. Index	=	137.50		

Columns A to D record the raw data, including the unit price in the period of interest (column B).

Column E records the result of the calculation of the consumption in the base period for each item (p_nq_o). This is then summed to give Σp_nq_o in cell E5 (14.00).

Column F records the result of the calculation of the consumption in the period of interest for each item (p_nq_n). This is then summed to give Σp_nq_n in cell F5 (19.25).

The result of the final part of the calculation is recorded in cell D7. The total consumption for the period of interest (Σp_nq_n) is divided by the total consumption for the base period (Σp_nq_o) and multiplied by 100.

Alternatively we could have calculated the consumption on each item and then substituted into the formula:

$$\text{Paasche's volume index} = \frac{(10.00 + 2.25 + 7.00)}{(7.50 + 3.00 + 3.50)} \times 100$$

$$= \frac{19.25}{14.00} \times 100$$

$$= 137.50$$

Thus we can say that the volume of our weekly shopping basket increased by 37.5% in terms of its value between 1983 and 1993 using 1993 consumption patterns. It should be noted that the disadvantages discussed in section 21.5 still apply.

A third index, the Irving Fischer index, uses the geometric mean of Laspeyre's and Paasche's indices. This is considered by some to provide the ideal index.

21.8 Summary

- The average price index and the average quantity index are used when the relative prices or amounts of each individual item in the index are not considered important.
- The weighted average price index and the weighted average volume index are used when we wish to attach different levels of importance to each of the items in our index.
- Laspeyre's price index is used when we wish to compare costs using the base period quantities (i.e. different prices, base consumption).
- Paasche's price index is used when we wish to compare costs using the period of interest quantities (i.e. different prices, current consumption).
- Laspeyre's volume index is used when we wish to compare quantities using the base period prices (i.e. different volumes, base price).
- Paasche's volume index is used when we wish to compare quantities using the period of interest prices (i.e. different volumes, current price).

Further reading:

Management Information Systems and Statistics (Chapter 12), Bee R and Bee F, IPM (1990)
Business Mathematics and Statistics (Chapter 23), Francis A, DP PUBLICATIONS (1993)
Quantitative Approaches in Business Studies (Chapter 6), Morris C, PITMAN (1989)
Statistics (Chapter 8), Owen F & Jones R, PITMAN (1990)

Unit 22: Index numbers: chain based index, splicing indices, deflating a series

22.1 Introduction – selecting a suitable base period

The base period for an index number should be one in which no unusual events have taken place, that is one where prices or volumes are normal (not particularly low or high).

It is also important to update the base period regularly in order that the indices do not differ too much from 100, making interpretation difficult, and so that the price or volume weightings are not too for removed from current trends. One example of an index that is regularly updated is the Retail Price Index last updated in January 1987.

22.2 Chain based index

The base of a *chain based index* changes each time a new index is calculated. The base is usually the previous year. This is particularly useful when we want to compare period on period (usually year on year) changes. Although the base is more up to date than the fixed base methods discussed in units 20 and 21, the chain based method makes multi-time period comparisons more difficult.

The chain based index is calculated using the formula:

$$\text{Chain based index} = \frac{\text{value for period of interest}}{\text{value for previous period}} \times 100$$

The table below illustrates the calculation of chain based price index numbers for the price of a packet of crisps using this formula. The fixed base price index has also been included to enable comparison between the two indices (figures have been rounded to 2 decimal places when necessary).

Chain Based and Fixed Base Price Index for a Packet of Crisps

Year	Price	Chain based Price Index	Fixed base Price Index
1985	12p	12/12 × 100 = 100.00	100.00
1986	12p	12/12 × 100 = 100.00	100.00
1987	14p	14/12 × 100 = 116.67	116.67
1988	15p	15/14 × 100 = 107.14	125.00
1989	16p	16/15 × 100 = 106.67	133.33
1990	18p	18/16 × 100 = 112.50	150.00
1991	20p	20/18 × 100 = 111.11	166.67
1992	22p	22/20 × 100 = 110.00	183.33
1993	23p	23/22 × 100 = 104.55	191.67

Source: MN Crisp Company

The chain based index is therefore particularly useful for answering questions such as 'Which year had the largest proportional price rise?' As we can see this was 1986 – 1987 with a chain based index of 116.67. By contrast, the fixed base index is more useful for answering questions such as 'What has been the proportional increase in price since the base year?'

22.3 Splicing indices

Often in business we need to combine two or more indices whose base years are different. To overcome this we can 'splice' the indices together.

The method for splicing is similar to that for chain based calculations. As the most recent data is usually considered the most important, the whole series is usually re-calculated on the latest base year.

We have been given three indices recording the price of our company's product The first records the years 1981 – 1983, the second 1983 – 1987 and the third 1997 – 1991. In order to interpret the changes in price over the whole period we need to splice the indices. The data and the spiced index are shown in the table below:

Original based indices and spliced index for price of a product

Year	Index 1977 = 100	Index 1983 = 100	Index 1987 = 100	Spliced Index 1987 = 100
1981	191.2			58.0
1982	194.8			59.1
1983	212.0	100.0		64.4
1984		112.8		72.6
1985		126.2		81.2
1986		135.5		87.2
1987		155.4	100.0	100.0
1988			110.3	110.3
1989			145.6	145.6
1990			145.7	145.7
1991			148.6	148.6

Source: Company Sales Report

To splice indices we usually keep the most recent index and work backwards. For our data above this means starting with the 1987 based index (1987 = 100). The indices for 1987 onwards are fine as these are already calculated to the 1987 base. The index numbers for 1983, 1984, 1985 and 1986 can be recalculated on the 1987 base simply by multiplying by:

$$\frac{100}{155.4}$$

as this is by what we need to multiply the 1987 (1983 base) figure to make it 100. As the original index numbers were to 1 decimal place the spliced index numbers have been calculated to 1 decimal place.

$$\text{Thus } 1986 = 135.5 \times \frac{100}{155.4} = 87.2$$

$$1985 = 126.2 \times \frac{100}{155.4} = 81.2$$

$$1984 = 112.8 \times \frac{100}{155.4} = 72.6$$

$$\text{and } 1983 = 100 \times \frac{100}{155.4} = 64.4$$

As there was also a change of base in 1983 we have to also take this factor into account. Therefore, in addition we have to multiply by:

$$\frac{100}{212}$$

as this is by what we would need to multiply the 1983 figure (1977 base) to make it 100.

We therefore need to multiply the index numbers for 1983, 1982 and 1981 by

$$\frac{100}{212} \times \frac{100}{155.4} = \frac{10000}{32944.8}$$

This gives the price index for each of the years as follows:

$$1983 \qquad 212.0 \times \frac{10000}{32944.8} = 64.4$$

$$1982 \qquad 194.8 \times \frac{10000}{32944.8} = 59.1$$

$$1981 \qquad 191.2 \times \frac{10000}{32944.8} = 58.0$$

These figures have been inserted into the final column of the table above to give the spliced price index. We can now see our product prices relative to 1987 = 100 for all the years.

22.4 Deflating a series

The price of the product produced by our company and prices in general have risen since 1981. We wish to know whether or not the price of our product has risen more or less than the rate of inflation over a number of years. We can use the Retail Price Index to deflate the prices of our product to obtain a relative value after taking general changes in prices into account.

The *Retail Price Index* (RPI) is used to measure the change in retail prices over a given period. It is generally regarded as a barometer of the cost of living. The RPI is compiled by the Department of Employment and is designed to measure the monthly degree of change in the relative prices of goods and services that a 'typical' household might spend its money on. The RPI consists of 10 main groups:

- Food
- Alcoholic drink
- Tobacco
- Clothing and footwear
- Housing
- Fuel and power
- Household goods and services
- Transport and communication
- Recreation
- Catering

The Department of Employment's officials visit shops to ascertain prices and then a price index for each of the chosen items is calculated relative to the base. The base year is currently 1987. The price indices for each item are averaged to find the 'United Kingdom price index' for each item. These are then weighted using weightings based on the Family Expenditure Survey which is a continuous survey into the breakdown of household expenditure (see unit 3.4). The RPI is therefore a weighted average price index.

The table below shows the price of our product and the retail price index for the period 1981-1991.

Company Product Price and General Index of Retail Prices 1981 – 1991
(1983 = 100)

Year	Price	RPI
1981	£1.55	86
1982	£1.65	95
1983	£1.80	100
1984	£1.90	105
1985	£2.00	111
1986	£2.20	116
1987	£2.25	121
1988	£2.35	125
1989	£2.50	135
1990	£2.70	145
1991	£3.20	158

Source of RPI Employment Gazette

We can now use the Retail Price Index to deflate our product's prices and obtain real change in its price.

To do this we use the general formula:

$$\text{Deflated price} = \frac{\text{Price for period n}}{\text{Retail Price Index for period n}} \times 100$$

where period n is a particular year.

For example:

Average product price for 1989 at 1983 prices $= \frac{2.50}{135} \times 100 = £1.85$

Average product price for 1991 at 1983 prices $= \frac{3.20}{158} \times 100 = £2.03$

This means that our product's price has increased in real terms by 18p over the 1989 – 1991 period at 1983 prices.

22.5 Summary

- The base period for an index should be one in which no unusual events have taken place, that is where prices or volumes are normal.
- Chain based indices are used for comparing period upon period, usually year on year, changes in prices or quantities.
- Splicing indices is undertaken to combine two or more overlapping indices where the bases are different.
- An index is usually deflated to remove the impact of inflation upon prices. This is normally done using the Retail Price Index.
- The Retail Price Index is used to measure changes in retail prices over a given period. It is a weighted average price index.

Further reading:

Management Information Systems and Statistics (Chapter 12), Bee R and Bee F, IPM (1990)
Business Mathematics and Statistics (Chapter 24), Francis A, DP PUBLICATIONS (1993)
Quantitative Approaches in Business Studies (Chapter 6), Morris C, PITMAN (1989)
Statistics (Chapter 8), Owen F & Jones R, PITMAN (1990)

Useful articles on the Retail Price Index include:

(1986) 'Forthcoming changes to the Retail Prices Index' *Employment Gazette* September 373-379
(1992) 'Retail prices index: updating of weights for 1992' *Employment Gazette* June 304-306

Unit 23: Theoretical and empirical probability

23.1 Introduction to probability

Within business we are often faced with the question 'What is the chance of..... .' This question may be something as crucial to the company's well-being as the chance of a new product being a success, or as mundane as the chance that it will rain on the day of the company's annual outing. In both cases we are asking what is the probability of an event occurring. In the first case, the event is the success of the new product; in the second, it is rain falling on the day of the annual outing. Knowing either probability prior to the event will help us in our decision making. If the probability of a new product being a success was high, we would put the product into production. Conversely, if the probability of rain on the day of the company's annual outing was high, we might be tempted to re arrange the outing on another day.

Probability is therefore a measure of certainty. It is usually expressed on a scale of 0 to 1. If the probability of an event is close to 1 then this event has a high chance of occurring. If the probability of an event is close to 0 then this event has a low chance of occurring.

There are two ways of calculating probability: empirical and theoretical probability. Empirical probability is calculated on the basis of some experiment, for example testing a sample of products from a production line to see they meet quality standards. Theoretical probability is calculated without an experiment being carried out.

23.2 Types of event

Mutually exclusive events

The events described in the introduction were clear cut. If we consider the occurrence of rain on the day of the company's annual outing, the outcome was one from the following list of possible events, we call this list the *event set*:

- rain on the day of the company's annual outing;
- no rain on the day of the company's annual outing.

In other words, for each event either it happened or it did not. We call such events *mutually exclusive*: if one happens it means that the remaining possible outcomes can, by definition, not happen. Other examples of mutually exclusive events from business are listed in their event sets below:

- the union recommends the work force accepts the annual pay award of a 10% increase. The union recommends the work force rejects the annual pay award of a 10% increase;
- the work force complete the order in under 2 days. The work force complete the order in two to under four days; the work force take four or more days to complete the order.

In some event sets the events will not be mutually exclusive. If a private cleaning firm employs males and females as cleaners and supervisors the two events 'female' and 'supervisor' would not be mutually exclusive as both events could happen simultaneously – a female supervisor.

Dependent events

Two events are said to be *dependent* on one another if the knowledge of one occurring alters the probability of the other event occurring. Mutually exclusive events are, by definition, dependent as the occurrence of one automatically excludes all other events in the event set. The event that the union will recommend that the pay award is accepted is, in effect, dependent upon the event that the union will recommend that the pay award is rejected not occurring.

Dependent events are not always mutually exclusive. Let us consider the two events:

- the company bids for the contract;
- the company wins the contract.

The probability of the company winning the contract is dependent upon the event the company bids for the contract having actually occurred. Thus the probability of both events occurring is the product of the independent probability of the event 'the company bids for the contract' occurring and, dependent upon this the probability of the event 'the company wins the contract' occurring.

Independent events

Two events are said to be *independent* if the knowledge that one has occurred has no effect on the probability of other occurring. Events which are not mutually exclusive may be independent. If we consider the two events 'females' and 'supervisors' within a cleaning firm's employees we would expect that these were independent because the occurrence of one would not affect the other. If this was not the case then we might suspect sexual discrimination.

Events occurring in two completely different event sets are also likely to be independent. For example, the event 'the company wins a new contract' will be independent of the event 'a current customer pays their outstanding account' to the same company.

23.3 Theoretical and empirical probability

Theoretical probability

Theoretical probability is used when all outcomes are assumed to be equally likely. It is the name given to a probability that is calculated by using information about the problem situation rather than by collecting empirical data.

We work in the quality control department of a large company manufacturing footwear. At present four different styles are manufactured in the following quantities:

Daily Production by type of Footwear 199-

Footwear type	Daily Production
Boots	2000
Shoes	5000
Sandals	1500
Plimsolls	1000
Total	9500

Source: Production Department

Footwear is selected at random for inspection to check that it meets the company's quality standards. As each piece of footwear that is inspected is chosen at random, each of the 9,500 pieces of footwear produced daily can be regarded as having an equal chance of being selected or not selected. This means we can use *theoretical probability* as each of the two events in the event set (chosen or not chosen) has an equally likely chance of occurring.

We need to know what the probability is of the footwear selected for inspection being a boot, a shoe, a sandal, or a plimsoll.

To calculate the theoretical probability we use the formula:

$$p(E) = \frac{n\ (E)}{n\ (U)}$$

where $p(E)$ is probability of event E occurring
$n(E)$ is number of outcomes in the event set E
$n(U)$ is total number of possible outcomes

Thus the theoretical probability (all calculated to 4 decimal places) of:

selecting a boot for inspection by quality control $= \frac{2000}{9500} = 0.2105$

selecting a shoe $= \frac{5000}{9500} = 0.5263$

selecting a sandal $= \frac{1500}{9500} = 0.1579$

selecting a plimsoll $= \frac{1000}{9500} = 0.1053$

In this situation we have calculated the probabilities to 4 decimal places as we have thousands of observations. These probabilities should sum to 1 unless we have made an error in our calculation:

$$0.2105 + 0.5263 + 0.1579 + 0.1053 = 1.0000$$

In addition we can calculate the probability of selecting a sandal **or** a plimsoll using the same general formula:

$$\frac{1500 + 1000}{9500} = 0.2632$$

This is the same as adding the individual probabilities 0.1579 (sandal) and 0.1053 (plimsoll) together because the events are mutually exclusive.

Empirical probability

Empirical probability is calculated using empirical data which has been collected through observation of actual outcomes (event sets). Because it is based on actual outcomes it is sometimes called *relative frequency*. This means we can use empirical probability when all the events in an event set do not have the same probability, in other words they are not equally likely.

We work for a small restaurant and have conducted a sample survey of customers' bills. As part of this survey we have collected the amount spent from each bill. This is shown in the table below:

Age Distribution of Customers at Restaurant

Amount spent	< £20	£20 –< £40	£40 –< £60	£60 –< £80	£80 plus	**Total**
Number of bills	3	25	30	35	30	**123**

Source: Sample Survey of Customers 199-

We wish to calculate the probability that a bill will be less than £20, and £60 or over.

To do this we use the general formula for the empirical probability. This is very similar to the formula for the mean of a frequency distribution (unit 11.3):

$$p(E) = \frac{f(E)}{\Sigma f}$$

where $p(E)$ is the empirical probability (relative frequency) of event E occurring
$f(E)$ is the total number of times event E has occurred
Σf is the total frequency – the total number of observations (in this case the total number of bills)

The probability that a bill will be less than £20 is therefore:

$$\frac{3}{123} = 0.024 \text{ (to 3 decimal places)}$$

and £60 or over is: $\frac{35 + 30}{123} = 0.528$ (to 3 decimal places)

In this situation we have calculated the probability to 3 decimal places as we have hundreds of observations. Thus we can say that less than 3% of our bills will be under £20 and over 52% of our bills will be for £60 or more.

We can also calculate the empirical probability for two dimensional tables. The table below records the number of data input errors made by computer operators at a credit reference agency by time of day for the previous month:

Data Input Errors for the Previous Month

	Operator				
Time of Day	**Tracey**	**Sharon**	**Charlene**	**Jean**	**Total**
08.01 – 12.00	10	5	3	2	**20**
12.01 – 16.00	15	7	3	5	**30**
16.01 – 20.00	20	3	2	10	**35**
Total	**45**	**15**	**8**	**17**	**85**

Source: Credit Company

We have received a complaint from a customer that we provided an incorrect reference between 4 p.m. and 8 p.m. Our investigations suggest that it is due to an error made by one of our computer operators. We want to know what the probability is that this error was made by Tracey. The event is therefore the error was made by Tracey between 4 p.m. and 8 p.m., the event set is the number of errors made between 4 p.m. and 8 p.m.

We use the same formula as before for the empirical probability. In this case the total number of times that the event has occurred is 20 and the total frequency is 35. The empirical probability is therefore:

$$p(E) = \frac{20}{35} = 0.57 \text{ (to 2 decimal places)}$$

In this situation we have calculated the probability to 2 decimal places as we have tens of observations. We can therefore be 57% percent certain that Tracey made the error.

23.4 Combining events

We have already seen that for two mutually exclusive (dependent) events from the same event set the probability of either one of them occurring is the sum of the probabilities. This rule can be applied more generally. We can express this using the following notation:

$$p(A \text{ or } B) = p(A) + p(B)$$

where $p(A)$ is the probability of A occurring
$p(B)$ is the probability of B occurring
and A and B are two mutually exclusive events.

This means that if we know that the probabilities of a factory completing an order are:

in less than 1 week	0.50;
in 1 to less than 2 weeks	0.25;
in 2 to less than 3 weeks	0.15;
in 3 plus weeks	0.10.

We can calculate the probabilities for completing the order in less than 2 weeks (0.50 + 0.25 = 0.75), 1 to 3 weeks (0.25 + 0.15 = 0.40) or any other combination of the original probabilities. This is known as the *addition rule* for probabilities.

Probabilities for independent events can be combined. This means we can calculate the probability of two or more events occurring. To do this we use the *multiplication rule*. This simply states that the probability of two or more independent events both occurring is the product of multiplying the probabilities. We can express this using the following notation:

$$p(A \text{ and } B) = p(A) \times p(B)$$

where $p(A)$ is the probability of A occurring
$p(B)$ is the probability of B occurring
and A and B are two mutually exclusive events.

Therefore if we know the probability of an employee being a male is 0.4, and the probability of an employee having green eyes is 0.1, then the probability of an employee being male and having green eyes is:

$$0.4 \times 0.1 = 0.04$$

23.5 Summary

- Probability is a measure of certainty. It is usually expressed on a scale of 0 to 1. If the probability of an event is close to 1 then this event has a high chance of occurring. If the probability of an event is close to 0 then this event has a low chance of occurring.
- The possible outcomes of any given situation are called events.
- An event or outcome set is all the possible events or outcomes than can occur for a given situation.
- Mutually exclusive events are those where if one event occurs the others in the event set cannot occur.
- Two event sets are independent if the knowledge that one has occurred does not affect the occurrence of the other.
- Mutually exclusive events are therefore by definition dependent.
- Theoretical probability is used when each event is equally likely. It is the name given to a probability that is calculated by using information about the problem situation rather than by collecting empirical data.
- Empirical probability is calculated using empirical data which has been collected through observation of actual outcomes (events). Because it is based on actual outcomes it is sometimes called relative frequency.
- The probability for either one of two or more mutually exclusive dependent events occurring can be calculated using the addition rule.
- The probability for two or more independent events both occurring can be calculated using the multiplication rule.

Further reading:

Management Information and Statistics (Chapter 7), Bee R and Bee F, IPM (1990)
Business Mathematics and Statistics (Chapters 36 & 37), Francis A, DP PUBLICATIONS (1993)
Quantitative Approaches in Business Studies (Chapter 7), Morris C, PITMAN (1989)

Unit 24: Expectation and conditional probability

24.1 Introduction

In the previous unit we considered the use of probability to answer simple questions for business use. These were of the type 'What is the chance of...' This enabled us to put a value on the likelihood of an event occurring. Probability can also be used to answer more involved questions within business. These questions fall into two types:

- 'What would we expect to happen....'
- 'What is the chance of .... given that the following has occurred....'

The former of these is known as *expectation* as we are calculating what we expect to happen. The latter is known as *conditional probability* as we are constraining our set of possible outcomes by stating a condition which must first be satisfied; in other words, we are calculating the probability after a condition has already been met.

24.2 Expectation

Expectation (or the expected value) is the arithmetic mean of a given set of values. It is calculated using probabilities rather than frequencies.

Expected income

We work for a small cafe which is open Monday to Sunday. Over the past year we have observed that our income varies according to the day of the week. These we have divided into Saturday, Market Day (Thursday) and Normal days. We have calculated our average (mean) income for each of these types of day over the past year, and the probability of each of these types of day occurring to 3 decimal places:

Mean Daily Income 199-

Type of Day	Mean daily income (x)	Probability (p)
Saturday	£600	0.143
Market Day	£750	0.143
Normal Days	£200	0.714

Source: Daily Takings Data

We have applied for a loan and been asked by the lender what our expected daily income will be. To calculate this we can use the formula:

$$\text{Expected value of } x = \Sigma(p\ x)$$

where x is the value of the variable (in our case mean daily income)
p is the probability of the value occurring

In effect we are calculating the arithmetic mean of the values using probabilities instead of frequencies. Although this is a relatively simple calculation it helps if we set it out as a table. This format also makes it easy to use a computer spreadsheet especially if we are undertaking longer calculations:

	A	B	C	D
1	Type of Day	Mean daily income x	Probability p	px
2	Saturday	£600	0.143	85.80
3	Market Day	£750	0.143	107.25
4	Normal	£200	0.714	142.80
5	Total			335.85

The first step is to note down our original daily income and probability data (columns A – C).

Next we multiply the probability (column C) by the mean daily income (column B) for each type of day (answer in column D). This is px.

Finally we sum result of multiplying column C by column B for each type of day – £335.85 (cell D5). This is Σpx.

We can therefore say that the expected mean daily income for the cafe is £335.85.

Expected profit

The lender has also asked us what we expect our daily average (mean) profit will be. The calculation above can be developed so that we can calculate these expected values.

We know that our overheads for the cafe are £150 a day for normal days, and £200 a day for Saturday and Market Day when we require extra staff. This data can be included in our calculation:

	A	B	C	D	E	F
1	Type of Day	Mean daily income	Mean daily expenditure	Profit (x)	Probability (p)	(px)
2	Saturday	£600	£200	£400	0.143	57.20
3	Market Day	£750	£200	£550	0.143	78.65
4	Normal	£200	£150	£50	0.714	35.70
5	Total					171.55

The first stage is to calculate the profit. This is simply income – expenditure, in other words column B – column C. The answer is given in column D.

We can then substitute our profit into the formula for the expected value shown above.

Next we multiply the probability (column E) by the mean daily profit (column D) for each type of day (answers in column F). This is px.

Finally we sum the result of multiplying column E by column D for each type of day and provides the answer – £171.55 (cell F5). This is Σpx.

We can therefore say that the expected mean daily profit for the cafe is £171.55.

24.3 Conditional probability

Conditional probability is the probability that an event happens given that another event has occurred. In such cases we are looking at probabilities where the outcome of the second event depends upon the outcome of the first. This means we have to take account of the event that has already occurred in finding the probability of the other event.

If we consider a firm whose employees are 70% female and 30% male. This means that if we were to select an employee at random the probability of them being female would be 0.7, and of them being male 0.3. We also know that 10% of female employees are of supervisory grade or above, compared with 50% of male employees. Therefore if we have selected an employee at random and they are female the probability of them being of supervisory grade and above is going to be 0.1. Conditional probability is expressed as:

$$p(A \mid B)$$

where p is the probability
$A \mid B$ that event A occurs given that event B has occurred.

Tabular method

We work for an electronics firm which has 1000 employees. Of these 800 are females and 200 are males. We also know that 400 are part time and 600 are full time. We need to find out

- the probability that an employee will be female, $p(F)$;
- the probability that an employee will be part time, $p(P)$;
- the probability that an employee is female and part time, $p(F) \times p(P)$;
- the probability that an employee is part time given that they are female, $p(P \mid F)$.

We can express the information given to us as a table:

	Male	Female	Total
Full time	A	B	**600**
Part time	C	D	**400**
Total	**200**	**800**	**1000**

The first stage in answering our questions is to work out the expected values for each of the cells in our table, this is known as the *tabular method*. To do this for full time males we can take the probability that an employee will be male (200/1000) and multiply it by the probability that an employee will be full time (600/1000):

$$\frac{200}{1000} \times \frac{600}{1000} = \frac{120000}{1000000} = 0.12$$

This gives the probability that an employee will be male and full time (0.12). As we have 1,000 employees we multiply this probability by 1000 to find the number of male full time employees.

This can be simplified to the following formula (the same that we used to find the expected values for chi square in unit 19.4):

$$\frac{\text{Column total for column containing cell} \times \text{Row total for row containing cell}}{\text{Grand total}}$$

Thus for cell A the expected value is: $\dfrac{200 \times 600}{1000} = 120$

and for cell B the expected value is: $\dfrac{800 \times 600}{1000} = 480$

and for cell C the expected value is: $\dfrac{200 \times 400}{1000} = 80$

and for cell D the expected value is: $\dfrac{800 \times 400}{1000} = 320$

We can now insert these values into our table:

	Male	Female	Total
Full time	120	480	**600**
Part time	80	320	**400**
Total	**200**	**800**	**1000**

and use them to calculate the probabilities.

Since there are 1000 employees of whom 800 are females the probability that an employee will be female, $p(F)$, is:

$$\frac{800}{1000} = 0.8$$

Since there are 1000 employees, of whom 400 are part time the probability that an employee will be part time, $p(P)$, is:

$$\frac{400}{1000} = 0.4$$

Since there are 1000 employees, of whom 320 are part time and females the probability that an employee will be part time and female, $p(F) \times p(P)$, is:

$$\frac{320}{1000} = 0.32$$

However, once we know the employee is female then the conditional probability that one of these female employees, $p(P \mid F)$, is part time is the number of part time female employees (320) divided by the total number of female employees (800):

$$\frac{320}{800} = 0.4$$

Bayes' theorem

Conditional probabilities can also be calculated using Bayes' theorem rather that the tabular method. This enables us to calculate a conditional probability providing we know its reverse. It uses the general formula:

$$p(A \mid B) = \frac{p(A) \times p(B \mid A)}{p(B)}$$

For our example above this translates as:

$$p(\text{employee is part time given know female}) = \frac{p(\text{part time}) \times p(\text{female given know part time})}{p(\text{female})}$$

The probability that an employee is part time, $p(P)$, is 0.4;

the probability that an employee is female given that they are part time, $p(F \mid P)$, is 0.8;

the probability that an employee is female, $p(F)$, is 0.8.

We can now substitute these figures into the formula and undertake the calculation.

$$p(P \mid F) = \frac{0.4 \times 0.8}{0.8} = 0.4$$

which agrees with the result for the tabular method.

24.4 Summary

- Expectation (the expected value) is when we calculate what we expect to happen using a given set of values and probabilities. It is calculated in a similar way to the arithmetic mean for a frequency distribution, except that probabilities are used instead of frequencies.
- Conditional probability is when we constrain our set of possible outcomes by stating a condition that must first be satisfied. We are therefore calculating the probability that an event occurs given that another event has already occurred.
- Conditional probability can either be calculated using the tabular method or Bayes theorem.
- Bayes theorem calculates the conditional probability given that the inverse of that conditional probability is known.

Further reading:

Business Mathematics and Statistics (Chapter 38), Francis A, DP PUBLICATIONS (1993)

Unit 25: Probability and the normal distribution

25.1 Introduction

We have already come across, and briefly discussed, the normal distribution in earlier units (12.5, 13.7, and 14.6). The normal distribution pattern is the most important distribution in statistics as its existence is a pre requisite for many statistical tests. Fortunately the normal distribution pattern occurs frequently in business data. To recap the normal distribution is the name given to a distribution of continuous data for a variable. When this data is plotted as a frequency curve it has the following characteristics:

- it is symmetrical about the mean of the distribution;
- the frequencies of the values tend to taper away either side of the mean giving the normal distribution curve a 'bell shape';
- the majority of values tend to cluster around the mean, with the greatest frequency at the mean. Therefore the mean, median and mode all have the same value.

The normal distribution curve can take any number of shapes within these rules as illustrated by the examples in unit 14.6.

25.2 The normal distribution and probabilities

Because the normal distribution is continuous it not possible for us to calculate the probability of a precise value occurring. It is only possible for us to find the probability of a range of values within the distribution. We can illustrate this using an example.

An electrical company manufactures reels of cable which are approximately 50 metres in length. The quality control manager knows from quality control checks on 1,000 reels that the actual length of cable on each reel is normally distributed. It is not possible for him to calculate the probability that a reel of cable will be exactly 50 metres in length. However he can calculate the probability that it will be between (for example) 49 and 51 metres, or between 49.9 and 50.1 metres.

To calculate either probability the manager needs to know both the mean and the standard deviation (units 11 and 14 respectively) of the distribution. Once they know these the manager can then calculate the *z* score. Normal distribution tables are then used to determine the probability that a *z* score will have a value less than or equal to the one specified.

25.3 Calculation of the z score

The quality control manager of the electrical company has asked us to calculate the probability that a machine will produce a real of cable of less than or equal to 50.1 metres in length. We know that the mean cable length produced by the machine is 50 metres, with a standard deviation of 0.24 metres.

The first stage is to calculate the *z* score using the formula:

$$z = \frac{x - \bar{x}}{\delta}$$

where z is the z score
x is the value specified (in this case 50.1)
$\bar{x}$ is the mean (in this case 50)
δ is the standard deviation (in this case 0.24)

$$\text{Therefore the } z \text{ score} = \frac{50.1 - 50.0}{0.24}$$

$$= 0.417$$

$$= 0.42 \text{ (to 2 decimal places)}$$

We round the z score to 2 decimal places as this is the accuracy required in the table 'Values of the Standard Normal Distribution' below. The process of calculating the z score is sometimes called *standardising the x value.*

25.4 The probability of the z score being less than that calculated

We now need to find the probability that a z score is less than 0.42. This probability is given in our normal distribution tables. The table below shows an extract of the normal distribution tables from appendix 5.

Values of the Standard Normal Distribution (extract)

x	0.00	0.01	0.02	0.03	0.04	0.05	0.06	0.07	0.08	0.09
0.0	.5000	.5040	.5080	.5120	.5160	.5199	.5239	.5279	.5319	.5359
0.1	.5398	.5438	.5478	.5517	.5557	.5596	.5636	.5675	.5714	.5754
0.2	.5793	.5832	.5871	.5910	.5948	.5987	.6026	.6064	.6103	.6141
0.3	.6179	.6217	.6255	.6293	.6331	.6368	.6406	.6443	.6480	.6517
0.4	.6554	.6591	.6628	.6664	.6700	.6736	.6772	.6808	.6844	6879
0.5	.6915	.6950	.6985	.7019	.7054	.7088	.7123	.7157	.7190	.7224
0.6	.7258	.7324	.....							

Source: Appendix 5

As our value of z is 0.42 we first look down the column headed x until we come to the value **0.4**, next we read across this row until we come to the column **0.02**. The probability of z being less than or equal to 0.42 is the value in this cell 0.6628.

In other words we are finding the area of the shaded portion under the normal distribution curve, given that the total area under the curve is 1. This is illustrated in the diagram below:

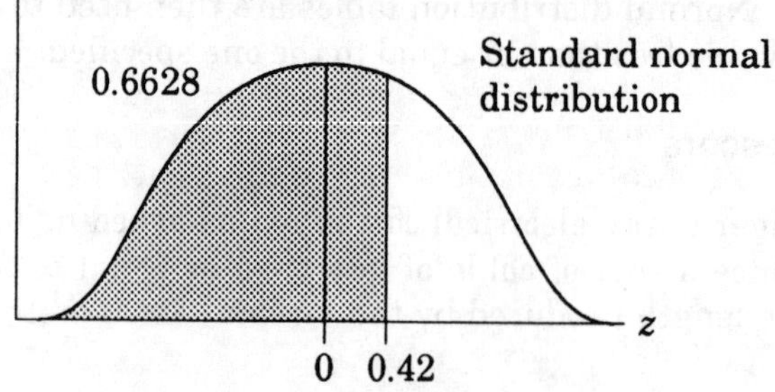

We can therefore say that the probability of a reel of cable being less than or equal to 50.1 metres in length is 0.6628.

This means that out of 1,000 reels of cable we would expect 663 to be less than or equal to 50.1 metres in length.

25.5 The probability of the z score being greater than that calculated

Once we have calculated the z score and looked up the probability of a z score being less than or equal to this value in the normal distribution tables we can use our knowledge of probability to calculate the probability of a score being greater.

The probability of the z score being less than or equal to the calculated z score is one of two mutually exclusive events:

1. the probability of the z score being less than or equal to the calculated z score;
2. the probability of the z score being greater than the calculated z score.

As we know that the probability of a reel of cable being less than or equal to 50.1 metres in length is 0.6628 then we can also calculate the probability that it is over 50.1 metres in length using the addition rule for probabilities (unit 23.4).

The probability that a reel of cable is over 50.1 metres in length therefore

= total probability – probability for less than or equal to 50.1 metres
= 1.0000 – 0.6628
= 0.3372

as the probabilities for two mutually exclusive events from the same event set must sum to 1.

In this example it means that out of 1,000 reels of cable we would expect 337 to be over 50.1 metres in length.

25.6 The problem of negative z scores

Suppose we had been asked by the Quality Control Manager of the electrical company to calculate the probability that the length of cable is less than or equal to 49.8 metres. Using our formula this would give us a z score of:

$$z = \frac{49.8 - 50.0}{0.24}$$

$$= -0.833$$

$$= -0.83 \text{ (to 2 decimal places)}$$

As our normal distribution tables only contain positive values of z this could cause us a problem! Fortunately, because the normal distribution is symmetric, we know that the probability that z is less than or equal to –0.83 is the equivalent to the probability of z being greater than 0.83. This is 1 – the tabulated value of z. This is 0.7967 from the Standard Normal Distribution Table (appendix 5).

Thus the probability that the length of cable is less than 49.8 metres is:

$$1 - 0.7967 = 0.2033$$

This means that out of every 1,000 reels of cable manufactured 203 would be less than or equal to 49.8 metres in length.

25.7 The probability of a value between two z scores

Often we need to know the probability that a value will lie within a specified range. We can use z scores to find the answer to this sort of problem.

For example an agricultural feed company sells feed in 50 kg bags. The mean weight of bags sold is in fact 50.5 kg with a standard deviation of 0.7 kg. We have been asked to find the probability of a bag's weight being between 50 and 52 kg.

First we calculate the probability that the bag will weigh less than or equal to 50 kg.

$$\text{In this case the } z \text{ score} = \frac{50.0 - 50.5}{0.7}$$

$$= -0.714$$

$$= -0.71 \text{ (to 2 decimal places).}$$

As the z score is negative this is equivalent to the probability of z being greater than 0.71. The tabulated value of z is 0.7612, therefore the probability that the bag will weigh less than 50 kg

$$= 1 - 0.7612$$

$$= 0.2388$$

Next we calculate the probability that the bag will weigh more than 52 kg. To do this we need to calculate the probability that the bag will weigh less than or equal to 52 kg and use the addition rule to calculate the probability that it will weigh more.

$$\text{In this case the } z \text{ score} = \frac{52.0 - 50.5}{0.7}$$

$$= 2.14 \text{ (to 2 decimal places)}$$

The tabulated value of z is 0.9838, therefore the probability that the bag will weigh more than 52 kg

$$= 1 - 0.9838$$

$$= 0.0162$$

To summarise we have now calculated that:

- the probability that a bag weighs 50 kg or less is 0.2388;
- the probability that a bag weighs more than 52 kg is 0.0162.

Using the addition rule of probability we can now calculate the probability that a bag of feed weighs between 50 and 52 kg:

$$\text{Probability} = 1 - (0.2388 + 0.0162)$$

$$= 1 - 0.255$$

$$= 0.745$$

This means that out of every 1,000 bags of feed sold 745 will weigh between 50 and 52 kg.

25.8 Summary

- The normal distribution is a distribution of continuous data of a variable. Its frequency curve is symmetrical and bell shaped.
- In order to calculate the probability of a range of values occurring (for normally distributed continuous data) we need to calculate the z score.
- We use the mean and the standard deviation to calculate the z score for the value specified; this is sometimes termed standardising the x value.

- Normal distribution tables only give the probability that the a z score will be less than or equal to the calculated z score for the value specified.

- This means we can only calculate the probability that an actual value will be less than or equal to the value specified.

- Using the fact that this event is mutually exclusive and the addition rule of probability it is possible to calculate the probability that an actual value will be greater than the value specified.

- It is also possible to calculate the probability that an actual value will lie between two other values (specified) using the addition rule.

Further reading:

Business Mathematics and Statistics (Chapter 42), Francis A, DP PUBLICATIONS (1993)
Statistics (Chapter 10), Owen F and Jones R, PITMAN (1990)

Section 3

Practice and development of skills and knowledge

This section gives you the opportunity to apply and build upon what you have learned so far. It does this by using a mixture of tasks and assignments. For tasks the necessary data is provided; assignments usually involve you in obtaining your own primary data or secondary data from company reports, newspapers or other appropriate business publications. The aim of assignments is to enable you to use the principles you have learned in the real world. The assignments also give you the opportunity to generate evidence for demonstrating your competence at NVQ level 4 in *Unit 8: Seek, evaluate and organise information for action* of the Occupational Standards for Managers.

Section 1 developed your understanding of Business Statistics in stages which followed the units in Section 2: The Information Bank. In the real world things are not so simple, and so the majority of tasks and assignments in Section 3 have been placed into a series of topics by grouping together units from Section 2 (and 1). You will find that the tasks in Section 3 are usually longer and involve more work than those in Section 1. The mathematical and statistical knowledge required for each task or assignment can be found by referring to the units in Section 2.

Section 3 Contents and outline

Section 3 is divided into nine topics each of which contains a number of tasks and assignments. An additional tenth 'topic' contains assignments which are designed to integrate a large number of units from the Information Bank:

Tasks and assignments

Within each topic there are a number of tasks and assignments. Answers are given for at least one task in each topic to give you the opportunity for further practice. This is indicated at the start of the task.

At the end of each task or assignment you are referred to the Information Bank (Section 2) for help. For those tasks with answers you are referred to the precise section of the unit in Section 2.

For other tasks and assignments you are only referred to the relevant unit or units in Section 2, as one of the purposes of this section is to give you practice in choosing the most appropriate techniques. The assignments in topic ten will cover many of the 25 units in Section 2.

Assignments are designed to provide you with the opportunity to investigate and analyse data from the real world. If you are studying at college the secondary data you require should be available in your college library, usually in the reference section. If you are in employment the secondary data you require should be available from your employer. If you are studying on your own the secondary data you require should be available in the nearest large public library, usually in the reference section.

Competency based programmes (NVQ 4 M1)

The assignments provide opportunities to generate evidence for competency based programmes, particularly NVQ 4 (M1) *Unit 8: Seek, evaluate and organise information for action* of the Occupational Standards for Managers. Against each assignment the element(s) and the performance criteria where the assignment could be used to generate evidence are given in brackets after the assignment number. By completing all the assignments you should be able to generate evidence for all the performance criteria of *Element 8.1: Obtain and evaluate information to aid decision making*; in some cases it may also be possible to generate evidence for the performance criteria of *Element 8.2: Record and store information.*

If you are taking a competency based programme the performance criteria will have been given to you at the start of your programme. You are reminded that, where possible, your evidence should be generated from performance in the workplace. You may also have to include a narrative with your evidence stating which performance criteria the evidence meets and how, as well as your reflections upon and review of the evidence. Remember it is your responsibility to convince the assessor that your evidence satisfies the performance criteria.

How to use this section

If you are studying at a College your Lecturer will advise you which tasks and assignments you should do and the sequence which best suits your particular course (or programme).

If you are studying on your own the following suggested study plan is recommended:

1. work through this section as you are directed at the end of each unit in Section 1. In most cases this will only coincide with the end of a topic. Work through the tasks in the order in which they are presented in Section 3 and then attempt the assignments. In this way you will be confirming and extending your knowledge of each topic prior to moving on to new ideas and concepts;
2. remember to refer to Section 2: The Information Bank (and the recommended additional reading in Section 2) as and when required. The process of continual checking and cross referencing will help you to develop your knowledge and understanding;
3. where an answer is provided for the task always attempt the task prior to looking at the answer, referring to Section 2 as necessary. This is an important learning technique;
4. each topic contains a number of assignments. You should attempt as many assignments as possible as they will help you apply your knowledge and understanding to real world situations, thereby developing real and worthwhile practical skills.

Topic 1: Data and information

■ Task 1.1

You are the managing director of a small electronics firm which produces a variety of components. You have been presented with the following table by your production manager and asked to make a decision about whether the firm should buy the necessary equipment to increase output for one of the components.

HELP See *Section 2: The Information Bank* Data and information: Unit 1, page 57; The value and characteristics of information: Unit 2, page 59

Does the table contain data or information?

Give reasons for your answer by evaluating the relevance, reliability, timeliness and sufficiency of the table.

Month	Order level	Production Capacity
January 1991	1500	1500
February 1991	1400	1500
March 1991	1600	1500
April 1991	1650	1450
May 1991	1600	1500
June 1991	1450	1500

■ Task 1.2

You are the owner of a small building equipment firm which produces a variety of equipment for use in the construction industry. For the past two years your company has been able to sell all the ladders it can produce without any need for marketing. You now have a full order book for ladders for the next year. The firm is meeting next month to decide whether to increase output of ladders by 20%. This will not entail purchasing new equipment but will necessitate the employment of an extra person.

HELP See *Section 2: The Information Bank* Data and information: Unit 1, page 57; The value and characteristics of information: Unit 2, page 59

Produce a list of the information that you will need to make this decision.

Your list should be in sufficient detail to enable someone else to obtain the relevant information.

■ Task 1.3 (with answers)

You are an assistant manager at a small sports centre which includes a swimming pool built in the early 1970s. You have been asked to look into the feasibility of upgrading the swimming pool to provide facilities that the public now expect. In your research you have discovered a Market Research Report on public expectations of sports centres. This is based upon an interview survey conducted last January with a sample size of 5,000. An extract from this report is given below:

HELP See *Section 2: The Information Bank* Business data: Unit 1.2, page 57; Business information: Unit 1.3, page 57; The characteristics of information: Unit 2.2, page 60

Public Expectations of Sports Centres EJS Market Research Ltd Page 17

As part of the survey a quota sample of members of the public were asked what features they would like to find at a swimming pool. The results are given in table 3.5 (below). Each Respondent was allowed to name up to three features.

Table 3.5: Percentage of respondents who would like to find various features at a swimming pool

Feature	Percentage of Respondents[1]
Water chute	74%
Wave machine	68%
Diving area with boards	45%
Lanes for serious swimmers	39%
Jacuzzi	29%
Shallow area for young children	23%
Others	17%
Total respondents (=100%)	5000

[1] **Percentages will total more than 100 as respondents were able to name up to 3 features**

Source: Market Research Survey January 199-

Does this extract from the Market Research Report contain data or information as far as you (the assistant manager) are concerned?

Give reasons for you answer.

■ Assignment 1.1 (NVQ 4 M1 Unit 8.1 b)

Examine a company report (you will find examples of these in your college library, or larger public reference libraries).

Imagine you are a shareholder in this company.

List the information you would ideally require from the company report.

HELP
See *Section 2: The Information Bank*
Data and information: Unit 1, page 57; The value and characteristics of information: Unit 2, page 59

Evaluate the relevance, sufficiency and usefulness of the contents of this report for you as a shareholder against your list.

Does the company report contain data or information as far as you (the shareholder) are concerned?

■ Assignment 1.2 (NVQ 4 M1 Unit 8.2a, b)

In a format of your choice list either the data and information that is available to you as a student for one aspect of your course, or the data and information that is available to you for one aspect of your current work.

HELP
See *Section 2: The Information Bank*
Data and information: Unit 1, page 57; The value and characteristics of information: Unit 2, page 59

By each item of data (and each item of information) note whether the format in which you received it was accurate, relevant, timely and easy to understand?

Evaluate your initial classification of each item. Are there any items you wish to change? (If there are, note them and give reasons why.)

■ **Assignment 1.3** (NVQ 4 M1 Unit 8.1b, c)

HELP: See *Section 2: The Information Bank* Data and information: Unit 1, page 57; The value and characteristics of information: Unit 2, page 59; Data sources: Unit 3, page 61

You wish to invest £5,000 by buying shares in up to 10 companies. Examine the financial pages of a national newspaper over at least two weeks.

Do these pages contain sufficient relevant information to enable you to make your investment decisions?

What other information sources do you think would also prove useful? Give reasons for each of the individual information sources you cited.

Topic 2: Collecting data

USING A COMPUTER FOR TOPIC 2 TASKS AND ASSIGNMENTS

Task 2.4 and assignment 2.3 can either be undertaken by hand or using a word processor. The use of a word processor will enable you to reword and rearrange the order of your questions with comparative ease.

■ **Task 2.1** (with answers)

HELP: See *Section 2: The Information Bank* How to sample: Unit 5.3, page 69

You have been asked to select a sample for a questionnaire survey of staff using simple random sampling. Your sampling frame is the internal telephone directory listed below.

Select two random samples, each of ten staff members using random number tables and mark those members of staff selected for each sample on the sampling frame.

Describe and compare the pattern of each of the samples selected as marked on the sampling frame.

Describe the characteristics of the staff members selected for each of the samples.

Is there any bias in either of the samples selected?

Name	Ext.	Name	Ext.	Name	Ext.	Name	Ext.
Claire	7646	George	5454	Barry	6335	Chris	6664
Graham	6453	Maureen	4242	Sarah	4222	Mike	5332
Susan	5354	Jean	2245	Maria	7463	Martin	6424
Benjamin	5425	Mark	7355	Kenneth	5353	Val	5432
Sue	4245	Peter	5656	Jenny	4227	Sarah	7898
Sharon	7497	Julia	4690	Margaret	6789	Denise	6789
Sean	7567	Phil	5456	Pete	5588	Angela	6557
Mike	6336	Steve	5535	Derek	7554	John	4224
Keith	4648	Douglas	4478	Gregory	5353	Jemma	5353
Jane	5426	Stacey	5335	Paul	5757	Eliza	5568
June	5422	Andy	5352	Ann	4649	Jackie	7570
Adrian	5211	Joan	5400	Edward	5698	Ivan	3560
David	7970	Norman	5435				

■ Task 2.2 (with answers)

Select a 20% systematic sample from the sampling frame used for task 2.1. Mark those members of staff selected on the sampling frame.

HELP: See *Section 2: The Information Bank* How to sample: Unit 5.3, page 69

Describe the pattern of the sample selected as marked on the sampling frame and compare it with that of the two random samples from task 2.1.

Once the first member of staff in your sample has been located on the sampling frame what is the likelihood of any other member of staff being selected?

■ Task 2.3

An Agricultural firm wishes to estimate the average (mean) area of farms in ten counties in order to plan a sales drive for fertilisers. Data is available on all five farms in each of the ten counties in the firm's sales area (see below). To assist you in selecting your samples the farms have been numbered from 0 to 49.

HELP: See *Section 2: The Information Bank* Populations, samples and sampling methods: Unit 5, page 68; Measures of central tendency: means: Unit 11, page 109

County		Ha.		Ha.		Ha.		Ha.		Ha.
Ashire	*0*	116.3	*1*	107.2	*2*	125.7	*3*	130.0	*4*	103.4
Bshire	*5*	104.3	*6*	99.8	*7*	108.1	*8*	110.0	*9*	90.6
Cshire	*10*	33.2	*11*	38.4	*12*	45.3	*13*	37.9	*14*	43.1
Dshire	*15*	205.7	*16*	193.5	*17*	182.2	*18*	163.4	*19*	175.6
Eshire	*20*	135.7	*21*	143.5	*22*	186.2	*23*	159.6	*24*	139.4
Fshire	*25*	20.2	*26*	15.7	*27*	26.4	*28*	27.4	*29*	30.2
Gshire	*30*	15.3	*31*	20.4	*32*	19.7	*33*	18.0	*34*	16.1
Hshire	*35*	14.5	*36*	10.2	*37*	9.3	*38*	15.7	*39*	16.3
Ishire	*40*	5.7	*41*	9.2	*42*	8.4	*43*	7.3	*44*	6.6
Jshire	*45*	1.0	*46*	0.7	*47*	2.9	*48*	3.9	*49*	5.5

Select a simple random sample of 5 farms and calculate the average (mean) farm size.

Select a systematic sample of 10% of the farms and calculate the average (mean) farm size.

Select one county at random and calculate the average (mean) farm size. What is this type of sample called?

The true average (mean) farm size is 66.09 hectares. Which method of sampling provides the poorest estimate of the true average (mean) farm size?

■ Task 2.4

You work for a national charity which up until this year has produced a Christmas gift catalogue. This catalogue has been sent to all charity members but response (in terms of value of purchases made from the catalogue) has been poor. You have been asked to design a questionnaire which is short enough to fit on one side of a postcard to find out the following from charity members:

HELP: See *Section 2: The Information Bank* Deciding what data must be collected: Unit 4, page 65; Collecting primary data: questionnaire and interview schedule design: Unit 6, page 75

- what members' views are on charity catalogues in general;
- what members like and dislike about the charity's own catalogue;
- whether members would be interested in a Christmas cards only catalogue;
- how much members would expect to spend in total on items from a charity catalogue.

The questionnaire will be accompanied by a covering letter explaining the purpose of the survey. This has already been drafted.

List the data that must be collected to find the answers to each of the charity's questions.

Design the questionnaire.

■ Assignment 2.1 (NVQ 4 M1 Unit 8.1d, e)

HELP
See *Section 2: The Information Bank*
Data sources: Unit 3, page 61

Which secondary sources do you need to consult to discover the following data?

- the total population of the county in which you live;
- the most recent summary national crime statistics;
- the most recent seasonally adjusted unemployment figure for the United Kingdom;
- the most recent seasonally adjusted gross domestic product figures by category of expenditure for the United Kingdom;
- the percentages of households in the United Kingdom in a series of different weekly income groups;
- the total gross domestic product at current factor cost for two industry sectors in the United Kingdom for a 10 year period.

Visit your college library (or nearest large public reference library) and obtain the appropriate data from each of these sources.

■ Assignment 2.2 (NVQ 4 M1 Unit 8.1c, e)

HELP
See *Section 2: The Information Bank*
The value and characteristics of information: Unit 2, page 59; Data sources: Unit 3, page 61

Obtain data on the same subject area (for example unemployment levels or company profits) from two different data sources.

Evaluate the two data sources for their usefulness, reliability and the ease of obtaining data in the future.

Which of the two sources do you feel is better? Give reasons for your answer.

■ Assignment 2.3 (NVQ 4 M1 Unit 8.1a, b, c, d, g; 8.2 d)

HELP
See *Section 2: The Information Bank*
Deciding what data must be collected: Unit 4, page 65; Populations, samples and sampling methods: Unit 5, page 68; Collecting primary data: questionnaire and interview schedule design: Unit 6, page 75

Design an interview schedule or a questionnaire on an issue of interest to you where the data cannot be collected from secondary sources. (For example it could be related to some aspect of college or work such as the quality of a service or product).

List the factors you want to find out as a series of detailed questions.

Decide whether or not you need to sample and give reasons for your decision. If you are going to sample what method of sampling would you use, and why?

Design a questionnaire or interview schedule to collect the information you need to answer these questions. It should not be more than 20 questions in length.

Pilot the questionnaire or interview schedule on at least five people who are representative of the intended respondents.

Evaluate the effectiveness and reliability of your questionnaire by establishing which questions worked well and why, and where there were problems such as inadequate or the wrong information being collected and why.

Topic 3: Presenting data

USING A COMPUTER SPREADSHEET FOR TOPIC 3 TASKS AND ASSIGNMENTS

Tasks 3.3, 3.4 and 3.5 and assignment 3.3 can either be undertaken by hand or using a computer spreadsheet. The data for these tasks can, with practice, be aggregated more quickly and with less chance of error using a spreadsheet (tasks 3.4 and 3.5). A spreadsheet will also enable you to achieve very high quality diagrams (tasks 3.3, 3.4, and 3.5 and assignment 3.3). A number of computer spreadsheets may not have the capability to construct histograms of unequal class widths so check your spreadsheet manual prior to attempting to draw histograms of unequal class width.

■ Task 3.1

Classify the following into categorical or quantitative data:

- number of people attending a rock concert;
- daily air temperatures at a holiday resort;
- number of applicants for a vacancy;
- length of service of an employee with a company;
- preferred method of payment by employees;
- most popular holiday destination for families.

HELP: See *Section 2: The Information Bank* Types of data and tabulating data: Unit 7, page 81

■ Task 3.2

The following questions has been taken from an application for a bank loan from the Midwest bank:

HELP: See *Section 2: The Information Bank* Types of data and tabulating data: Unit 7, page 81

1. Full name: Forenames. .... Surname ....
2. Address: Number .... Street ....
   Town... County..
   Postcode ....
3. Date of Birth: Day............Month............Year............
4. Details of current bank account: Bank ....
   Branch.. Sort code ....
   Account Number. ....
   (If none write "NONE")
5. Amount required for loan: £...................................
6. Purpose of loan: ....
   ....
7. Current Employer: ....
   ....

8. Employer's address: Street..
Town... County...
Postcode ....

9. What is your gross annual salary?
Up to £5,000 ❐ £5,001 to £10,000 ❐
£10,001 to £15,000 ❐ £15,001 to £20,000 ❐
£20,001 to £30,000 ❐ £30,001 to £40,000 ❐
Over £40,000 ❐

Classify the data which is likely to be collected by each of these questions into categorical, continuous, discrete or grouped.

■ Task 3.3 (with answers)

You have been given the following table of data by the personnel department of the company in which you work.

HELP
See *Section 2: The Information Bank*
Multiple bar charts: Unit 8.3, page 91

Employee Grades at BMK Office Services

	Managerial & professional grade employees	Supervisory grade employees	Junior grade employees
Male	38	56	12
Female	17	14	89

Source: Personnel Department 199-

Draw two diagrams using all this data. The first should facilitate a comparison between males and females; the second should facilitate a comparison between grades of employees.

■ Task 3.4

The list below contains the responses from a sample of 50 managers who were asked "Does your employer provide you with a company car?" as part of a telephone survey. The survey was conducted last week by MJ Market Research Ltd.

HELP
See *Section 2: The Information Bank*
Types of data and tabulating data: Unit 7, page 81; Diagrams for categorical and discrete data: pie charts and pictograms: Unit 9, page 97

Y Y Y Y Y N N Y Y N
N Y Y Y N Y Y Y N N
N N N Y Y Y Y Y Y Y
Y Y Y N Y Y Y Y Y N
N Y Y Y Y Y Y N Y Y

Produce a frequency distribution from this data. Add an extra column (or row) to show the percentage in each category.

Illustrate this data using the most suitable form of diagram to show the relative proportions of responses.

■ Task 3.5

You work for a large museum. The number of visitors for each of the last 150 days has been automatically recorded by the turnstile (see below). However it is difficult to see at a glance what the pattern of visitors has been over this period. You therefore decide to construct a frequency distribution and graph the data.

> **HELP** See *Section 2: The Information Bank* Types of data and tabulating data: Unit 7, page 81; Diagrams for continuous and grouped discrete data: histograms and frequency polygons: Unit 10, page 102

1000	1075	2084	3014	3199	4258	3462	3078	2419	2686
2121	3422	2988	405	2612	2245	1402	2522	2718	4283
2943	2677	2152	2747	2826	2734	3341	2618	942	***25***
1521	2681	2945	1902	1985	2901	1757	3411	3006	1706
3061	370	3727	2313	2504	***4815***	3418	3267	2735	2553
3229	4110	2918	3667	592	2622	2731	2871	1835	4307
1304	3143	1921	2048	2529	3847	713	2851	2829	3402
2191	2713	3155	1314	2687	3641	2424	2924	3727	1463
2827	2243	2114	3194	3278	2455	3229	3328	2593	3401
893	4003	3143	2615	2595	2617	2857	1809	2822	2133
1918	3687	501	3232	1772	537	4703	2745	3741	3927
2903	3925	3715	1632	3888	2761	2147	2719	2287	989
1845	1647	2315	1873	3417	3247	2727	2418	2984	3766
2487	3458	3633	3902	2222	2623	214	2321	2683	1451
3319	2495	2105	3176	2589	2384	2830	2675	3443	3148

Construct a frequency distribution from the raw data using class widths of 500. (N.B. the lowest and the highest numbers of visitors are shown in bold and italics).

Illustrate this data using the most suitable form of diagram.

■ Task 3.6

You are employed as a financial consultant offering investment advice to clients. A client brings you three diagrams all of which she has taken from advertisements for competing life assurance companies. She asks you in which one of the three companies, if any, you would recommend her to invest a lump sum of £3,000. She tells you that she wishes to invest her money for a 10 year period.

> **HELP** See *Section 2: The Information Bank* Diagrams for categorical and discrete data: bar charts: Unit 8, page 88; Diagrams for continuous and grouped discrete data: histograms and frequency polygons: Unit 10, page 102

Examine each of the three diagrams (below) and list all the factors that make you wary of the message portrayed by each diagram.

Based on these factors provide a justified recommendation for your client.

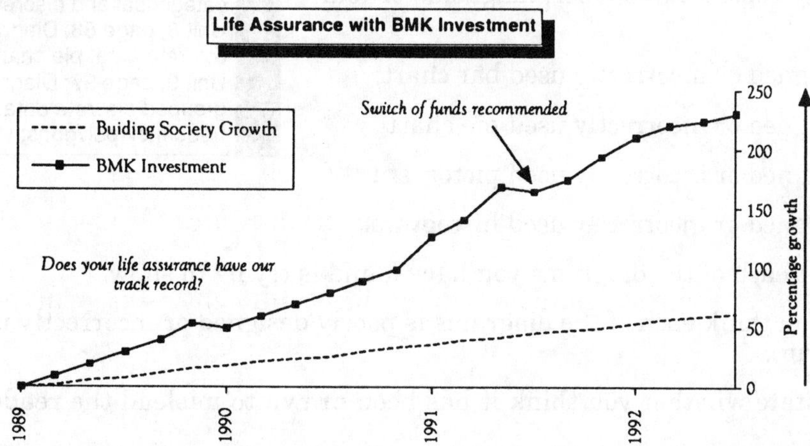

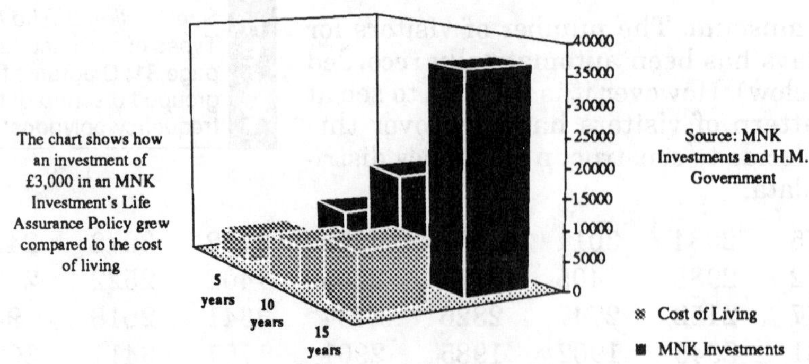

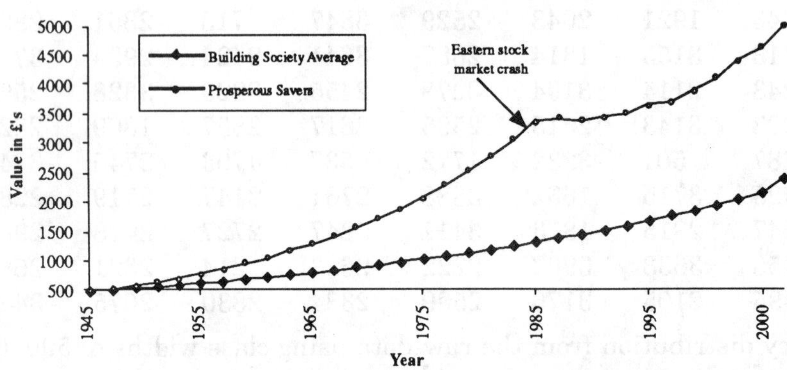

The data was prepared by a major financial consultant in the City of London

■ Assignment 3.1 (NVQ 4 M1 Unit 8.1h, i)

Find an example of a poorly designed table of data which has appeared in a company report, newspaper, magazine or journal.

HELP See *Section 2: The Information Bank* Data sources: Unit 3, page 61; Types of data and tabulating data: Unit 7 , page 81

List the reasons why this table of data is poorly designed and may be unsuitable as an aid to decision making.

What clues does this table provide about the validity and reliability of the data it contains?

■ Assignment 3.2 (NVQ 4 M1 Unit 8.1h, i)

Find one example of each of the following which has appeared in a company report, newspaper, magazine or journal:

- a poorly designed or incorrectly used bar chart;
- a poorly designed or incorrectly used pie chart;
- a poorly designed or incorrectly used pictogram;
- a poorly designed or incorrectly used histogram.

HELP See *Section 2: The Information Bank* Data sources: Unit 3, page 61; Diagrams for categorical and discrete data: bar charts: Unit 8, page 88; Diagrams for categorical and discrete data: pie charts and pictograms: Unit 9, page 97; Diagrams for continuous and grouped discrete data: histograms and frequency polygons: Unit 10, page 102

Briefly explain what each of the diagrams you have found is trying to show.

Give reasons why you think each of the diagrams is poorly designed or incorrectly used (in other words in an unsuitable form).

For each diagram state whether you think it has been drawn to mislead the reader and give reasons for your answer.

■ **Assignment 3.3** (NVQ 4 M1 Unit 8.1f, h, i)

Select a table of data from a company report, newspaper, magazine or journal. This might, for example, be data on company profits over the past 5 years.

Draw two diagrams to represent all or part of this data. The first should illustrate the data in the most favourable light, the second should illustrate the data in the least favourable light. (N.B. your diagrams need not be drawn correctly).

HELP: See *Section 2: The Information Bank* Types of data and tabulating data: Unit 7, page 81; Diagrams for categorical and discrete data: bar charts: Unit 8, page 88; Diagrams for categorical and discrete data: pie charts and pictograms: Unit 9, page 97; Diagrams for continuous and grouped discrete data: histograms and frequency polygons: Unit 10, page 102

Write a brief commentary explaining the techniques you have used to illustrate the data in the most favourable and least favourable light.

Summarise those aspects of your diagrams where you feel a reader would need to seek clarification and assistance to understand what was being shown.

Topic 4: Measures of central tendency

USING A COMPUTER SPREADSHEET FOR TOPIC 4 TASKS AND ASSIGNMENTS

Tasks 4.1, 4.2, 4.3 and 4.4 and assignment 4.2 can either be undertaken by hand or using a computer spreadsheet. The calculations for these tasks and the assignment are, with practice, quicker and less prone to error using a spreadsheet. The spreadsheet also enables you to achieve very high quality diagrams where necessary. For task 4.1 you will either need to use a either calculator or a computer spreadsheet to work out the nth root as part of the calculation.

■ **Task 4.1**

The annual rates of return for money invested in two expanding offshore companies for each of the past five years are:

Good Return: 6.9%, 7.8%, 9.3%, 7.7%, 8.8%
Safe n' Sure: 7.8%, 6.7%, 11.2%, 8.4%, 8.1%

HELP: See *Section 2: The Information Bank* Measures of central tendency: means: Unit 11, page 109

Calculate the average rate of return for each of these companies.

Which company has the best average rate of return over the past five years?

■ **Task 4.2** (with answers)

A holiday company wishes to promote a resort for all year "beach" holidays. As part of this promotion you have been asked to examine the following monthly climate data for the resort:

HELP: See *Section 2: The Information Bank* The arithmetic mean from raw data: Unit 11.2, page 109; The median from raw data: Unit 12.1, page 116; The mode: Unit 12.4, page 119

Month	**Jan**	**Feb**	**Mar**	**Apr**	**May**	**Jun**
Temperature (°C)	13	14	16	19	21	23
Rainfall (mm)	50	23	10	1	1	1
Month	**Jul**	**Aug**	**Sep**	**Oct**	**Nov**	**Dec**
Temperature (°C)	24	25	24	22	20	17
Rainfall (mm)	1	1	1	3	15	54

Calculate the mean, median and modal temperature and rainfall for the resort.

Which average for each of temperature and rainfall would you choose to promote the resort for all year "beach" holidays.

■ Task 4.3

You are the personnel manager of a company with three similar production facilities. You are concerned that the salary budgets in some of these production facilities may be over target. The target salary budget for each production facility is £3,750 per week. All the employees are paid between £100 and £200 per week, the actual amount being determined by responsibility. This means that the distribution of each facility's salaries should be positively skewed.

HELP See *Section 2: The Information Bank* Measures of central tendency: means: Unit 11, page 109; Measures of central tendency: medians and modes: Unit 12, page 116

Identify which of the production facilities' salary budgets are over target.

Calculate the mean and median for salary for each of the three production facilities.

Based on these figures state why some production facilities' salary budgets are over target.

Salaries at each production facility in £'s

Lancaster	Preston	Blackpool
115	141	196
143	134	186
197	180	180
100	187	178
196	177	109
106	191	111
122	100	179
125	130	175
195	132	100
111	135	185
125	175	179
193	106	116
113	114	182
125	100	102
128	133	200
198	171	119
178	189	182
125	198	114
134	194	198
130	130	184
190	115	195
193	199	105
198	104	200
110	190	120
200	125	122

Source: Personnel Department 199-

■ Task 4.4

A clothing company has 100 machinists sewing shirts. The number of shirts sewn by each machinist over a day is recorded in the table below. The production manager wants to record the average number of shirts sewn using as high a number as possible.

HELP See *Section 2: The Information Bank* Measures of central tendency: means: Unit 11, page 109; Measures of central tendency: medians and modes: Unit 12, page 116

Calculate the mean, median and modal group of shirts sewn by a machinist in a day.

Which average would the production manager use?

Frequency Distribution of Shirts Sewn in a Day

Number of shirts sewn	Number of machinists
111 – 115	1
116 – 120	3
121 – 125	7
126 – 130	14
131 – 135	27
136 – 140	16
141 – 145	12
146 – 150	11
151 – 155	9

Source: Production Department 199-

■ Assignment 4.1 (NVQ 4 M1 Unit 8.1 h, j)

Examine company reports, national newspapers, journals or other business publications.

HELP See *Section 2: The Information Bank* Types of data and tabulating data: Unit 7, page 81; Measures of central tendency: means: Unit 11, page 109; Measures of central tendency: medians and modes: Unit 12, page 116

Find at least one example for each of three of the following:

- arithmetic mean
- median
- mode
- geometric mean
- harmonic mean

For each example state the type of data for which it has been calculated, and the conclusion(s) drawn from its use in the publication.

Assess the validity of the conclusions drawn and the suitability of the particular average for the data.

■ Assignment 4.2 (NVQ 4 M1 Unit 8.1 i, j)

Select a table of data from a company report, newspaper, magazine or journal. This might, for example, be data on a company's sales over the past 15 years.

HELP See *Section 2: The Information Bank* Data sources: Unit 3, page 61; Types of data and tabulating data: Unit 7, page 81; Measures of central tendency: means: Unit 11, page 109; Measures of central tendency: medians and modes: Unit 12, page 116

Calculate the most suitable measure of central tendency for the data selected.

Justify your choice of measure of central tendency in terms of the type of the data and what you are trying to show.

What do you conclude from your calculations (give reasons for your conclusion)?

Topic 5: Measures of dispersion

USING A COMPUTER SPREADSHEET FOR TOPIC 5 TASKS AND ASSIGNMENTS

Tasks 5.1, 5.2, 5.3 and 5.4 and assignment 5.1 can either be undertaken by hand or using a computer spreadsheet. The calculations for these tasks and the assignment are, with practice, quicker and less prone to error using a spreadsheet. In addition you will be able to achieve very high quality diagrams where required.

■ Task 5.1 (with answers)

A national company is thinking about relocating their head offices due to high rental of their current property. As part of this relocation they are interested in the rent of commercial property per square foot. They telephone commercial lettings' agencies in three areas and obtain a range of rentals for each area.

HELP See *Section 2: The Information Bank* Principles of good tabulation: Unit 7.3, page 82; The median from raw data: Unit 12.1, page 116; The mode: Unit 12.4, page 119; The upper and lower quartiles and the inter-quartile range from raw data: Unit 13.3, page 124

Calculate the median, quartiles and inter-quartile range for each of the three areas.

Summarise your findings in a table.

How would you advise the company on the basis of these findings?

Give reasons for your answer.

Southam:	£4.89	£7.20	£9.50	£13.25	£13.00
	£10.40	£10.93	£5.87	£11.04	£11.40
	£11.80	£15.92	£9.36	£5.98	£7.37
	£6.98	£11.10	£7.40	£8.65	£7.80
	£10.34	£8.82			
Northam:	£12.09	£13.67	£14.99	£11.89	£12.34
	£14.99	£12.69	£13.27	£12.86	£13.14
	£13.78	£12.50	£12.90	£14.65	£14.59
	£12.87	£14.21			
Westham:	£10.70	£12.71	£9.75	£10.90	£11.99
	£7.40	£11.99	£8.70	£6.99	£7.44
	£9.97	£9.53	£8.28	£9.71	£10.57
	£10.60	£8.09	£10.40	£7.20	£9.99
	£6.59				

■ Task 5.2

The table below records the number of employees in different salary bands for three departments in a company.

HELP See *Section 2: The Information Bank* Measures of central tendency: means: Unit 11, page 109; Measures of central tendency: medians and modes: Unit 12, page 116; Measures of dispersion: ranges, quartiles, deciles and percentiles: Unit 13, page 123

Calculate the mean, median and the inter-quartile range of the salaries for each department.

What do these statistics tell you about variability in salaries between departments?

Salary Band of Employees in 3 departments

Salary band	Admin. Dept.	Marketing Dept.	Sales Dept.
£6,000 – < £8,000	3	0	6
£8,000 – < £10,000	5	1	5
£10,000 – < £12,000	3	1	3
£12,000 – < £14,000	2	2	1
£14,000 – < £16,000	1	1	1
£16,000 – < £18,000	0	1	1
£18,000 – < £20,000	0	0	1

Source: Personnel Section, Admin. Department 199-

■ Task 5.3

A clothing company has 100 machinists sewing shirts. The number of shirts sewn by each machinist over a day is recorded in the table below. The manager hears that 95% of a rival company's machinists sew between 116 and 145 shirts a day.

HELP See *Section 2: The Information Bank* Measures of central tendency: means: Unit 11, page 109; Measures of dispersion: variance, standard deviation and coefficient of variation: Unit 14, page 129

Frequency Distribution of Shirts Sewn in a Day

Number of shirts sewn	Number of machinists
111 – 115	5
116 – 120	7
121 – 125	10
126 – 130	15
131 – 135	29
136 – 140	16
141 – 145	11
146 – 150	5
151 – 155	2

Source: Production Department 199-

Using the data in the table calculate the mean and the standard deviation for the number of shirts sewn.

Is the number of shirts sewn by machinists in this clothing company more or less variable than the number sewn in rival company?

■ Task 5.4

You work in the computer section of a large department and are responsible for the service contract for the department's personal computers. The three companies that have tendered all have quoted an average call out time of 24 hours. In order to check this statement you ask the companies to send you details of the actual call out times for their last 15 visits.

HELP See *Section 2: The Information Bank* Measures of central tendency: means: Unit 11, page 109; Measures of dispersion: ranges, quartiles, deciles and percentiles: Unit 13, page 123; Measures of dispersion: variance, standard deviation and coefficient of variation: Unit 14, page 129

Compuquick:	24	11	20	23	24	25	19	13	37	33
	25	25	27	29	25					
PC Repairs:	20	24	21	24	24	28	22	23	24	24
	27	23	25	26	25					
Kwik Chip:	23	25	24	22	23	24	25	26	24	23
	24	24	25	24	24					

Check the claimed mean call out time for each company.

Calculate the most suitable measures of dispersion to establish which company has the greatest and which company has the least variation in call out time. (N.B. you can assume the data is normally distributed.)

To which company would you award the contract?

Give reasons for your answer.

■ **Assignment 5.1** (NVQ 4 M1 Unit 8.1i, j)

Select a table of quantitative data from a company report, newspaper, magazine or journal. This might, for example, be data on the number of employees at a company over the past 15 years.

Calculate the most suitable measures of central tendency and dispersion for the data selected.

Justify your choice of measures of central tendency and dispersion in terms of the characteristics of the data and what you are trying to show.

What do you conclude from your calculations (give reasons for your conclusion)?

HELP
See *Section 2: The Information Bank*
Data sources: Unit 3, page 61; Measures of central tendency: means: Unit 11, page 109; Measures of central tendency: medians and modes: Unit 12, page 116; Measures of dispersion: ranges, quartiles, deciles and percentiles: Unit 13, page 123; Measures of dispersion: variance, standard deviation and coefficient of variation: Unit 14, page 129

Topic 6: Time Series

USING A COMPUTER SPREADSHEET FOR TOPIC 6 TASKS AND ASSIGNMENTS

Tasks 6.1, 6.2 and 6.3 and assignment 6.2 can either be undertaken by hand or using a computer spreadsheet. The calculations for these tasks and the assignment are, with practice, quicker and less prone to error using a spreadsheet. In addition you will be able to achieve very high quality diagrams where required.

■ **Task 6.1** (with answers)

The table below records the output in millions of tonnes from a stone quarry. The new owner of the quarry is worried as output in 1992 was at a lower level than in 1991. He has asked you to work out what the overall trend in output has been over the period 1981 – 1992.

HELP
See *Section 2: The Information Bank*
Determining the trend: moving averages: Unit 15.3, page 144

Quarry Output 1981 – 1992

Year	Output in million tonnes	Year	Output in million tonnes
1981	11	1987	13
1982	15	1988	18
1983	8	1989	11
1984	11	1990	15
1985	16	1991	18
1986	9	1992	11

Source: Company Statistical Returns

Determine the trend in output using a three period and a five period moving average.

Plot the raw data, the three year moving average and the five year moving average on the same diagram.

Describe the trend.

Which of the two moving averages is better for determining the trend for this data? Give one reason for your answer.

■ Task 6.2

Your local coal merchant has achieved the following sales of sacks of coal over the past three and a half years:

HELP See *Section 2: The Information Bank* Time series: variations and moving average: Unit 15, page 141; Times series: forecasting and seasonal variation: Unit 16, page 149

Sales of Sacks of Coal by Gormeley's Coal Merchants 1990 – 1993

Year	Quarter	Sacks sold
1990	Jan – Mar	2,840
	Apr – June	1,080
	Jul – Sept	3,240
	Oct – Dec	4,120
1991	Jan – Mar	2,600
	Apr – June	1,000
	Jul – Sept	3,480
	Oct – Dec	3,960
1992	Jan – Mar	2,520
	Apr – June	840
	Jul – Sept	3,240
	Oct – Dec	3,720
1993	Jan – Mar	2,440
	Apr – June	800

Source: Gormeley's Coal Merchants

Determine the trend in output using an appropriate period moving average.

Plot the raw data and the moving average on the same diagram.

Calculate the average variation per quarter.

What is the long term trend?

■ Task 6.3

You have been asked to forecast sales of swim wear for the remaining quarters of 1993 and all of 1994 for a local sportswear shop using seasonal variation.

HELP See *Section 2: The Information Bank* Time series: variations and moving averages: Unit 15, page 141; Times series: forecasting and seasonal variation: Unit 16, page 149

Using the data in the table below undertake this forecast.

Illustrate the actual and forecast sales 1989 – 1994 using the most suitable diagram.

Sales of Swim wear 1989 – 1993

Year	Quarter	Sales
1989	1	37
	2	62
	3	79
	4	42
1990	1	35
	2	58
	3	77
	4	47
1991	4	41
	2	63
	3	75
	4	41
1992	1	33
	2	57
	3	79
	4	44
1993	1	35

Source: Sales Receipts

■ **Assignment 6.1** (NVQ 4 M1 Unit 8.1d, g)

Select a report for a particular company, government department, or a market research report for a particular product sector, or some other appropriate source of trend data.

HELP

See *Section 2: The Information Bank*
Data sources: Unit 3, page 61; Time series: variations and moving averages: Unit 15, page 141

Examine your trend data and identify examples of each of the following trend features:

- long term trend;
- seasonal variations;
- cyclical fluctuations;
- residual influences.

■ **Assignment 6.2** (NVQ 4 M1 Unit 8.1d, i, j)

Obtain a time series of data from a company report for a particular company or some other business publication over at least 15 periods. (Examples of such data would include the number of unemployed from the *Employment Gazette* or the values of the FT S-E 100 as recorded daily in the *Financial Times*.)

HELP

See *Section 2: The Information Bank*
Data sources: Unit 3, page 61; Types of data and tabulating data: Unit 7, page 81; Time series: variations and moving averages: Unit 15, page 141; Times series: forecasting and seasonal variation: Unit 16, page 149

Record this data as a table.

Plot the raw data using the most suitable form of diagram.

Determine the trend and forecast seasonally adjusted future data values for the next three periods.

What conclusions do you draw from your forecast (give reasons for your conclusion)?

Topic 7: Relationships between variables

USING A COMPUTER FOR TOPIC 7 TASKS AND ASSIGNMENTS

Tasks 7.1, 7.2, 7.3, 7.4, and 7.5 and assignments 7.1, 7.2 and 7.3 can either be done by hand or using a computer spreadsheet. The calculations for these tasks and assignments are, with practice, quicker and less prone to error using a spreadsheet. The spreadsheet will also enable you to achieve very high quality diagrams (needed for tasks 7.1, 7.2, 7.3 and assignments 7.1, 7.2).

■ Task 7.1 (with answers)

A recent survey asked car purchasers to rank 15 features of a car in order of importance to them. The results of two customer groups (young males and retired females) are shown in the table below.

See *Section 2: The Information Bank* Spearman's rank correlation: Unit 17.3, page 157

Importance of Features to Car Purchasers

Feature	Young males	Retired females
85% recyclable	15th	3rd
Acceleration	2nd	14th
Boot size	7th	6th equal
Catalytic converter	12th	5th
Depreciation	9th	2nd
Driver's air bag	13th	4th
Driving enjoyment	1st	10th
Fuel economy	14th	1st
Handling and ride	3rd	13th
Insurance costs	4th	8th
Metallic paint	10th	15th
Price	5th	11th
Quality and equipment	6th	12th
Rear doors	11th	9th
Servicing costs	8th	6th equal

Source: Survey of Car Purchasers 199-

Illustrate the relationship between the variables using a suitable diagram.

What does this diagram suggest about the relationship between the requirements of the two customer groups?

Calculate and interpret a correlation coefficient.

■ Task 7.2

The reaction times of 24 drivers were tested by a research programme after they had consumed varying amounts of alcohol. The results are recorded in the table below.

See *Section 2: The Information Bank* Relationships between variables: regression: Unit 18, page 163

Units of Alcohol Consumed and Reaction Time (Raw Data) 199-

Alcohol units consumed	0	1	2	3	4	5	6	7	8	9	10
Reaction time in seconds	0.14 0.19 0.23	0.23	0.33 0.45	0.41 0.59	0.35 0.58 0.71	0.69	0.74 0.80 0.91	0.80 0.93	0.99 1.21	1.15 1.16	1.09 1.25 1.30

Source: Drivers' Research Ltd

Illustrate the relationship between the variables using a suitable diagram.

What does this diagram suggest about the relationship between units of alcohol consumed and reaction time?

Calculate the regression equation for the data.

By how much would a driver's reaction time increase if the driver had drunk 8 units as opposed to 3 units of alcohol?

Calculate and interpret the regression coefficient for the data.

■ Task 7.3

You have been asked to conduct an investigation into the impact of speed of working on number of faulty products ("waste") on a production line. The Work Study Unit have collected data on the number of items produced and the number of items which are faulty and therefore classified as "waste" for a sample of 11 workers. These are recorded in the table below.

HELP See *Section 2: The Information Bank* Relationships between variables: correlation: Unit 17, page 155; Relationships between variables: regression: Unit 18, page 163

Total Items and Waste Items Produced an Hour

Worker	Total items produced an hour	Waste items produced an hour
George	94	4
Eric	98	5
Stephen	106	6
Martin	114	7
Mark	107	6
Mike	93	5
Antony	98	6
Pete	87	4
Simon	95	5
Jake	103	7
Dave	79	3

Source: Sample Survey by Quality Control 199-

Illustrate the relationship between the variables using a suitable diagram.

What does this diagram suggest about the relationship between speed of working and "waste"?

Calculate and interpret a correlation coefficient for the data.

Calculate the regression equation for the data.

How many waste items would be produced if a worker produced 100 items an hour?

■ Task 7.4

A random sample of 1000 shoppers leaving a hypermarket were asked which washing powder they used. The results were:

> **HELP** See *Section 2: The Information Bank* Testing for significance: the chi square test: Unit 19, page 168

Powder	Frequency
Zad	187
Ecological Blue	221
Softerwash	193
Sunshine White	204
Blanco	195
Total	**1000**

You have been asked whether the shoppers have displayed any significant preference in their use of washing powder.

State your null hypothesis and hypothesis.

Calculate a chi square statistic using the appropriate method. Is there a significant preference in washing powder choice?

■ Task 7.5

A group of people were asked whether they intended to visit the new local theme park. Their responses were as follows:

> **HELP** See *Section 2: The Information Bank* Testing for significance: the chi square test: Unit 19, page 168

Gender	Yes	No	Don't know
Female	118	62	25
Male	82	78	35

You have been asked whether there was any significant difference in intentions between males and females.

State your null hypothesis and hypothesis.

Calculate a chi square statistic using the appropriate method. Was there a significant difference between the genders in their intentions?

■ Task 7.6

You work for a national company selling domestic televisions, satellite dishes, videos and photographic goods. Recently they commissioned research into consumer preferences by a reputable market research organisation. Initial results (see below) from a quota sample of 500 people have been received. You have been asked to summarise these results and their implications for your company's future advertising policy by the next board meeting.

> **HELP** See *Section 2: The Information Bank* Relationships between variables: correlation: Unit 17, page 155; Testing for significance: the chi square test: Unit 19, page 168

Produce a summary of the results below (N.B. in some cases you will need to state hypotheses and complete the calculations).

List the likely implications of these results for your company's future advertising policy.

Market Research Report:
Technical Summary of Initial Results

Correlations:

number of hours spent watching satellite programmes and number of hours spent watching television programmes — r = -0.831 (n = 142);

number of hours spent watching pre recorded video cassettes and annual income — r = 0.237 (n = 243);

number of hours spent watching television and annual income — r = -0.659 (n = 489).

Chi square test tables:

Newspaper read	Intend to purchase a satellite dish	Do not intend to purchase a satellite dish
Tabloid Express	38	27
Daily Reflector	33	22
The Moon	45	13
The Daily Quality	12	38
The Daily Messenger	21	57

Chi square of 51.60.

Number of satellite dishes	Upper income band	Middle income band	Lower income band
0	13	43	29
1	11	65	77

Chi square of 7.57.

■ Assignment 7.1 (NVQ 4 M1 Unit 8.1d, h, i, j)

HELP See *Section 2: The Information Bank* Data sources: Unit 3, page 61; Types of data and tabulating data: Unit 7, page 81; Relationships between variables: correlation: Unit 17, page 155

Find or create a table which contains quantitative data on two variables which you feel might be related. You will probably find the data for such a table in a company report, newspaper, magazine or journal. This might, for example, be data on sales of two similar products at a number of different outlets, or data on number of employees and annual turnover for a series of firms.

Record your data as a table.

Draw the most suitable diagram to represent the relationship between the variables and describe the relationship it suggests.

Calculate a correlation coefficient.

What do you conclude about the strength of the relationship (give reasons for your conclusion)?

■ Assignment 7.2 (NVQ 4 M1 Unit 8.1d, h, i, j)

HELP See *Section 2: The Information Bank* Data sources: Unit 3, page 61; Types of data and tabulating data: Unit 7, page 81; Relationships between variables: correlation: Unit 17, page 155; Relationships between variables: regression: Unit 18, page 163

Find or create a table which contains quantitative data on two variables where you feel the values of one variable are dependent upon the values of the other. You will probably find the data for such a table in a company report, newspaper, magazine or journal. The table might, for example, be data on daily sales of ice cream and daily temperature for a four week period; or number of employees and annual turnover for a number of companies.

Record your data as a table.

Draw the most suitable diagram to represent the relationship between the variables and describe the relationship it suggests.

Calculate a regression equation and use this to predict two other values of the dependent variable.

Calculate the coefficient of determination.

What do you conclude about the strength of the relationship (give reasons for your conclusion)?

■ Assignment 7.3 (NVQ 4 M1 Unit 8.1d, h, i, j)

> **HELP** See *Section 2: The Information Bank* Data sources: Unit 3, page 61; Types of data and tabulating data: Unit 7, page 81; Testing for significance: the chi square test: Unit 19, page 168

Find or create a cross tabulation which contains categorical data on two variables. You will probably find data for such a table in a company report, newspaper, magazine or journal. This might for example be a table of gender by voting intention at the next election; or second car ownership by social class.

Record your data as a table.

Examine the table and state your null hypothesis and hypothesis.

Calculate a chi square statistic.

What do you conclude about the relationship between the two variables (give reasons for your conclusion)?

Topic 8: Index Numbers

USING A COMPUTER FOR TOPIC 8 TASKS AND ASSIGNMENTS

Tasks 8.1, 8.2, 8.3 and 8.4 and assignments 8.1 and 8.2 can either be undertaken by hand or using a computer spreadsheet. The calculations for these tasks and assignments are, with practice, quicker and less prone to error using a spreadsheet. A spreadsheet will enable you to achieve very high quality diagrams (needed for task 8.1 and assignment 8.1).

■ Task 8.1

> **HELP** See *Section 2: The Information Bank* Index numbers using one item: quantity and price indices, value indices: Unit 20, page 174

You work for a local authority education department and have been asked to compare the forecast growth in pre-school and school age population for your local authority with that of the region. The authority's education officer has told you that he is interested in 3 different age groups:

- pre-school (0 – 4)
- primary school (5 – 11)
- secondary school (12 – 16)

Using the data in the table below calculate the index numbers for the local authority and the region for the period 1991 – 2001 for each of the age groups using 1991 as the base period.

Present the index numbers for the local authority and the region on three separate graphs, one for each of the age groups.

Summarise the relative trends for the local authority and the region for each of the age groups over the period 1991 – 2001.

Population for 3 Age Groups – Local Authority (LA) and Region

Year	0 – 4 LA	0 – 4 Region	5 – 11 LA	5 – 11 Region	12 – 16 LA	12 – 16 Region
1991	7900	57000	15100	94300	8200	63200
1992	7500	56800	14800	95700	8500	64800
1993	7300	53300	14300	97000	8800	66000
1994	7000	52500	14000	98500	9100	67300
1995	6600	51100	13800	99700	9400	68300
1996	7000	49000	13100	99400	9900	69300
1997	7400	46200	12800	96700	9500	70400
1998	7800	49000	12300	91900	9100	73200
1999	7900	51800	11600	89400	8800	71000
2000	8000	54600	12200	85700	8300	69100
2001	8200	55300	12800	82000	8700	65600

Source: Local Authority Planning Department and Regional Forum 199-

■ Task 8.2

You work for an investment analyst and have been asked which of two factories have performed the best over the period 1989 – 1992 in terms of:

- quantity of production;
- value of production.

HELP See *Section 2: The Information Bank* Index numbers using one item: quantity and price indices, value indices: Unit 20, page 174

The data is given in the table below:

Units Produced and Unit Prices for Two Factories 1989 – 1992

Factory		1989	1990	1991	1992
Bottles Ltd	Units produced	10,000	12,000	13,000	14,000
	Unit price	£0.25	£0.30	£0.40	£0.50
Cars Ltd	Units produced	500	650	800	900
	Unit price	£10,000	£11,000	£12,000	£13,000

Source: Market Information Report

Use the appropriate index numbers to determine the answers to these two questions.

■ Task 8.3 (with answers)

You work for a clothing shop. Your manager tells you that the quantity of items sold in the shop has declined over the past 3 years and he is thinking of closing the shop. You feel that he has only taken the actual number of items into account and not their relative prices. You decide to investigate further by comparing the quantity purchased three years ago with current quantities for typical weeks. The data you wish to use is given below:

HELP See *Section 2: The Information Bank* Laspeyre's volume index: Unit 21.6, page 184; Paasche's volume index: Unit 21.7, page 185

Purchase	Unit price (3 years ago)	Unit price (now)	Quantity purchased (3 years ago)	Quantity purchased (now)
Vests	£4.80	£7.30	40	32
Underpants	£0.80	£1.90	75	60
Boxer shorts	£6.40	£8.50	30	45
Hankies	£1.90	£2.10	12	11
Ties	£8.10	£9.50	12	11
Shirts	£9.80	£12.60	20	19
Trousers	£14.00	£17.00	11	10

Calculate the total number of items sold for each of the typical weeks. Is the manager correct?

Calculate a base weighted and a current weighted volume index.

Which of these two indices do you feel is most appropriate to an argument that the shop be kept open. Give at least one reason for your answer.

■ Task 8.4

You are preparing an advertising campaign on behalf of a building societies' trade association to try and persuade people to buy houses. The campaign is intended to target all types of house buyer throughout the United Kingdom. You have been given data on the average price of houses for the past twelve years and an index of retail prices for these years (see below).

> **HELP** See *Section 2: The Information Bank* Index numbers: chain based index, splicing indices, deflating a series: Unit 22, page 187

Average House Prices and Index of Prices 1981 – 1992

Year	Average House Price	Index of Prices
1981	£25,100	86
1982	£26,500	95
1983	£27,300	100
1984	£30,800	105
1985	£34,100	111
1986	£37,500	116
1987	£39,100	121
1988	£51,600	125
1989	£73,400	135
1990	£84,300	145
1991	£68,400	158
1992	£67,600	167

Source: A Building Societies' Trade Association

Deflate the average prices of houses to 1983 prices.

Plot the deflated price data on the most suitable diagram.

Devise a short informative piece of text to persuade people to buy houses which makes use of your calculations (no more than one paragraph in length).

■ **Assignment 8.1** (NVQ 4 M1 Unit 8.1i, j)

> **HELP** See *Section 2: The Information Bank* Data sources: Unit 3, page 61; Types of data and tabulating data: Unit 7, page 81; Index numbers using one item: quantity and price indices, value indices: Unit 20, page 174

Obtain a series of data from a company report for a particular company or some other business publication over at least 10 equal width time periods. (Examples of such data would include a company's profits for successive years, the number of houses sold by an estate agency chain for successive months or the estimated population of a county for successive years.)

Record your data as a table.

Calculate either a price or a quantity index (as appropriate) using the first time period as the base.

Plot the index numbers on the most suitable diagram.

Draw conclusions based on reasoned argument from what your diagram shows.

■ **Assignment 8.2** (NVQ 4 M1 Unit 8.1c, f, i, j)

> **HELP** See *Section 2: The Information Bank* Data sources: Unit 3, page 61; Types of data and tabulating data: Unit 7, page 81; Index numbers: chain based index, splicing indices, deflating a series: Unit 22, page 187

Obtain a series of price data over at least a ten year period from a market research report, government report, or some other business publication. (For example the price of a company's shares or the price of a litre of leaded petrol).

Record your data as a table.

Deflate these prices to take account of inflation using the Retail Price Index (one possible source is the *Employment Gazette*).

Draw conclusions from your calculations about the changes in real terms of prices.

Topic 9: Probability

■ **Task 9.1**

> **HELP** See *Section 2: The Information Bank* Theoretical and empirical probability: Unit 23, page 191

A company bids for a small, a medium and a large cleaning contract, each with a separate firm. The manager knows the number of previously successful bids for each of these type of contracts. These are shown on the computer print-out below.

CONTRACT TYPE	NUMBER SUCCESSFUL BIDS	NUMBER UNSUCCESSFUL BIDS
LARGE CLEANING	21	84
MEDIUM CLEANING	33	100
SMALL CLEANING	55	125

He wishes to know the probability of:

- winning the small cleaning contract;
- winning the medium cleaning contract;
- winning the large cleaning contract;
- winning both the small and the medium cleaning contracts.

Calculate the probabilities for each of these events.

■ Task 9.2

The quality control department of a refrigerator manufacturing company keeps a record of the number of faults found in refrigerators. These are shown in the table below:

HELP See *Section 2: The Information Bank* Theoretical and empirical probability: Unit 23, page 191

Number of Faults with Refrigerators

Number of faults	0	1	2	3	4	5 plus
Number of refrigerators	98,280	760	340	290	230	100

Source: Quality Control Department 199-

Use this information to calculate the probability that:

- a refrigerator has no faults;
- a refrigerator has between 1 and 3 faults (inclusive);
- a refrigerator has 4 or more faults.

What is the probability that a refrigerator checked by the quality control department will have at least 1 fault?

If the quality control department checks 1,500 refrigerators each week how many refrigerators with at least one fault are they likely to find in a (52 week) year?

■ Task 9.3

A Burger Bar offers free gifts with its children's meals. The current promotion provides one of four possible dinosaur gifts free with each meal. 100 free gifts are placed in the free gift box by the wholesaler. In each box he puts:

HELP See *Section 2: The Information Bank* Theoretical and empirical probability: Unit 23, page 191

- 40 Stegosauruses
- 30 Pterodactyls
- 20 Diplodocuses
- 10 Brontosauruses

A free gift is then chosen at random from the box by the member of counter staff selling the meal.

What is the probability that a child receives a Stegosaurus or a Diplodocus from a new box of free gifts?

If the first five free gifts from a new box are three Brontosauruses, one Pterodactyl and one Diplodocus what is the probability that the next child receives a Stegosaurus or a Diplodocus from the same box?

■ Task 9.4 (answers provided)

A small cafe owner expects the sales of cups of tea on market day to follow the pattern shown below:

HELP See *Section 2: The Information Bank* Expectation: Unit 24.2, page 197

Sales	0	50	100	150	200
Probability	0.1	0.2	0.4	0.2	0.1

The ingredients for each cup of tea costs him 6p, and he sells each cup of tea for 30p. At the end of the day he has to throw away any unused milk, this costs him 4p for each cup of tea.

The cafe owner is unsure whether to purchase sufficient ingredients for 200 or 150 cups of tea and asks you for help.

Calculate his expected profit for tea on market day if he buys sufficient ingredients for:

- 200 cups of tea;
- 150 cups of tea.

How would you advise the cafe owner?

■ Task 9.5

HELP: See *Section 2: The Information Bank* Expectation and conditional probability: Unit 24, page 196

A charter flight company has an exclusive contract with a hotel local to the airport. The charter flight company uses this hotel for passengers whose flights are going to be delayed over night and who live more than half an hour's drive from the airport. Company records show that 20% of passengers live within half an hour's drive of the airport. So far this year each flight has carried a full complement of 80 passengers. Only 2 of the 100 flights this year have been delayed over night.

How many passengers have had their flights delayed over night so far this year?

How many passengers have stayed at the hotel so far this year because of flights being delayed over night?

What is the probability of a passenger's flight being delayed over night?

What is the probability of a passenger's flight being delayed over night and them staying at the hotel?

Given that a passenger's flight was delayed over night, what is the probability that they stayed at the hotel?

■ Task 9.6

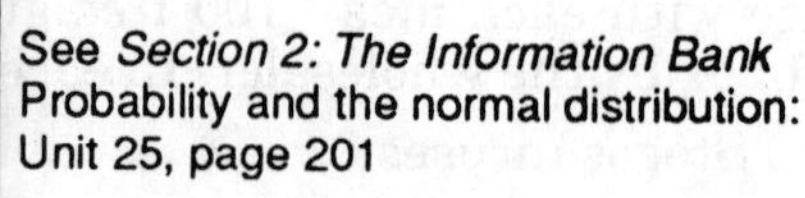
HELP: See *Section 2: The Information Bank* Probability and the normal distribution: Unit 25, page 201

You work for a manufacturing company making matches. The average content of each box is advertised as 30. However recently the Trading Standards Office have informed you of a series of complaints that there are fewer than 30 matches in each box. You decide to sample 1000 boxes of matches from your production line and discover that the average (mean) contents of each box is 33 with a standard deviation of 1.3.

The Trading Standards Office have told you that if the average contents of your match box falls below that stated for more than 1% of boxes, then you will have to withdraw your matches from the shops.

Calculate the probability that there are 29 or less matches in each box.

Will you have to withdraw the matches from shops?

■ Task 9.7

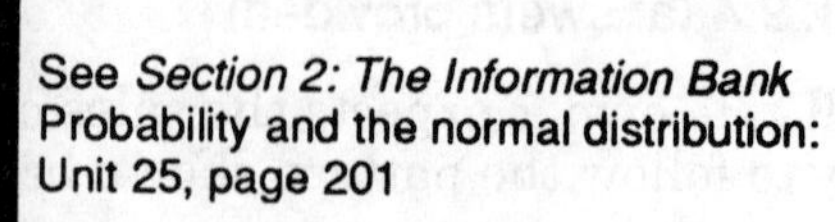
HELP: See *Section 2: The Information Bank* Probability and the normal distribution: Unit 25, page 201

The owner of Brown Lay Eggs has read in the Egg Producers Gazette that a new kind of feed increases the number of eggs laid by hens significantly. At present each hen lays an average (mean) of 8 eggs a week with a standard deviation of 1.5 eggs.

Having used the new diet on a random sample of 100 hens the owner finds that each hen now lays an average (mean) of 8.3 eggs.

Calculate the appropriate z score. Would you advise the owner of Brown Lay Eggs to change over to the new kind of feed?

■ **Assignment 9.1** (NVQ 4 M1 Unit 8.1b, i)

Obtain a set of sales data which divides sales by categories, either from a company report for a particular company or from a newspaper or some other business publication. (For example total sales of new cars by manufacturer over the past month).

HELP See *Section 2: The Information Bank*
Data sources: Unit 3, page 61; Types of data and tabulating data: Unit 7, page 81; Theoretical and empirical probability: Unit 23, page 191

Record your data as a table.

Calculate the probability of a sale being in each of the categories.

Are these events mutually exclusive?

Topic 10: Integrating assignments

Assignment 10.1 is written for students who are not following a competency based course of study; the second assignment (10.2) is written for students who are following a competency based course (programme) of study. Assignment 10.3 includes the data necessary for you to undertake the assignment; it can be used for either type of course.

USING A COMPUTER FOR TOPIC 10 ASSIGNMENTS

All assignments can be undertaken by hand or using a computer spreadsheet. It is likely that the calculations for all assignments (especially with large data sets such as 10.3) will with practice be quicker and less prone to error using a spreadsheet. The use of a spreadsheet for these assignments will also enable you to achieve very high quality diagrams where necessary.

■ Assignment 10.1

The purpose of this assignment is to provide you with the opportunity to put into practice a wide range of the techniques and skills you have developed during your course of study. In particular the assignment enables you to demonstrate your ability to apply data collection, analysis and presentation to an issue of your choice. You are recommended to allow at least three weeks for this piece of work.

Stage 1

Identify an area that is known to you which you would like to investigate. You may find the following questions useful in helping you to select a suitable area for investigation and in deciding the likely approach you will take:

1. what do you want to do? – Briefly describe what your investigation aims to find out;
2. how are you going to collect the data to find this out? – Briefly outline data collection methods – if you are using secondary data make sure it is available at this stage;
3. how are you going to present this data? – Briefly outline the likely diagrams and tables you are going to use;
4. how are you going to analyse this data? – Briefly outline the likely statistical techniques you are going to use.

Stage 2

Building upon Stage 1 produce a report that satisfies the assessment criteria given below.

Assessment Criteria

1. Your report should be between 1,500 and 2,000 words excluding diagrams, tables and appendices.
2. Your report must involve the collection of primary and/or secondary data and demonstrate understanding of the collection method(s). Where possible the raw data should be included in the appendices.
3. Your analysis and interpretation must make use of appropriate diagrams. When diagrams are used tables of base data must be included in the appendices.
4. Your analysis and interpretation must make use of appropriate statistical techniques. When statistical techniques are used the full working and raw data must be included in the appendices. If a computer spreadsheet is used there should be a printout showing cell values, and a printout showing cell formulae for each calculation.
5. You should note that a report that does not contain both graphs and statistical analysis is unlikely to be awarded a pass.

■ Assignment 10.2 (NVQ 4 M1 competencies as identified in bold)

The purpose of this assignment is to provide you with an opportunity to gather evidence of competence in the management of information. In particular the evidence produced in completing the assignment may contribute to your portfolio of evidence at NVQ level 4 (M1) for *Unit 8 Seek evaluate and organise information for managers* of the Occupational Standards for Managers.

In completing this assignment it is important that you use the knowledge and understanding you have gained by working through Sections 1 and 3 of this book and apply it, preferably to a real situation. Remember competent performance includes the demonstration of underpinning theories and techniques, in this case those applicable to Managing Information.

Your overall aim for this assignment is to present information which is organised into a suitable form to enable a decision to be made.

The task

1. Within an organisation, or situation with which you are familiar, identify a 'decision' which needs to be made. Preferably this should be 'real'. For example if your organisation is intending to purchase a new computer system then the 'decision' might be "which one will meet our needs?" If you have difficulty in finding a real 'decision' then you may use a simulation. For example, if there is no budget to purchase a computer you could still go through the process to decide which one to purchase if the finance were available.
2. Collect data to assist you in your decision making using techniques which you have covered in the book. For example in the case of the new computer system you could design a questionnaire to find views on what is required from a variety of sources within the organisation:

   i) Senior Managers (strategic view),

   ii) Middle managers (operational view),

   iii) Technical managers (specialist view). **(8.1 a)**
3. Establish clear criteria to ensure that the data you obtain is accurate, up-to-date, sufficient and relevant to the decision. N.B. Remember to demonstrate knowledge and understanding. (For example what time scales were you working to? How did you decide upon the method to select the sample?) Distinguish between data which is categorical and that which is quantitative. **(8.1 b, d)**.
4. Remember to identify and use other appropriate data sources, for example books, journals, and reports. In the example this could be computer suppliers' catalogues or data from other organisations who have recently purchased a computer system. **(8.1 e)**.

5. Review the data you have collected and make sure it is clear, easy to understand and adequate. If this is not the case seek clarification and assistance and, if necessary, gather additional data. (**8.1 f, g**).

6. Assess the data you have collected for its validity and reliability. (**8.1 h**).

7. Conduct a thorough analysis of all the data you have gathered using those techniques which are most appropriate. The technique(s) you use will depend upon the nature of your data. The knowledge you have gained from working through Sections 1 and 3 of this book should be used, for example, measures of central tendency and dispersion, time series analysis, correlation and regression, index numbers and z scores. (**8.1 i**).

8. Present your findings in an appropriate and suitable form using appropriate techniques, including tables and diagrams. Ensure that a clear decision can be made based upon the information you have presented. Your findings should be checked to ensure that they are relevant, clear, sufficiently accurate and supplied at the appropriate level of detail. (**8.1b, i, j**).

9. Write a report indicating what you have learnt from the exercise and how you could apply that learning to other situations.

■ Assignment 10.3 (NVQ 4 M1 competencies may be identified by the student)

The purpose of this assignment is to provide you with the opportunity to put into practice a wide range of the techniques and skills you have developed during your course of study. In particular this assignment enables you to demonstrate your ability at data analysis and presentation.

Scenario:

You have been invited for an interview as a research officer by your local authority's Road Safety Division. In preparation for the interview they have provided you with two related tables of road safety data and asked you to analyse them as outlined in their brief (given below).

The two tables are arranged so that there is one line for each police force in England. The column headings for each table and the explanatory notes describe the data.

The Brief

The post of Research Officer (Road Safety Division) requires the post holder to be able to analyse business data and present their findings graphically and in writing. To enable the interview panel to assess your skills you are requested to provide answers to the following questions. You should make sure that your analysis and interpretation (including full working for calculations) arrive by the stated date. If a computer spreadsheet is used there should be a printout showing cell values, and a printout showing cell formulae for each calculation.

1. *Population and force strength*

   i Calculate the mean and median of the English police forces' areas' population.

   ii Calculate the mean and median of the English police forces' strength.

   iii If you were asked to state the "average" for the English police forces' areas' population and strength which of these would you choose?

   Give one reason for your answer.

2. *Range of force strength*

   i Calculate the inter-quartile range of the English police forces' strength.

   ii Interpret your finding.

3. *Variability in breath testing between forces*

   i Calculate the mean, the standard deviation, and the coefficient of variation for:

   a. total breath tests in England in 1989;
   b. total breath tests in England in 1992;
   c. positive breath tests in England in 1989;
   d. positive breath tests in England in 1992.

   ii What do these statistics tell you about the variability in breath testing between English forces?

   Has the variability altered between 1989 and 1992?

4. *Proportion of positive breath tests*

   i Calculate the proportion of total breath tests in England that were positive in 1989, 1990, 1991 and 1992.

   ii Represent the proportion of total breath tests that were positive for each of these years on one diagram.

   iii Interpret your findings.

5. *Trends in breath testing and accidents*

   i Calculate the appropriate simple indices for the years 1989 – 1992 for:

   a. total breath tests in England;
   b. positive breath tests in England;
   c. total injury accidents in England.

   ii Plot these indices on the same diagram.

   iii Describe the trends in total breath tests, positive breath tests and total injury accidents over the period 1989 – 1992.

   iv What are the advantages of plotting the indices, rather that the raw data, on the graph?

6. *Differences between years*

   i Calculate the cell values for the following table:

Christmas Breath test results for England 1989 – 1992

Breath test result	1989	1990	1991	1992	Total
Positive					
Negative					
Total					

Source: ACPO and OPCS

   ii Calculate a statistical test to see if there is any significant difference in the result of the breath test between the years.

   iii Interpret your findings.

7. *Relationship between positive breath tests and total injury accidents*

   i Illustrate the relationship between data on positive breath tests and total number of injury accidents in 1992 using an appropriate diagram.

   ii Calculate a statistical test to see if there is any relationship between the number of positive breath tests and the total number of injury accidents in 1992.

   iii Interpret your findings.

8. *Summary*

Based on your answers to questions 1 – 7 summarise the main points of your findings in numbered point form (Not more than 300 words).

Number of Random Breath Tests Administered over Christmas Period by Police Forces' Areas' Populations and Forces' Strengths 1989 – 1992

Police Force	Population[1]	Strength[2]	Random breath tests 1989	1990	1991	1992
Avon & Somerset	1379.9	3130	718	754	1173	514
Bedfordshire	514.2	1097	341	962	479	702
Cambridgeshire	640.7	1220	1758	1600	936	1558
Cheshire	937.3	1905	833	1032	903	826
City of London	4.0	829	141	98	111	86
Cleveland	541.1	1483	332	794	898	621
Cumbria	486.9	1180	450	611	689	757
Derbyshire	914.6	1788	1241	818	674	807
Devon & Cornwall	1467.5	2928	2156	1830	1244	1263
Dorset	645.2	1306	469	527	422	626
Durham	589.8	1384	504	750	710	1015
Essex	1495.6	2904	1606	3107	2129	2754
Gloucester	520.6	1170	441	383	493	408
Greater Manchester	2454.8	7075	6650	5799	4711	5126
Hampshire	1638.5	3219	1650	1762	1958	1982
Hertfordshire	951.5	1690	699	613	606	428
Humberside	835.2	1997	1253	1168	984	525
Kent	1485.1	3091	1250	2101	2175	2029
Lancashire	1365.1	3210	2072	1764	1347	1423
Leicestershire	860.5	1853	846	1413	1216	1086
Lincolnshire	573.9	1198	1136	1294	1063	941
Merseyside	1376.8	4737	223	687	1151	566
Metropolitan	6373.9	28472	15248	18075	12347	12379
Norfolk	736.4	1410	4910	2992	3486	917
Northamptonshire	572.9	1190	805	697	778	728
Northumbria	1387.6	3551	407	470	533	383
North Yorkshire	698.7	1397	499	925	1175	665
Nottinghamshire	980.6	2341	3483	3462	609	342
South Yorkshire	1248.5	3031	1151	1271	1098	831
Staffordshire	1020.3	2184	698	947	932	505
Suffolk	629.9	1234	759	1235	896	638
Surrey	998.0	1673	943	1411	1721	1188
Sussex	1363.4	2981	1120	1100	806	741
Thames Valley	1889.8	3877	4245	4620	2855	3856
Warwickshire	477.0	994	301	527	188	205
West Mercia	1069.4	2043	571	891	939	1184
West Midlands	2499.3	6897	876	2254	1344	1160
West Yorkshire	1984.7	5052	848	1493	1886	1638
Wiltshire	553.3	1123	703	975	1034	919

[1] = Population of area in thousands 1991 [2] = Total number of police 1992

Source: Association of Chief Police Officers and 1991 Census (preliminary data)

Number of Positive Breath Tests Administered and Total Injury Accidents over Christmas Period by Police Force Area 1989 – 1992

Police force	Positive breath tests				Total injury accidents[3]			
	1989	1990	1991	1992	1989	1990	1991	1992
Avon & Somerset	99	113	107	85	179	225	65	150
Bedfordshire	52	54	60	59	48	82	42	85
Cambridgeshire	77	47	38	39	51	92	49	81
Cheshire	124	106	97	78	115	126	96	69
City of London	13	10	10	9	7	7	5	2
Cleveland	43	52	87	52	52	52	58	33
Cumbria	49	56	61	33	65	66	46	29
Derbyshire	91	67	49	61	82	104	90	92
Devon & Cornwall	163	152	114	119	137	161	97	135
Dorset	70	47	42	62	27	22	36	41
Durham	116	72	77	67	42	77	46	35
Essex	143	148	124	105	242	145	133	171
Gloucester	51	59	45	25	59	54	42	36
Greater Manchester	423	425	350	297	312	328	239	299
Hampshire	226	164	149	134	134	149	112	137
Hertfordshire	120	74	62	49	114	93	70	68
Humberside	141	95	91	65	123	117	96	87
Kent	161	134	120	109	111	123	89	153
Lancashire	159	131	146	127	270	249	171	153
Leicestershire	82	86	96	54	66	78	56	59
Lincolnshire	57	47	33	49	112	147	71	51
Merseyside	127	140	145	130	203	221	244	230
Metropolitan	926	838	835	804	1005	1053	844	789
Norfolk	103	53	59	35	110	108	63	66
Northamptonshire	54	50	35	33	54	70	48	41
Northumbria	189	157	122	118	194	166	196	153
North Yorkshire	98	60	69	38	94	88	72	63
Nottinghamshire	134	114	79	80	121	153	124	109
South Yorkshire	138	133	150	95	80	132	56	62
Staffordshire	130	98	82	69	105	144	100	127
Suffolk	61	51	50	68	68	79	56	59
Surrey	81	81	83	43	54	119	106	96
Sussex	143	95	102	71	124	136	87	122
Thames Valley	230	199	154	131	153	156	123	184
Warwickshire	45	50	33	24	65	78	43	53
West Mercia	89	100	99	98	77	114	89	103
West Midlands	256	304	251	205	300	288	215	278
West Yorkshire	212	230	240	188	194	229	227	223
Wiltshire	67	60	51	40	44	44	42	41

[3] = Total number of accidents involving an injury

Source: Association of Chief Police Officers and 1991 Census (preliminary data)

Appendix 1: Answers to tasks in Section 1

Unit 1 **Task 1.1**

The Stock Control Manager would consider the Weekly Stock Control Report to be information. As the recipient he can interpret it, understand it and it is useful to him in his role of managing stock levels.

Example of data: the Weekly Stock Control Report is data as far as Liz is concerned when she first reads it.

Example of information: the Monthly Sales Report for the Store Manager is information as far as the Store Manager is concerned.

Unit 2 **Task 2.1**

The Store Manager says that the first two Management Information Reports are useless to him in his role as Store Manager because:

Daily Balance of Stock and Re-order Report: the data is not relevant to him in his role as Store Manager; the task would be done by the Stock Control Manager. The data is far too detailed for the Store Manager's purposes, he would probably only find time to look at the reports on a monthly basis which would be too late to re-order stock!

Weekly Report of Items Which Have Not Sold: the data is not relevant to him in his role as Store Manager; the task would be done by the Stock Control Manager. The data is far too detailed for the Store Manager's purposes.

Unit 3 **Task 3.1**

Primary Data Sources
Questionnaire Survey of Customers,
Discussion with store staff about this problem.

Secondary Data Sources
Local Authority Planning Department,
Office of Population Censuses and Surveys County Report for Gloucestershire,
Personnel Database,
Daily Balance of Stock and Reorder Report,
Published Market Research Report on Shopping Trends,
Value Added Tax Returns.

Task 3.2

Internal Secondary Data Sources
Daily Balance of Stock Reorder Report,
Personnel Database,
Value Added Tax Returns.

External Secondary Data Sources
Local Authority Planning Department,
Office of Population Censuses and Surveys County Report for Gloucestershire,
Published Market Research Report on Shopping Trends.

Task 3.3

The Government Survey Reports most likely to be useful for keeping abreast of national trends are:

The Family Expenditure Survey because it contains data on household spending on the full range of goods and services.

Household Food Consumption because it contains a brief analysis of the consumption and expenditure on main food groups by household composition, income group, and region.

Both of these would be of considerable use to a supermarket selling such items.

Task 3.4

The advantages of using secondary data sources to keep abreast of national trends are:

1. to gain access to complex data which one could not hope to collect;
2. it removes the need to spend time or effort in data collection.

The disadvantages of using secondary data sources to keep abreast of national trends are:

1. the data may not always be up to date;
2. the data may not always be in sufficient detail for the required purpose;
3. it may be unclear how the data was collected. In the case of data collected by the surveys Liz listed from the Store Manager's Annual Report it is usually assumed that valid techniques have been used. However for some data sources this may not be the case;
4. it may not be clear what is meant by the terminology used in the reports;
5. the data may contain errors due to typing. However this is unlikely to be the case for the data sources mentioned in the Store Manager's Annual Report.

Unit 4

Task 4.1

Detailed question	Data required	Likely Values	Source
What proportion of customers would shop at the Gloucester store on Sundays if it was open?	Number of customers who would shop at the store on Sundays. Number of customers who would not shop at the store on Sundays.	Do shop, Don't shop, Don't know	Customer (primary data source)
Do the Gloucester store's customers shop at any of Brunley's competitors on Sundays?	Number of customers who do shop at competitors' stores on Sundays. Number of customers who do not shop at competitors' stores on Sundays.	Do shop, Don't shop	Customer (primary data source)
Which competitors' stores were these (for the past month)?	Name(s) of competitors' stores shopped at in past month.	Tesbury, Springfield's, Gaterose, Greenland's, Other	Customer (primary data source)
Do the Gloucester store's customers shop at any of Brunley's competitors during the week?	Number of customers who do shop at competitors' stores during the week. Number of customers who do not shop at competitors' stores during the week.	Do shop, Don't shop	Customer (primary data source)
Which competitors' stores were these (for the past month)?	Name(s) of competitors' stores shopped at in past month.	Tesbury, Springfield's, Gaterose, Greenland's, Other	Customer (primary data source)
How much do the Gloucester store's customers think they would spend each Sunday if they were to shop at the store?	Amount the customers would spend in £'s. (N.B. only interested in those who would shop on a Sunday)	To the nearest £*	Customer (primary data source)
How do the Gloucester store customers intend to get to the store to shop on a Sunday?	How customers intend to get to store on Sunday. (N.B. only interested in those who would shop on a Sunday)	Foot, Car, Bus, Other	Customer (primary data source)
How many times a week do customers visit the Gloucester store?	Number of times a week customers visit the store.	4 or more times a week, 2-3 times a week, Once a week, 2-3 times a month, Once a month, Less than once a month, First time ever*	Customer (primary data source)

*Liz would need to check the level of detail required for these questions with the Deputy Manager, Jemma Douglas. Your answers may differ from those above in the likely values you record.

Unit 5 **Task 5.1**

Liz cannot define her sampling frame. Although she knows there are 'over 10,000' customers 'of whom over 90% live locally' she cannot obtain a complete list of these customers.

Task 5.2

Liz should use quota sampling because it is not possible to list every member (customer) of the sampling frame.

Liz will devise a quota of customers to interview. This will split the customers into age and gender groups based on the proportions in the table 'Gloucester Store: Estimated Proportion of Customers by Age and Gender.' The quota will probably total between 100 and 200 customers. She will then specify the exact number (quota) she needs to interview from each group to fill her sample. She can then decide which customers she interviews until the quotas for each of the groups are filled.

Task 5.3

It would be impossible to list all the possible examples. However the key features for each type of sampling which should appear in your answer are in italics in the examples below.

Random sampling: to select a *representative sample, usually* of *over a few hundred* customers, for a particular product *from a sampling frame* of all customers.

Systematic sampling: to select a *representative sample, often of less than a hundred* customers, for a particular product *from a sampling frame* of all customers *where any underlying pattern in the sampling frame will not produce bias in the sample.*

Stratified sampling: to select a *representative sample* of staff working at Brunley's Gloucester store, *which represents all (strata)* grades of staff , *from a sampling frame* of all staff.

Multi-stage sampling: to select a *representative sample* for a national survey of customers so that those selected are in a few geographically discrete areas. This will require *a number of distinct sampling frames*, in this case two. The first will select the geographical areas, the second the customers.

Cluster sampling: to select a *representative sample* for a national survey of customers where the *sampling frame is not known*, and there is a need to *cluster the sample* geographically.

Unit 6 **Task 6.1**

It would be impossible to list all the possible examples. However the key features for each type of primary data collection method which should appear in your answer are in italics in the examples below.

Interview (using a check list of points): *in-depth interviews* with a *small number of people* such as departmental managers *where the interviewer records the responses.*

Questionnaire: asking the *same questions* to a *large number of people*, such as all members of staff, when *face to face contact is not needed and the information will be recorded by the respondent.*

Direct observation: *watching* a process such as shelf restocking, *recording* how it is done but *not interfering* in any way.

Task 6.2

Filter question is number: 8 (first one).
Open questions are numbers: 1, 6, 7, 9 and 14.
Pre-coded questions are numbers: 2, 4, 8 (first one), 10, 11, 12, 13 and 15.
Self coded question is number: 3.

Check question is number 14, this checks the answer to question 8 (second one).

Task 6.3

Faults identified with wording of individual questions will include:

1. uses language which is difficult to understand;
2. is biased, the question expects the respondent to say working conditions are unsatisfactory;
3. is likely to get the official tea break length rather than how long people actually spend;
5. uses language which would be unclear to many respondents;
6. asks a question to which many staff will not know the answer. This data could be collected more easily from the personnel department;
7. is biased. There are no questions asking staff what they like about the canteen;
8. is two questions in one. It would be impossible to interpret the answers;
9. uses a poorly defined expression 'all he can.' It is not clear what this means;
10. nearly every respondent will answer this question 'Yes.' It is therefore wasted;
12. (see comments for question 6). In addition it is unclear which box to tick if the respondent wishes to say that 5, 10, 15, 20, or over 25 staff have left their jobs;
13. (see comments for question 8). In addition it implies that the current union is neither strong nor fair minded.

Other faults identified will include:

- the introduction to the survey does not communicate the survey's objectives, it gives no idea of the time it will take to fill in and no assurances of confidentiality;
- there are no 'thanks' at the end of the survey;
- the section headed 'Your Union' contains questions which do not relate to unions (questions 11 and 12);
- the questions do not follow a logical order;
- the layout is, at times, cramped. Open ended questions (especially 1 and 7) have very little space in which the respondent can record their answers;
- There are two question 8's.
- some closed questions have boxes in which the respondent can record their answers, others (questions 5 and 8) do not.

Task 6.4

Liz will need to find out the customer's age and gender in order to check the sample is representative. Age will need to be split into the same groupings as the table 'Estimated Proportion of Customers by Age and Gender' in unit 5. These are: under 20, 20 – 29, 30 – 44, 45 – 59, 60 plus.

Task 6.5

The exact design of your interview schedule is likely to differ from that below. However it should contain questions which will enable all the required data to be collected. You should evaluate your questionnaire against the answer below, and the principles discussed in section 2 units 6.3 and 6.4.

Brunley's Supermarkets: Gloucester Store
Interview schedule

(Instructions to the interviewer are in italics; they should not be read to the respondent)

'Good morning / afternoon. My name is Liz Reynolds and I work for Brunley's Supermarkets (***show respondent identification card***). We are undertaking a survey to find our customers' views on Sunday opening of this supermarket. Would you mind answering a few questions? It will only take a few minutes of your time and your replies will be anonymous.'

'I would like to start by asking you about shopping on Sundays....'

1 Do you already shop at a supermarket on a Sunday? Yes ☐
(if no go to question 3) No ☐

2 *(if yes)* Which of the following supermarkets have you shopped at on a Sunday during the past month?
(read out list)
Other:...

Gaterose ☐
Greenland's ☐
Springfield's ☐
Tesbury ☐
Other *(note which)* ☐

3 Would you shop at this supermarket on a Sunday if it was open?
(if no go to question 6)

Yes ☐
No ☐
Don't know ☐

4 *(if yes or don't know)* If this supermarket was open on a Sunday how would you usually get here?

Foot ☐
Car ☐
Bus ☐
Other ☐
Don't Know ☐

5 How much do you think you would spend at this supermarket each Sunday if you were to shop here? *(record answer to the nearest pound)*

£ ....

'I would now like to ask your some more general questions....'

6 How often do you shop at this supermarket?
(record respondent's answer in the appropriate box)

4 + times a week ☐
2-3 times a week ☐
Once a week ☐
2-3 times a month ☐
Once a month ☐
First time ever ☐

7 Which of the following supermarkets have you shopped at during the past month?
(read out list)
Other:...

Gaterose ☐
Greenland's ☐
Springfield's ☐
Tesbury ☐
Other *(note which)* ☐

'And finally a question about yourself....'

8 Which one of the following age groups would you place yourself in?
(read out list)

Under 20 ☐
20 – 29 ☐
30 – 44 ☐
45 – 59 ☐
60 plus ☐

'Thank you for your time and help, it was most kind of you.'
To be filled in by the interviewer immediately after the interview:

9 *Gender of respondent:*

Male ☐
Female ☐

Day of Survey:

Weekday ☐
Saturday ☐

Remember to check your quota

Task 6.6

Liz should pilot test her interview schedule as this would enable her to detect any errors or problems in the layout and design of the survey, as well as the likely responses each question would generate. Mistakes could then be rectified prior to the main survey.

Unit 7

Task 7.1

A correctly constructed version of this table is given in unit 8, Task 8.4. Errors with the table include:

1. **no title;**
2. **no heading for column containing the names of the supermarkets;**
3. **no source of data;**
4. **data in the columns is not in a logical sequence, it would be better if they were either in alphabetical order or order of magnitude with 'none' at the end;**
5. **no footnote to explain why the numbers in the 'Visited' column do not sum to the total for that column;**
6. **poor use of lines and boxes.**

Task 7.2

The responses to this question are categorical data.

Tally and Number of Customers who would shop at Brunley's on Sundays

Shop on Sunday?	Tally	Number
Yes	卌 卌 卌 卌 卌 卌 卌 卌 卌 卌 卌 卌 I	61
No	卌 卌 卌 卌 卌 卌 卌 卌 IIII	44
Don't know	卌 卌 卌	15
Total		**120**

Source: Sample Survey of Customers 199-

Task 7.3

Percentage who responded yes = $\frac{61}{120} \times 100 = 50.8\%$ (to 1 decimal place)

Percentage who responded no = $\frac{44}{120} \times 100 = 36.7\%$ (to 1 decimal place)

Percentage who responded don't know = $\frac{15}{120} \times 100 = 12.5\%$

Number and Percentage of Customers who would shop at Brunley's on Sundays

Shop on Sunday?	Number	Percentage*
Yes	61	50.8
No	44	36.7
Don't know	15	12.5
Total	**120**	**100.0**

*percentages rounded to 1 decimal place where necessary

Source: Sample Survey of Customers 199-

Task 7.4

The responses to this question are quantitative data.

Amount Customers would spend at Brunley's Gloucester Store each Sunday

Amount in £'s	Tally	Number of Customers
0.5 – < 20.5	~~IIII~~ ~~IIII~~ ~~IIII~~ I	16
20.5 – < 40.5	~~IIII~~ ~~IIII~~ ~~IIII~~ ~~IIII~~ I	21
40.5 – < 60.5	~~IIII~~ ~~IIII~~ ~~IIII~~ II	17
60.5 – < 80.5	~~IIII~~ ~~IIII~~ II	12
80.5 – < 100.5	~~IIII~~	5
100.5 – < 120.5		0
120.5 – < 140.5	III	3
140.5 – < 160.5		0
160.5 – < 180.5	I	1
180.5 – < 200.5	I	1

Source: Sample Survey of Customers 199-

Task 7.5

Gender by Intended Transport of likely Sunday Customers at Brunley's Gloucester Store

Transport	Female	Male	Total
Car	8	8	16
Foot	3	0	3
Bus	0	0	0
Other	1	0	1
Total	**12**	**8**	**20**

(Source: Extract of data from Sample Survey of Customers 199-)

Unit 8

Task 8.1

'You can use a number of different types of bar chart to present categorical and discrete data such as simple bar charts, multiple bar charts, or stacked bar charts. Alternatively, Liz, you could use pie charts or pictograms. It depends upon what you are trying to show.'

Task 8.2

Improvements to the bar chart include:

1. adding a title which clearly describes what the bar chart shows;
2. adding a 'source' stating from where the data was obtained;
3. clearly labelling the frequency (vertical) axis.

Task 8.3

The chart distorts or misrepresents the data because the frequency (vertical) axis does not start at zero, and this is not made clear to the reader. The frequency axis should start at zero and the break in the scale should be represented by a zig-zag line.

Task 8.4

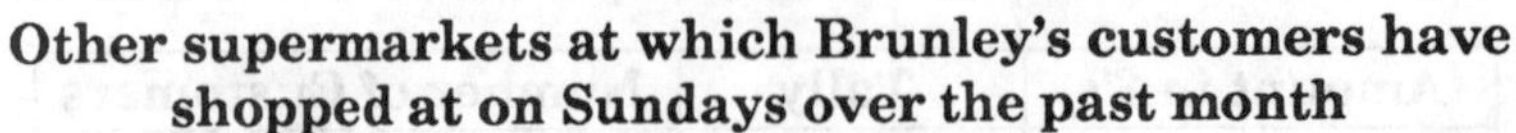

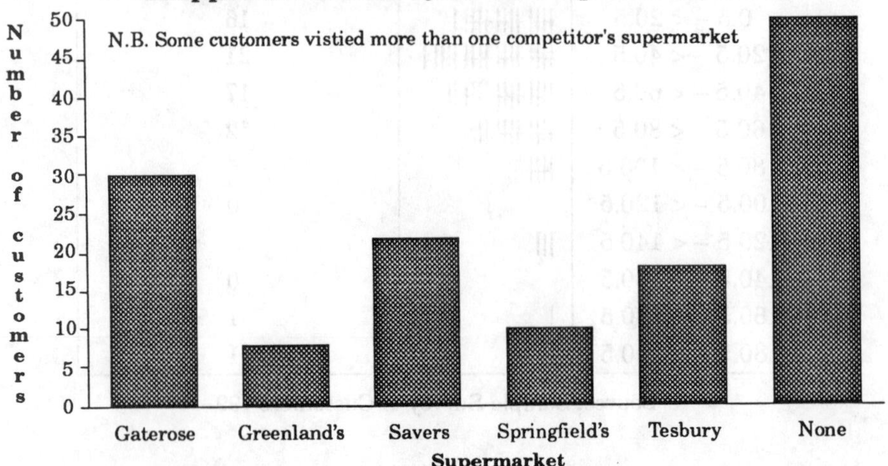

Source: Sample survey of 120 Customers 199-

Over half of Brunley's Gloucester store customers have shopped at a supermarket on Sunday in the past month. The most popular supermarket was Gaterose (25% of customers) followed by Savers (18% of customers) and Tesbury (15% of customers).

Task 8.5

Liz should use a stacked bar chart. A multiple bar chart would use a separate bar for each gender, so it could not show the totals for each of the 'number of visits' categories. A percentage component bar chart, whilst enabling comparison between genders, would not enable the totals for each of the 'number of visits' categories to be compared as they would all be represented by 100%.

Task 8.6

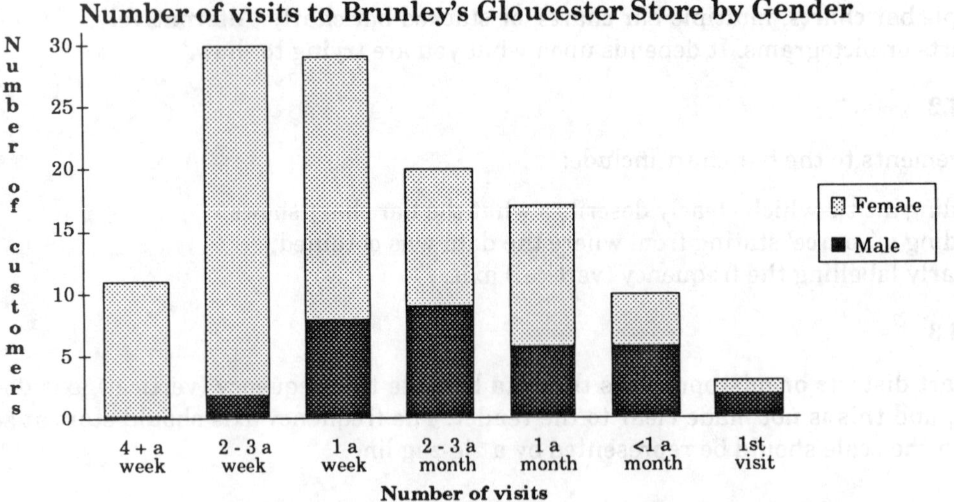

Source: Sample Survey of Customers 199-

Unit 9 Task 9.1

A pie chart was suggested because it is an excellent method of displaying the share that each component has of a particular variable; in this case the proportions of customers who responded 'yes,' 'no' and 'don't know' to the question.

Task 9.2

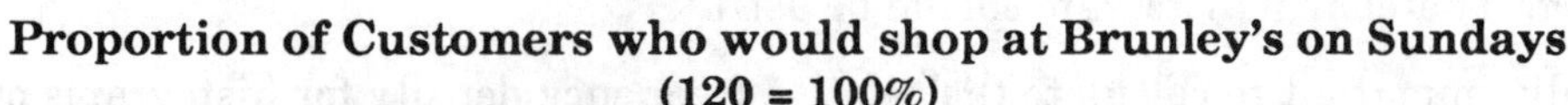

Proportion of Customers who would shop at Brunley's on Sundays (120 = 100%)

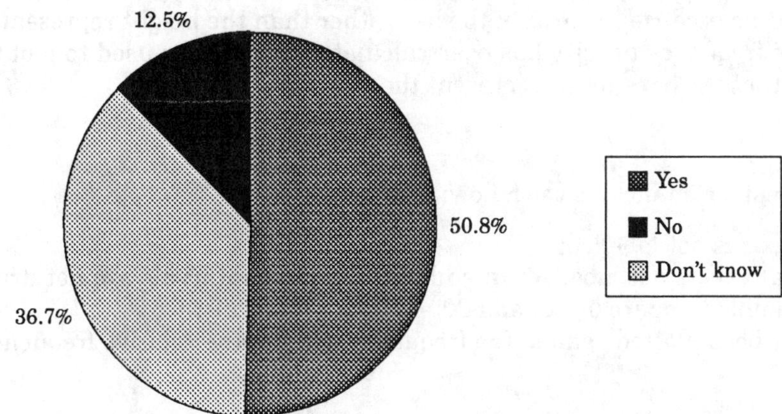

Source: Sample Survey of Customers 199-

Over half of Brunley's current customers would shop at Brunley's on a Sunday if the store was open. Approximately one third of current customers would not shop at Brunley's on a Sunday if the store was open.

Task 9.3

Ways in which the pie charts mislead the reader include:

1. The two pies represent different numbers of people and yet they are of the same area. The pie chart for females represents 3 times as many customers as the pie chart for males;
2. it is unclear to what each of the segments refers as there is no key;
3. it is unclear where the data came from as their is no source.

Task 9.4

Most likely means of transport of Customers who would shop at Brunley's on Sundays (N.B. One person represents 5 customers)

Other

Bus

Foot

Car

Source: Sample Survey of Customers 199-

The most likely means of transport to the store on a Sunday is the car. Other means of transport are rarely used.

Unit 10 Task 10.1

As the data has already been grouped (1st table) and is, in addition, continuous (2nd table) it is unclear exactly what values it could take. Only the class interval within which each data value falls is known. Therefore a histogram should be used.

It is especially important to calculate the relative frequency density for histograms of data with unequal class widths because the area of the bar rather than the height represents the frequency. Once the relative frequency density has been calculated this can be used to plot the bar heights. This will ensure that the bars' areas represent the frequencies.

Task 10.2

Errors with the histogram include the following:

1. the vertical axis is not labelled;
2. the horizontal axis is not labelled. In addition the class intervals are not drawn to the same scale (for example compare 0 – 20 and 20 – 30 class intervals.);
3. the bars have been plotted against the frequency and not the relative frequency density.

Task 10.3

N.B. The histogram below has been drawn using a computer spreadsheet and does not show the break in scale on the x axis correctly. There should be a 0 plotted.

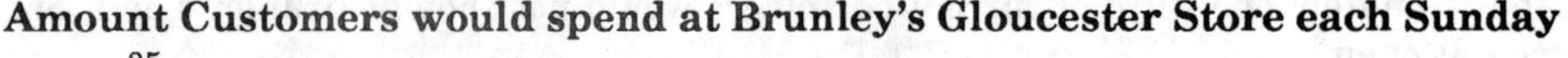

Amount Customers would spend at Brunley's Gloucester Store each Sunday

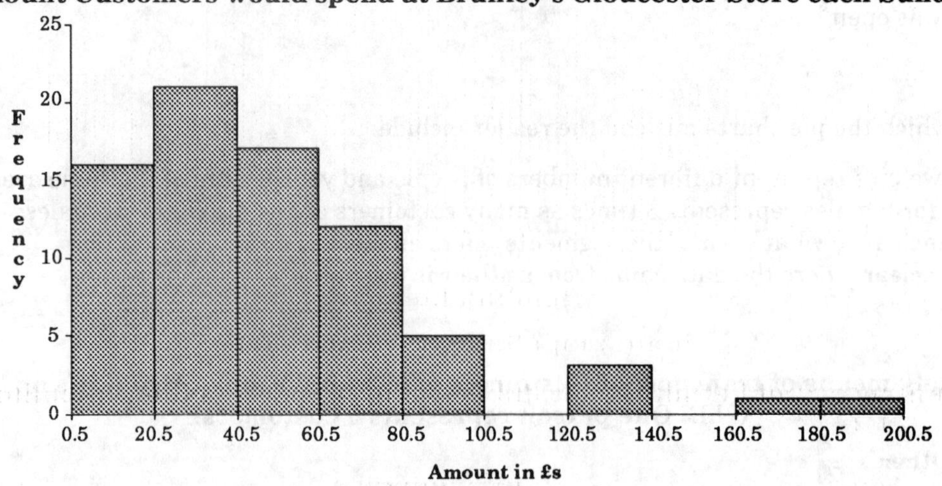

(Source: Sample Survey of Customers 199-)

The vast majority of customers who would shop at Brunley's on a Sunday would spend under £60.50. Very few customers would spend over £100.50.

Task 10.4

Calculation of relative frequency density for male customers (numbers rounded to 4 decimal places where necessary):

Age	Frequency	Relative frequency	Class width	rfd
10 – < 20	3	0.0909	2	0.0455
20 – < 30	7	0.2121	2	0.1061
30 – < 45	10	0.3030	3	0.1010
45 – < 60	8	0.2424	3	0.0808
60 – < 75	5	0.1515	3	0.0505
Total	33			

Calculation of relative frequency density for female customers (numbers rounded to 4 decimal places where necessary):

Age	Frequency	Relative frequency	Class width	rfd
10 – < 20	8	0.0920	2	0.0460
20 – < 30	17	0.1954	2	0.0977
30 – < 45	26	0.2989	3	0.0996
45 – < 60	24	0.2759	3	0.0920
60 – < 75	12	0.1379	3	0.0460
Total	87			

Age Structure of Male Customers shopping at Brunley's Gloucester Store

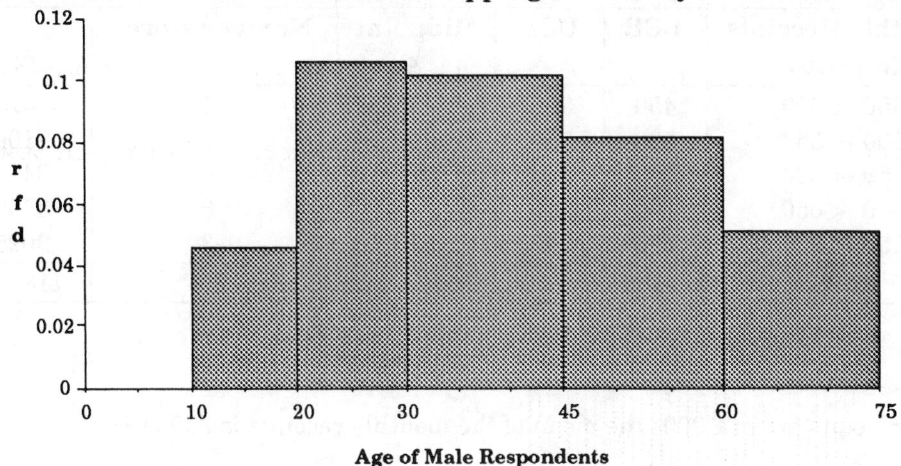

(Source: Sample Survey of Customers 199-)

Age Structure of Female Customers shopping at Brunley's Gloucester Store

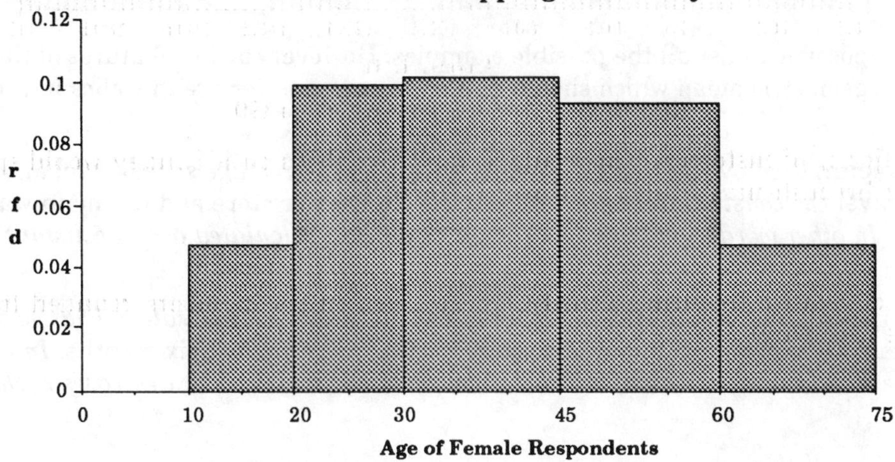

(Source: Sample Survey of Customers 199-)

The histograms show that the age structures of Brunley's male and female customers are similar.

Unit 11 **Task 11.1**

$$\text{Mean} = \frac{135000 + 151000 + 158000 + 165000}{4} = \frac{609000}{4} = £152,250$$

Task 11.2

Number of deliveries *x*	Number of suppliers *f*	*fx*
1	25	25
2	15	30
3	7	21
4	2	8
total	49	84

$$\text{Mean} = \frac{84}{49} = 1.71 \text{ (to 2 decimal places)}$$

Task 11.3

Monthly Receipts in £'000s	LCB	UCB	Midpoint *x*	Number stores *f*	*fx*
450 -< 500	450	500	475	1	475
500 -< 550	500	550	525	4	2100
550 -< 600	550	600	575	6	3450
600 -< 650	600	650	625	6	3750
650 -< 700	650	700	675	3	2025
Total				20	11800

$$\text{Mean} = \frac{11800}{20} = 590$$

As monthly receipts are in £'000s the mean of the monthly receipts is £590,000.

Therefore the mean of the monthly receipts of the '20 similar stores' is below the mean of the monthly receipts for the Gloucester store.

Task 11.4

It would be impossible to list all the possible examples. However the key features of the harmonic mean and the geometric mean which should appear in your answer are in italics in the examples below.

Harmonic mean: used by the Head Cashier to calculate the *average* speed (*rate*) at which delivery lorries travel the *constant distance* between the Gloucester store and the main warehouse in Cheltenham. *In other words your example should be a mean calculated over a constant numerator unit.*

Geometric mean: used by the Head Cashier to calculate the *average rate of change* of the monthly percentage (*proportional)* increase in store profits over the past six months. *In other words your example should be the mean of a series of proportional increases or decreases such as percentages.*

Task 11.5

$$\text{Harmonic mean} = \frac{2}{\frac{1}{25} + \frac{1}{20}} = \frac{2}{0.04 + 0.05} = \frac{2}{0.09}$$

$$= 22.22 \text{ miles per gallon (to 2 decimal places)}$$

Task 11.6

$$\text{Geometric mean} = \sqrt[5]{(10.2)(11.4)(14.3)(9.1)(8.2)} = \sqrt[5]{124078.43}$$

$$= 10.44\% \text{ (to 2 decimal places)}$$

nit 12

Task 12.1

Name	Annual Salary (£'s)	Rank
Denise	7300	1
Rosalie	7300	2
Sarah	7400	3
Gillian	8100	4
Malcolm	13800	5
Martin	14000	6

$$\text{Median pointer} = \frac{6+1}{2} = 3.5$$

therefore median salary is halfway between the salaries of Sarah and Gillian.

$$\text{Median salary} = \frac{7400 + 8100}{2} = £7,750$$

Task 12.2

Liz and the Personnel Manager should calculate the mode for the average day off because it is the only average that can sensibly be calculated from categorical data.

The modal (average) day off is Monday.

Task 12.3

Brunley's should use the median or the mode to calculate average salary if they want to keep the pay award to a minimum.

The median will provide a lower average than the mean when there are more people on low salaries than high salaries. Unlike the mean the median does not take into account extreme values. (If you are unsure of this calculate the mean for the salaries in task 12.1 and compare it with the median of £7,750). The mode will only provide a lower average if the majority of low-paid employees have the same salary.

Task 12.4

Claim in miles	UCB	Number of Employees *f*	Cumulative Frequency *F*	*F%**
0	0	2400	2400	45.5
>0 – < 10	10	1100	3500	66.3
10 – < 20	20	900	4400	83.3
20 – < 30	30	400	4800	90.9
30 – < 40	40	280	5080	96.2
40 – < 50	50	200	5280	100.0
Total		5280		

*percentages rounded to 1 decimal place where necessary.

Plot as a cumulative frequency curve and read off at 50% to give the median.

Cumulative frequency curve showing distribution of a sample of Brunley's travel claims

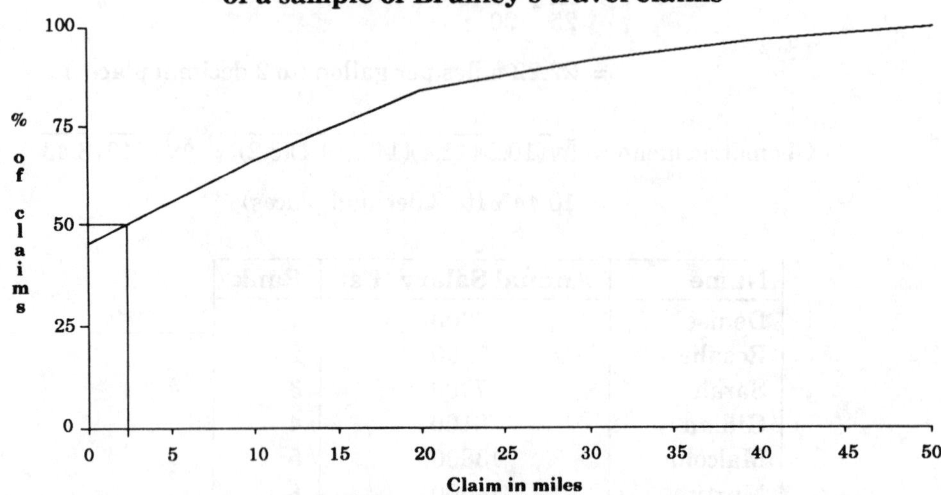

Source: Brunley's Supermarkets Head Office 199-

The median staff travel claim from the Head Office data is approximately 2.4 miles.

The median staff travel claim at the Gloucester store is higher than the median from the Head Office data.

Task 12.5

Male employees: the mean is less than the median which is less than the mode. This suggests that the data is negatively skewed. In other words more male employees at the Gloucester store are above the mean age of 34 than below it.

Female employees: the mean is greater than the median which is greater than the mode. This suggests that the data is positively skewed. In other words more female employees at the Gloucester store are below the mean age of 35 than above it.

Unit 13 Task 13.1

Contractor	Bid price	Rank
Jay's Haulage	£21,000	1
Pete's Transport	£26,000	2
Jeff's Haulage	£28,000	3
SA Ltd	£29,000	4
EJW	£29,500	5
KAGR Transport Group	£31,000	6

Range = 31000 – 21000 = £10,000

Median pointer $= \frac{6+1}{2} = \frac{7}{2} = 3.5$

Therefore median is half way between 3rd and 4th bid price.

Median $= \frac{28000 + 29000}{2} = £28{,}500$

Lower quartile pointer $= \frac{6+1}{4} = \frac{7}{4} = 1.75$

Therefore lower quartile is 0.75 of the way between 1st and 2nd bid price.

$$\begin{aligned}\text{Lower quartile} &= 21000 + 0.75 \times (26000 - 21000)\\ &= 21000 + 0.75 \times (5000)\\ &= 21000 + 3750\\ &= £24,750\end{aligned}$$

Upper quartile pointer $= \dfrac{3 \times (6+1)}{4} = \dfrac{21}{4} = 5.25$

Therefore upper quartile 0.25 of way between 5th and 6th bid price.

$$\begin{aligned}\text{Upper quartile} &= 29500 + 0.25 \times (31000 - 29500)\\ &= 29500 + 0.25 \times (1500)\\ &= 29500 + 375\\ &= £29,875\end{aligned}$$

Inter-quartile range = 29875 – 24750 = £5,125

Task 13.2

The bid prices are negatively skewed because the upper quartile is closer to the median than the lower quartile.

Therefore there is less variation in prices for bids above the median bid price than for bids below the median bid price.

Task 13.3

'Percentiles divide the distribution into 100 equal parts in the same way as the median divides the distribution into two equal parts. Percentiles enable us to calculate values at any given percentage.'

'Deciles divide the distribution into 10 equal parts. Therefore the first decile is the 10th percentile.'

Task 13.4

EJW Contractors

Number of lorries out of Service	Number of days occurred f	Cumulative frequency F
0	21	21
1	30	51
2	20	71
3	11	82
4	5	87
5	3	90
Total	90	

Lower quartile pointer $= \dfrac{90+1}{4} = \dfrac{91}{4} = 22.75$

Therefore lower quartile is 1 lorry out of service.

Upper quartile pointer $= \dfrac{3 \times (90+1)}{4} = \dfrac{273}{4} = 68.25$

Therefore upper quartile is 2 lorries out of service.

Inter-quartile range $= 2 - 1 = 1$ lorry out of service.

Median pointer $= \frac{90 + 1}{2} = 45.5$

Therefore median number of lorries out of service is 1.

SA Ltd

Number of lorries out of Service	Number of days occurred f	Cumulative Frequency F
0	47	47
1	22	69
2	10	79
3	9	88
4	2	90
5	0	90
Total	90	

Lower quartile pointer $= \frac{90 + 1}{4} = \frac{91}{4} = 22.75$

Therefore lower quartile is 0 lorries out of service.

Upper quartile pointer $= \frac{3 \times (90 + 1)}{4} = \frac{273}{4} = 68.25$

Therefore upper quartile is 1 lorry out of service.

Inter-quartile range $= 1 - 0 = 1$ lorry out of service.

Median pointer $= \frac{90 + 1}{2} = 45.5$

Therefore median number of lorries out of service is 0.

Although both contractors' lorry fleets have the same inter-quartile range for lorries out of service, the upper and lower quartiles and the median are lower for SA Ltd. SA Ltd therefore appear to be the most reliable.

Task 13.5

Value of bid	UCB	Number bidding f	Cumulative frequency F	F%*
£18,000 – < £20,000	20000	1	1	7.1
£20,000 – < £22,000	22000	1	2	14.3
£22,000 – < £24,000	24000	2	4	28.6
£24,000 – < £26,000	26000	3	7	50.0
£26,000 – < £28,000	28000	5	12	85.7
£28,000 – < £30,000	30000	0	12	85.7
£30,000 – < £32,000	32000	1	13	92.9
£32,000 – < £34,000	34000	1	14	100.0
Total		14		

*percentages rounded to 1 decimal place where necessary.

Plot as a cumulative frequency curve and read off at 25%, 50% and 75% points to give the lower quartile, median and upper quartile respectively.

N.B. The cumulative frequency curve below has been drawn using a computer spreadsheet and does not show the break in the x axis correctly. There should be a zig-zag line between 0 and 18000.

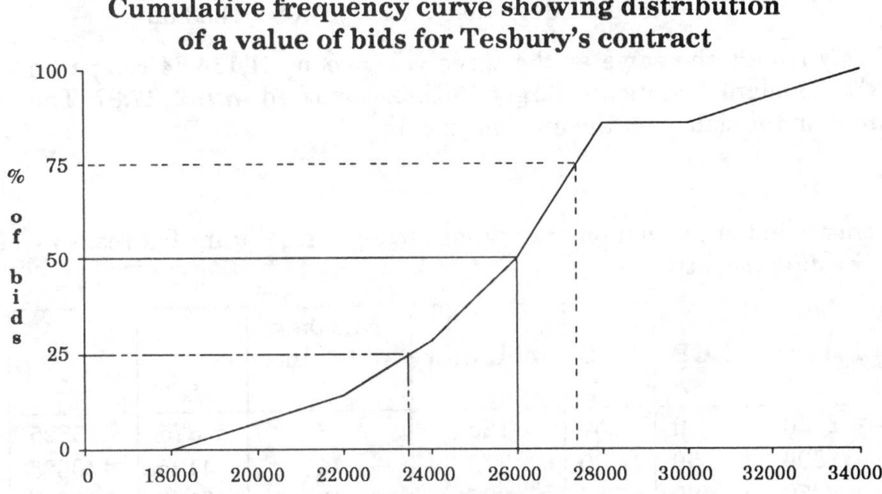

Source: Tesbury Supermarkets Head Office 199-

The median contract bid is therefore approximately £26,000, the upper quartile is approximately £27,500 and the lower quartile £23,500.

The median is therefore less than that for the bids received by Brunley's.

The inter-quartile range is 27500 – 23500 = £4,000. This is also less than the inter-quartile range of bids received by Brunley's.

It would therefore seem likely that the bids received by Brunley's are higher and more variable than those received by Tesbury.

Unit 14 Task 14.1

Liz calculated the standard deviation rather than the variance because the variance expresses the data as the square of the values, in this case pounds squared! This would make it difficult to interpret the variance as the mean is expressed in pounds. As the standard deviation is the square root of the variance this converts pounds squared back to pounds.

N.B. for calculations numbers have been rounded to 2 decimal places where necessary; spreadsheet answers may therefore differ slightly.

Vehicle	Amount Claimed x	Deviation $x - \bar{x}$	(Deviation)^2 $(x - \bar{x})^2$
J123 ABC	£1504.50	389.66	151834.91
K234 BBC	£544.85	-569.99	324888.60
J345 CBC	£1275.00	160.16	25651.23
K59 CBC	£1217.99	103.15	10639.92
J19 XBC	£645.24	-469.60	220524.16
J452 MBC	£1501.45	386.61	149467.29
Total	£6689.03	*-0.01	883006.11

*N.B. this does not sum to 0 due to rounding errors.

$$\text{Mean} = \frac{6689.03}{6} = £1,114.84$$

$$\text{Variance} = \frac{883006.11}{6} = 147167.68$$

$$\text{Standard deviation} = \sqrt{147167.68} = £383.62$$

The mean is virtually the same as the three year mean, £1,114.84 compared with £1,115.88. However, the standard deviation is larger £383.62 compared with £317.87. Thus there has been more variation in the claims for the previous month.

Task 14.2

N.B. components in the calculation are rounded to eight significant figures; spreadsheet answers may therefore differ slightly.

Value of claim	LCB	UCB	Midpoint x	Number of Claims f	fx	x^2	fx^2
£0 – < £250	0	250	125	3	375	15625	46875
£250 – < £500	250	500	375	11	4125	140625	1546875
£500 – < £750	500	750	625	13	8125	390625	5078125
£750 – < £1000	750	1000	875	3	2625	765625	2296875
£1000 – < £1250	1000	1250	1125	1	1125	1265625	1265625
Total				31	16375		10234375

$$\text{Mean} = \frac{16375}{31} = £528.23 \text{ (to 2 decimal places)}$$

$$\text{Standard deviation} = \sqrt{\frac{10234375}{31} - \left(\frac{16375}{31}\right)^2}$$

$$= \sqrt{330141.12 - 528.2258^2}$$

$$= \sqrt{330141.12 - 279022.49}$$

$$= \sqrt{51118.63}$$

$$= £226.09$$

95% of claims will be within plus or minus 1.96 standard deviations from the mean. Therefore 95% of claims will lie in the range:

£528.23 plus or minus 1.96 × 226.09 = 443.14

= £85.09 to £971.37

Task 14.3

$$\text{Windscreen} = \frac{6.7}{178.25} \times 100 = 3.759 \text{ (to 3 decimal places)}$$

$$\text{Theft / Break-in} = \frac{796.89}{1984.78} \times 100 = 40.150 \text{ (to 3 decimal places)}$$

$$\text{Collision (Brunley's fault)} = \frac{280.76}{915.42} \times 100 = 30.670 \text{ (to 3 decimal places)}$$

Collision (3rd party's fault) = $\dfrac{317.87}{1115.88} \times 100 = 28.486$ (to 3 decimal places)

Car-park = $\dfrac{226.08}{528.23} \times 100 = 42.800$ (to 3 decimal places)

The claim type with the least variation is windscreens (coefficient of variation of 3.759). The greatest variation is in car-park claims (coefficient of variation of 42.800), although the variability for theft / break-in claims is similar (40.150).

Unit 15 Task 15.1

It would be impossible to list all the possible examples. However the key features of cyclical fluctuations and residual influences which should appear in your answer are in italics in the examples below.

Cyclical fluctuation: the overall business *cycle* of boom followed by recession, probably over approximately a 7 year period, would affect Brunley's. *Any variation which is repeated over a number of years will probably be correct.*

Residual influence: an *unforeseen* scare of baby food products being contaminated with ground glass would affect Brunley's sales figures. *Any unforeseen or random event which affects sales figures will probably be correct.*

Task 15.2

Year	Quarter	Profit (£ million)	4 quarter total (£ million)	4 period average (£ million)	Centred (moving) average (£ million)
1989	2	22.7			
	3	28.3			
			109.7	27.425	
	4	31.4			27.5625
			110.8	27.700	
1990	1	27.3			27.9125
			112.5	28.125	
	2	23.8			28.0500
			111.9	27.975	
	3	30.0			28.1750
			113.5	28.375	
	4	30.8			28.6000
			115.3	28.825	
1991	1	28.9			29.0125
			116.8	29.200	
	2	25.6			29.5750
			119.8	29.950	
	3	31.5			30.2125
			121.9	30.475	
	4	33.8			30.7000
			123.7	30.925	
1992	1	31.0			31.4875
			128.2	32.050	
	2	27.4			32.6375
			132.9	33.225	
	3	36.0			33.6125
			136.0	34.000	
	4	38.5			
1993	1	34.1			

Operating Profits 1989 – 1993 and Overall Trend (Moving Average)

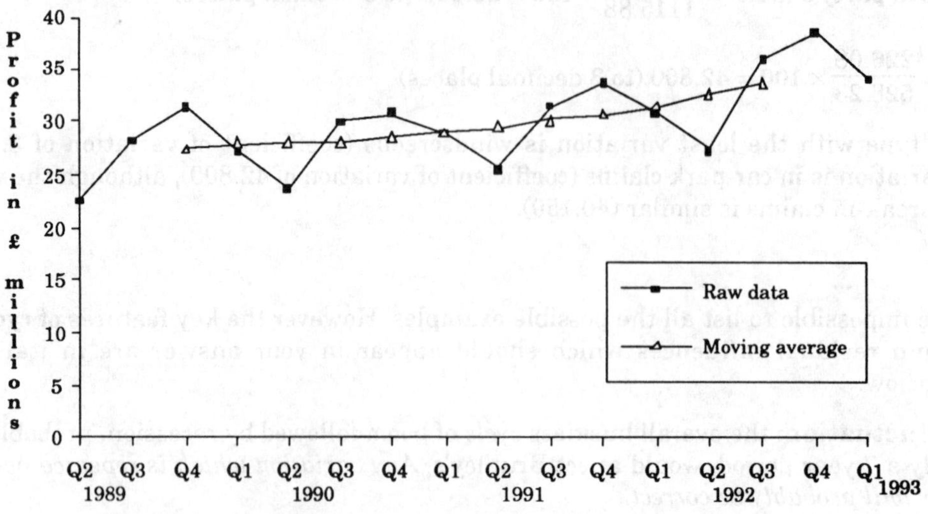

Source: Brunley's Supermarkets Corporate Sales Report 199-

The overall trend is an increasing operating profit over the period 1989 to 1993.

nit 16 **Task 16.1**

Year	Quarter	Profit (£ million)	Centred moving average (£ million)	Variation from previous quarter (£ million)
1989	2	22.7		
	3	28.3		
	4	31.4	27.5625	
1990	1	27.3	27.9125	0.3500
	2	23.8	28.0500	0.1375
	3	30.0	28.1750	0.1250
	4	30.8	28.6000	0.4250
1991	1	28.9	29.0125	0.4125
	2	25.6	29.5750	0.5625
	3	31.5	30.2125	0.6375
	4	33.8	30.7000	0.4875
1992	1	31.0	31.4875	0.7875
	2	27.4	32.6375	1.1500
	3	36.0	33.6125	0.9750
	4	38.5		
1993	1	34.1		
Total				6.0500

$$\text{Average variation} = \frac{6.05}{11} = 0.55$$

Forecast of future quarterly sales using average variation:

Year	Quarter	Previous quarter trend (£ million)	Average variation (£ million)	Basic trend forecast (£ million)
1992	4	33.6125	0.55	34.1625
1993	1	34.1625	0.55	34.7125
	2	34.7125	0.55	35.2625
	3	35.2625	0.55	35.8125
	4	35.8125	0.55	36.3625
1994	1	36.3625	0.55	36.9125
	2	36.9125	0.55	37.4625
	3	37.4625	0.55	38.0125
	4	38.0125	0.55	38.5625

Task 16.2

'Seasonally adjusting the data means taking into account the effect of regular (seasonal) variations which usually recur year after year in the same months or quarters. For example when unemployment data is seasonally adjusted this means the regular variations that occur month after month have been taken into account; thus the data is adjusted to take account of the fact that a larger number of people are out of work in the winter than the summer.'

Task 16.3

Forecasting using the moving average does not take seasonal variations into account; these are smoothed out by the use of the moving average. Therefore if there is any seasonality in the data this will not be included in the forecast. By contrast forecasting using seasonal variations takes the average variation for each 'season' into account when making the forecast.

Task 16.4

Calculation of the variation from the trend:

Year	Quarter	Profit (£ million)	Centred Moving Average (Trend) (£ million)	Variation from trend (£ million)
1989	2	22.7		
	3	28.3		
	4	31.4	27.5625	3.8375
1990	1	27.3	27.9125	-0.6125
	2	23.8	28.0500	-4.2500
	3	30.0	28.1750	1.8250
	4	30.8	28.6000	2.2000
1991	1	28.9	29.0125	-0.1125
	2	25.6	29.5750	-3.9750
	3	31.5	30.2125	1.2875
	4	33.8	30.7000	3.1000
1992	1	31.0	31.4875	-0.4875
	2	27.4	32.6375	-5.2375
	3	36.0	33.6125	2.3875
	4	38.5		
1993	1	34.1		

Calculation of corrected seasonal variation (N.B. figures rounded to 4 decimal places, spreadsheet answers may differ slightly):

Year	Quarter 1 (£ million)	Quarter 2 (£ million)	Quarter 3 (£ million)	Quarter 4 (£ million)
1989				3.8375
1990	-0.6125	-4.2500	1.8250	2.2000
1991	-0.1125	-3.9750	1.2875	3.1000
1992	-0.4875	-5.2375	2.3875	
Total	-1.2125	-13.4625	5.5000	9.1375
Average (mean)	-0.4042	-4.4875	1.8333	3.0458

Total average seasonal variation = -0.4042 + (-4.4875) + 1.8333 + 3.0458

= -0.0126

$$\text{Average correction} = \frac{-0.0126}{4} = -0.0032$$

	Quarter 1 (£ million)	Quarter 2 (£ million)	Quarter 3 (£ million)	Quarter 4 (£ million)
Average seasonal variation	-0.4042	-4.4875	1.8333	3.0458
Average correction	-0.0032	-0.0032	-0.0032	-0.0032
Corrected seasonal variation	-0.4010	-4.4843	1.8365	3.0490

To check corrected seasonal variation is right:

-0.4010 + (-4.4843) + 1.8365 + 3.0490 = 0.0002 (due to rounding errors)

therefore correct.

Forecast using seasonal variation:

Year	Quarter	Previous quarter trend (£ million)	Average variation (£ million)	Basic trend forecast (£ million)	Average seasonal variation (£ million)	This quarter trend (£ million)
1992	4	33.6125	0.55	34.1625	3.0490	37.2115
1993	1	34.1625	0.55	34.7125	-0.4010	34.3115
	2	34.7125	0.55	35.2625	-4.4843	30.7782
	3	35.2625	0.55	35.8125	1.8365	37.6490
	4	35.8125	0.55	36.3625	3.0490	39.4115
1994	1	36.3625	0.55	36.9125	-0.4010	36.5115
	2	36.9125	0.55	37.4625	-4.4843	32.9782
	3	37.4625	0.55	38.0125	1.8365	39.8490
	4	38.0125	0.55	38.5625	3.0490	41.6115

Operating Profits 1989 – 1994 (Actual and Predicted)

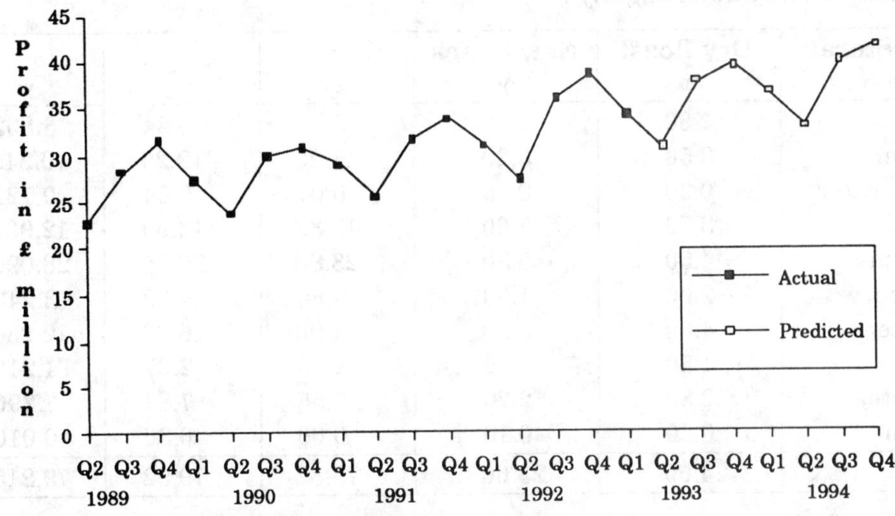

Source: Brunley's Supermarkets Corporate Sales Department

Operating profits vary seasonally, peaking in the fourth quarter of each year. Profits are forecast to increase in 1993 and 1994 following the same pattern of seasonal variations as in earlier years.

Unit 17 **Task 17.1**

Liz is correct, she could use either Spearman's Rank Correlation Coefficient or Pearson's Product Moment Correlation Coefficient. Pearson's Product Moment Correlation Coefficient could be calculated using the data without amendment. If the data was ranked then Spearman's Rank Correlation Coefficient could be calculated.

Task 17.2

Scatter graph of Dry Roast Peanut Sales against New Snack Sales

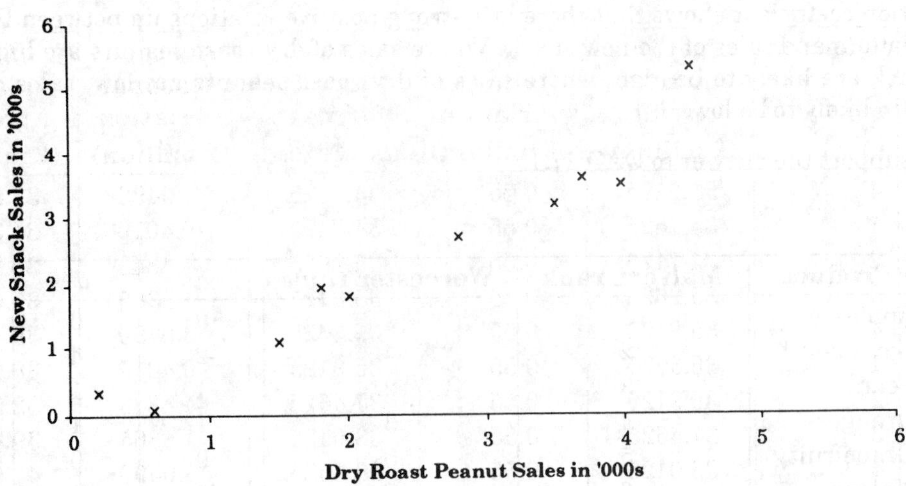

Source: Brunley's Trials in 10 Stores 199-

Calculation of correlation coefficient (N.B. numbers rounded to 2 decimal places in calculation – spreadsheet answers may differ slightly):

Trial Store	Dry Roast x	New Snack y	xy	x^2	y^2
Malvern	1.80	1.95	3.51	3.24	3.8025
Worcester	3.50	3.20	11.20	12.25	10.2400
Kidderminster	0.20	0.35	0.07	0.04	0.1225
Hereford	3.70	3.60	13.32	13.69	12.9600
Cheltenham	4.50	5.30	23.85	20.25	28.0900
Tewkesbury	2.00	1.80	3.60	4.00	3.2400
Gloucester	4.00	3.50	14.00	16.00	12.2500
Stroud	1.50	1.10	1.65	2.25	1.2100
Cirencester	2.80	2.70	7.56	7.84	7.2900
Evesham	0.60	0.10	0.06	0.36	0.0100
Total	24.60	23.60	78.82	79.92	79.2150

$$r = \frac{(10 \times 78.82) - (24.6 \times 23.6)}{\sqrt{(10 \times 79.92 - (24.6)^2)\,(10 \times 79.215 - (23.6)^2)}}$$

$$= \frac{788.2 - 580.56}{\sqrt{(799.2 - 605.16)\,(792.15 - 556.96)}}$$

$$= \frac{207.64}{\sqrt{194.04 \times 235.19}}$$

$$= \frac{207.64}{\sqrt{45636.27}}$$

$$= \frac{207.64}{213.63}$$

$$= 0.97 \text{ (to 2 decimal places)}$$

The correlation coefficient shows that there is a strong positive relationship between the sales of dry roast peanuts and sales of the new snack. Where sales of dry roast peanuts are high, sales of the new snack are likely to be high; where sales of dry roast peanuts are low, sales of the new snack are also likely to be low.

Yes it does support the answer to QAQ 17.1.

Task 17.3

Product	Malvern rank	Worcester rank	d	d^2
Apples	1	1	0	0
Bananas	2	4	-2	4
Pears	3	2	1	1
Oranges	4	3	1	1
Grapefruit	5	5	0	0
Melons	6	7	-1	1
Grapes	7	6	1	1
Kiwi Fruits	8	9	-1	1
Cherries	9	8	1	1
Fresh Figs	10	10	0	0
Total				10

$$r^s = 1 - \frac{6 \times 10}{10\,(10^2 - 1)}$$

$$= 1 - \frac{60}{10 \times (100 - 1)}$$

$$= 1 - \frac{60}{10 \times 99}$$

$$= 1 - \frac{60}{99}$$

$$= 1 - 0.06 = 0.94 \text{ (to 2 decimal places)}$$

There is a strong correlation between the rank order of sales of fruits in the Malvern and Worcester stores; this means that fruits with higher numbers of sales in the Malvern store are likely to be similar to fruits with higher number of sales in the Worcester store.

Unit 18 **Task 18.1**

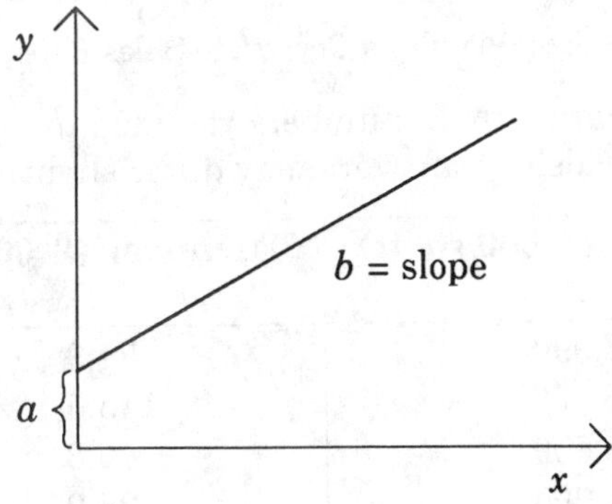

y represents the dependent variable, in this case sales.

x represents the independent variable, in this case floor area.

a represents the intercept (where the regression line crosses the y axis). This has a constant value which can be either negative or positive.

b represents the angle of slope of the regression line. This is the factor we need to multiply floor area when predicting profit.

Task 18.2

Interpolation refers to predicting the dependent variable (in this case turnover) between known data points for the independent variable; in this case between floor areas of 2,100 and 18,500 square feet.

Extrapolation is predicting the dependent variable (turnover) outside known data points for the independent variable; in this case outside the range of floor areas of 2,100 to 18,500 square feet.

Liz says that extrapolation is a 'bit dodgy' because any regression equation is only based upon the values within the data range. Extrapolation involves values outside the data range and so is likely to be less accurate.

Task 18.3

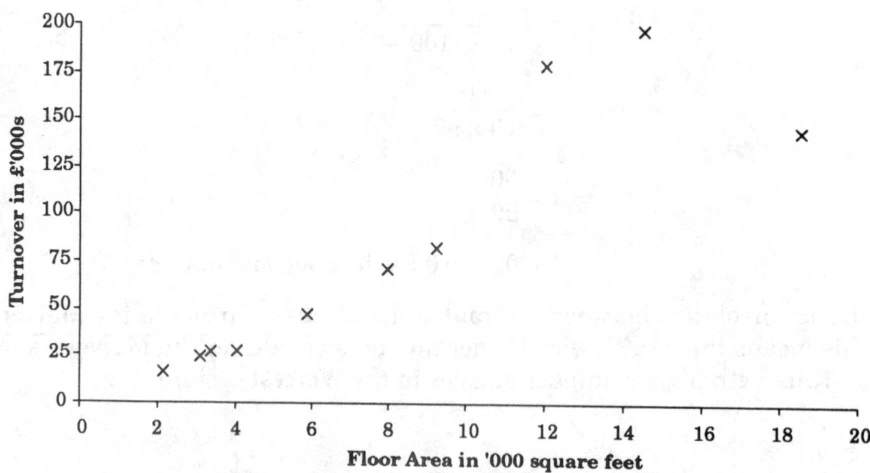

Source: Brunley's Corporate Sales Report 199-

Calculation of regression equation (N.B. numbers rounded to 4 decimal places or to 8 significant figures where necessary, spreadsheet answers may differ slightly):

Store	Floor area ('000 sq. ft)	Turnover (£ '000s)		
	x	y	xy	x^2
Monmouth	7.990	71.9	574.481	63.8401
Bristol	18.500	145.0	2682.500	342.2500
Ross on Wye	5.850	46.8	273.780	34.2225
Chippenham	4.000	28.0	112.000	16.0000
Trowbridge	3.075	24.6	75.645	9.4556
Bath	14.500	199.0	2885.500	210.2500
Wells	3.400	27.2	92.480	11.5600
Bridgewater	9.200	82.8	761.760	84.6400
Swindon	12.000	179.0	2148.000	144.0000
Marlborough	2.100	16.8	35.280	4.4100
Total	80.615	821.1	9641.426	920.6282

$$\text{Gradient (b)} = \frac{(10 \times 9641.426) - (80.615 \times 821.1)}{(10 \times 920.6282) - 80.615^2}$$

$$= \frac{96414.26 - 66192.976}{9206.282 - 6498.7782}$$

$$= \frac{30221.284}{2707.5038}$$

$$= 11.1620$$

$$\text{Intercept (a)} = \frac{821.1 - (11.1620 \times 80.615)}{10}$$

$$= \frac{821.1 - 899.82463}{10}$$

$$= -7.8672 \text{ (to 4 decimal places)}$$

therefore the regression equation is:

turnover (£'000s) = -7.8672 + (11.1620 × floor area ('000s sq ft))

If the floor area is 8,000 square feet predicted value of sales is £81,428.80

If the floor area is 15,000 square feet predicted value of sales is £159,562.80

Task 18.4

To calculate the coefficient of determination we also need to know Σy^2 for the sum of squares before regression.

Calculation of y^2:

Store	Turnover (£ '000s) y	y^2
Monmouth	71.9	5169.61
Bristol	145.0	21025.00
Ross on Wye	46.8	2190.24
Chippenham	28.0	784.00
Trowbridge	24.6	605.16
Bath	199.0	39601.00
Wells	27.2	739.84
Bridgewater	82.8	6855.84
Swindon	179.0	32041.00
Marlborough	16.8	282.24
Total	821.1	109293.93

Sum of squares explained by regression (N.B. numbers rounded to 4 decimal places or to 8 significant figures where necessary, spreadsheet answers may differ slightly):

$$= \frac{\left(9641.426 - \frac{80.615 \times 821.1}{10}\right)^2}{920.6282 - \frac{80.615^2}{10}}$$

$$= \frac{(9641.426 - 6619.2976)^2}{920.6282 - 649.8778}$$

$$= \frac{9133260.1}{270.7504}$$

$$= 33733.136$$

Sum of squares before the regression

$$= 109293.93 - \frac{(821.1)^2}{10}$$

$$= 109293.93 - 67420.521$$

$$= 41873.409$$

$$\text{Coefficient of determination} = \frac{33733.136}{41873.409}$$

$$= 0.8055 \text{ (to 4 decimal places)}$$

This means that 80.55% of the variation in weekly turnover of stores can be explained by the stores' floor areas.

Unit 19 **Task 19.1**

Null hypothesis: there is no significant difference in the number of sales of mayonnaise before and after the promotion period.

Hypothesis: there is a significant difference in the number of sales of mayonnaise before and after the promotion period.

Calculation of Chi Square (N.B. numbers rounded to 2 decimal places where necessary):

Period	Observed	Expected	$O-E$	$\lvert O-E\rvert-0.5$	$(\lvert O-E\rvert-0.5)^2$	$\frac{(\lvert O-E\rvert-0.5)^2}{E}$
Before	230	275	-45	44.5	1980.25	7.20
After	320	275	45	44.5	1980.25	7.20
Total						14.40

Degrees of freedom = 2 – 1 = 1

From appendix 4 the critical value of chi square with 1 degree of freedom is 6.63 at the 0.01 level. As our calculated value is 14.40 (greater) we can reject the null hypothesis and accept the hypothesis.

Brunley's should therefore introduce this promotion into the rest of their stores.

Task 19.2

Liz needed to use Yate's correction because the table only had one degree of freedom.

Task 19.3

Null hypothesis: there is no significant relationship between the social class of potential customers and whether they purchase salad cream or mayonnaise.

Hypothesis: there is a significant relationship between the social class of potential customers and whether they purchase salad cream or mayonnaise.

Expected values rounded to 2 decimal places where necessary:

Class	Salad Cream	Mayonnaise	Total
Upper	75.41	74.59	150
Middle	193.56	191.44	385
Lower	186.02	183.98	370
Total	455.00	450.00	905

Calculation of Chi Square (N.B. numbers rounded to 2 decimal places where necessary):

Class	Purchase	Observed	Expected	$O-E$	$(O-E)^2$	$\frac{(O-E)^2}{E}$
Upper	Salad	60	75.41	-15.41	237.47	3.15
	Mayonnaise	90	74.59	15.41	237.47	3.18
Middle	Salad	175	193.56	-18.56	344.47	1.78
	Mayonnaise	210	191.44	18.56	344.47	1.80
Lower	Salad	220	186.02	33.98	1154.64	6.21
	Mayonnaise	150	183.98	-33.98	1154.64	6.28
Total		905	905			22.40

Degrees of freedom = (3 – 1) × (2 – 1) = 2

From appendix 4 the critical value of chi square with 2 degrees of freedom is 9.21 at the 0.01 level. As our calculated value is 22.40 (greater) we can reject the null hypothesis and accept the hypothesis.

Brunley's should therefore target the mayonnaise promotion by social class. They should target their upper and middle class customers as these people are more likely to purchase mayonnaise than salad cream.

Unit 20 Task 20.1

Liz decided not to use 1984 as the base year because it was not a typical year. Brunley's had only sold blank video tapes for four months of that year.

N.B. numbers rounded to 2 decimal places where necessary.

$$\text{Quantity index for 1984} = \frac{45000}{171000} \times 100 = 26.32$$

$$\text{Quantity index for 1985} = \frac{171000}{171000} \times 100 = 100.00$$

$$\text{Quantity index for 1986} = \frac{175000}{171000} \times 100 = 102.34$$

$$\text{Quantity index for 1987} = \frac{180000}{171000} \times 100 = 105.26$$

$$\text{Quantity index for 1988} = \frac{190000}{171000} \times 100 = 111.11$$

$$\text{Quantity index for 1989} = \frac{195000}{171000} \times 100 = 114.04$$

$$\text{Quantity index for 1990} = \frac{200000}{171000} \times 100 = 116.96$$

$$\text{Quantity index for 1991} = \frac{206000}{171000} \times 100 = 120.47$$

$$\text{Quantity index for 1992} = \frac{213000}{171000} \times 100 = 124.56$$

Task 20.2

N.B. numbers rounded to 2 decimal places where necessary.

$$\text{Quantity index for 1986} = \frac{175000}{175000} \times 100 = 100.00$$

$$\text{Quantity index for 1987} = \frac{180000}{175000} \times 100 = 102.86$$

$$\text{Quantity index for 1988} = \frac{190000}{175000} \times 100 = 108.57$$

$$\text{Quantity index for 1989} = \frac{195000}{175000} \times 100 = 111.43$$

$$\text{Quantity index for 1990} = \frac{200000}{175000} \times 100 = 114.29$$

$$\text{Quantity index for 1991} = \frac{206000}{175000} \times 100 = 117.71$$

$$\text{Quantity index for 1992} = \frac{213000}{175000} \times 100 = 121.71$$

Sales of blank video tapes have increased more rapidly at Brunley's than at supermarkets in general since 1986.

Task 20.3

$$\text{Price index for Brunley's baked beans} = \frac{27}{18} \times 100 = 150.00$$

$$\text{Price index for Hugo's baked beans} = \frac{32}{24} \times 100 = 133.33 \text{ (to 2 decimal places)}$$

Brunley's baked beans have experienced the largest price rise in the period 1988 – 1992.

Task 20.4

$$\text{Expenditure index for Brunley's baked beans} = \frac{27 \times 49}{18 \times 68} \times 100$$

$$= \frac{1323}{1224} \times 100 = 108.09 \text{ (to 2 decimal places)}$$

$$\text{Expenditure index for Hugo's baked beans} = \frac{32 \times 27}{24 \times 36} \times 100$$

$$= \frac{864}{864} \times 100 = 100$$

The average customer's expenditure on Brunley's baked beans has increased by 8.09% over the period 1988 – 1992.

The average customer's expenditure on Hugo's baked beans has remained constant.

Unit 21 **Task 21.1**

(N.B. numbers rounded to 2 decimal places where necessary)

Item	Price 5 yrs ago p_o	Price today p_n	Price Index $\frac{p_n}{p_o} \times 100$
Baked beans	£0.22	£0.28	127.27
Milk	£0.20	£0.26	130.00
Corn flakes	£0.99	£1.29	130.30
Butter	£0.45	£0.63	140.00
Bread	£0.54	£0.69	127.78
Coffee	£1.19	£1.59	133.61
Cola	£0.49	£0.59	120.41
Beef	£3.99	£5.99	150.13
Total			1059.50

$$\text{Average price index} = \frac{1059.50}{8} = 132.44$$

This calculation gives a lower increase for Brunley's than that in the Gaterose advertisement.

Task 21.2

Item	5 years ago		Today	Expenditure 5 years ago	Expenditure today
	p_o	q_o	p_n	p_oq_o	p_nq_o
Baked Beans	£0.22	3	£0.28	0.66	0.84
Milk	£0.20	4	£0.26	0.80	1.04
Corn flakes	£0.99	1	£1.29	0.99	1.29
Butter	£0.45	2	£0.63	0.90	1.26
Bread	£0.54	4	£0.69	2.16	2.76
Coffee	£1.19	1	£1.59	1.19	1.59
Cola	£0.49	2	£0.59	0.98	1.18
Beef	£3.99	3	£5.99	11.97	17.97
Total				19.65	27.93

Laspeyre's price index $= \frac{27.93}{19.65} \times 100 = 142.14$ (to 2 decimal places)

This calculation does suggest the same increase as the Gaterose advertisement. The Gaterose advertisement says 'over £142', it would have said 'over £143' if the index number had been 143 or above.

Task 21.3

Item	5 years ago	Today		Expenditure 5 years ago	Expenditure today
	p_o	q_n	p_n	p_oq_n	p_nq_n
Baked Beans	£0.22	2	£0.28	0.44	0.56
Milk	£0.20	3	£0.26	0.60	0.78
Corn flakes	£0.99	1	£1.29	0.99	1.29
Butter	£0.45	1	£0.63	0.45	0.63
Bread	£0.54	4	£0.69	2.16	2.76
Coffee	£1.19	1	£1.59	1.19	1.59
Cola	£0.49	3	£0.59	1.47	1.77
Beef	£3.99	2	£5.99	7.98	11.98
Total				15.28	21.36

Paasche's price index $= \frac{21.36}{15.28} \times 100 = 139.79$ (to 2 decimal places)

This calculation gives a lower increase than that suggested by the Gaterose advertisement.

The price index that shows the increase in the price of Brunley's weekly shopping basket to the best advantage is the average price index.

Unit 22 Task 22.1

(N.B. Numbers rounded to two decimal places when necessary.)

Year	Hourly rate	Chain based index
1981	£1.98	1.98 / 1.98 × 100 = 100.00
1982	£2.18	2.18 / 1.98 × 100 = 110.10
1983	£2.30	2.30 / 2.18 × 100 = 105.50
1984	£2.43	2.43 / 2.30 × 100 = 105.65
1985	£2.67	2.67 / 2.43 × 100 = 109.88
1986	£2.86	2.86 / 2.67 × 100 = 107.12
1987	£3.12	3.12 / 2.86 × 100 = 109.09
1988	£3.41	3.41 / 3.12 × 100 = 109.29
1989	£3.75	3.75 / 3.41 × 100 = 109.97
1990	£3.89	3.89 / 3.75 × 100 = 103.73
1991	£4.04	4.04 / 3.89 × 100 = 103.86
1992	£4.19	4.19 / 4.04 × 100 = 103.71
1993	pending	

Barry's suggestion that the union negotiator is basing the pay claim on 1989 because it was the year the checkout operators had their last large pay rise is correct.

Task 22.2

'Splice the inflation index' means combining two or more overlapping indices whose base years are different. As the most recent data is usually considered the most important the spliced indices are usually recalculated on the latest base year; in this case 1990.

Deflating the checkout operators' hourly rate to 1990 prices enables the checkout operators' hourly rate to be calculated for all years at 1990 prices. The effect of increases in the hourly rate which took account of inflation have therefore been removed.

Task 22.3

The first stage is to spice the indices for the inflation index using 1990 as the base year. The answers are given in the table below.

For the years 1984 – 1990 the original index numbers are multiplied by $\frac{100}{145}$

For the years 1981 – 1983 the original index numbers are multiplied by $\frac{100}{180} \times \frac{100}{145}$

(N.B. all index numbers have been rounded to 2 decimal places)

Year	Inflation Index	Spliced Index
1981	155	59.39
1982	171	65.52
1983	180 (=100)	68.97
1984	105	72.41
1985	111	76.55
1986	116	80.00
1987	121	83.45
1988	125	86.21
1989	135	93.10
1990	145 (=100)	100.00
1991	109	109.00
1992	112	112.00
1993	114	114.00

The next stage is to deflate the hourly rates to 1990 prices. This is done by dividing each years hourly rate by the spliced index and then multiplying by 100.

Year	Spliced Index	Hourly rate	Hourly rate @ 1990 prices
1981	59.39	£1.98	£3.33
1982	65.52	£2.18	£3.33
1983	68.97	£2.30	£3.33
1984	72.41	£2.43	£3.36
1985	76.55	£2.67	£3.49
1986	80.00	£2.86	£3.58
1987	83.45	£3.12	£3.74
1988	86.21	£3.41	£3.96
1989	93.10	£3.75	£4.03
1990	100.00	£3.89	£3.89
1991	109.00	£4.04	£3.71
1992	112.00	£4.19	£3.74
1993	114.00	£4.27	£3.75

The hourly rate for checkout operators has fallen well behind the rate of inflation since 1989.

The union negotiator chose 1989 as the year on which to base the pay claim as this was the year in which the checkout operators' hourly rate was at its highest, once the effects of inflation have been taken into account.

Unit 23 Task 23.1

The probability of a store employee having had an accident in the past year is:

$$\frac{832}{22700} = 0.03665 \text{ (to 5 decimal places)}$$

Yes, it is a mutually exclusive event. The event set consists of two possible events:

- employee has had an accident in the past year;
- employee has not had an accident in the past year.

If an employee has had an accident in the past year then, by definition, they could not have not had an accident in the past year.

Task 23.2

Given a store employee has had an accident in the past year, the probability the employee was a....

checkout operator is: $\frac{11000}{22700} = 0.48458$ (to 5 decimal places)

shelf stacker is: $\frac{9850}{22700} = 0.43392$ (to 5 decimal places)

member of administration staff is: $\frac{1600}{22700} = 0.07048$ (to 5 decimal places)

member of managerial staff is: $\frac{250}{22700} = 0.01101$ (to 5 decimal places)

The probability that the accident involved either a checkout operator or a shelf stacker is:

$$\frac{11000 + 9850}{22700} = 0.91850 \text{ (to 5 decimal places)}$$

Task 23.3

If an accident occurred at a store during the past year the probability that it was at a....

town centre store is: $\frac{10050}{22700} = 0.44273$ (to 5 decimal places)

suburban store is: $\frac{9100}{22700} = 0.40088$ (to 5 decimal places)

out of town store is: $\frac{3550}{22700} = 0.15639$ (to 5 decimal places)

Probability of an accident occurring at an out of town store and involving a female employee is:

$0.7 \times 0.15639 = 0.10947$ (to 5 decimal places)

Task 23.4

Memorandum BRUNLEY'S SUPERMARKETS

From: Liz Reynolds, Personnel Department
To: Fred Smith, Health and Safety Committee
Subject: Employee Accidents
Date: 18th June 199-

Further to your recent communication with Barry Bacon of this department please find below the information you requested:

1. The probability of a store employee having had an accident in the past year is 0.03665.

2. Given that a store employee has had an accident in the past year, the probability that the employee was:

   a checkout operator is 0.48458;
   a shelf stacker is 0.43392;
   a member of administrative staff is 0.07048;
   a manager is 0.01101.

3. If an accident occurred at a store during the past year what was the probability it was at:

   a town centre store is 0.44273;
   a suburban store is 0.40088;
   an out of town store 0.15639.

4. Given that 70% of our store employees are female the probability that an accident occurs at an out of town store and involves a female employee is 0.10947.

All probabilities have been calculated to 5 decimal places. Please do not hesitate to contact me if you require further information.

Liz Reynolds

Unit 24 Task 24.1

(N.B. Numbers rounded to 2 decimal places where necessary)

Claim type	Mean value x	Probability p	px
Windscreen	£178.25	0.08	14.26
Theft / Break – in	£1984.78	0.27	535.89
Collision (Brunley's fault)	£915.42	0.26	238.01
Collision (3rd party's fault)	£1115.88	0.25	278.97
Car – park	£528.23	0.14	73.95
Total			1141.08

Mean expected insurance claim is £1141.08

Task 24.2

Calculation of expected values:

Age	Had accident	Did not have accident	Total
Under 35	57	63	120
35 or over	38	42	80
Total	95	105	200

Probability of each of the following occurring:

a company car driver aged under 35 having an accident: $\frac{57}{200} = 0.285$

a company car driver aged 35 or over having an accident: $\frac{38}{200} = 0.190$

a company car driver aged under 35 not having an accident: $\frac{63}{200} = 0.315$

a company car driver aged 35 or over not having an accident: $\frac{42}{200} = 0.210$

The probability that, given a company car driver is aged 35 or over, they have an accident is:

$$\frac{38}{80} = 0.475$$

Task 24.3

Probability company car driver has an accident, $p(A) = 0.475$

Probability that a company car driver is aged 35 or over given they have an accident, $p(T|A) = 0.400$

Probability that a company car driver is aged over 35, $p(T) = 0.400$

$$\text{Bayes' theorem} = p(A|T) = \frac{p(A) \times p(T|A)}{p(T)}$$

$$= \frac{0.475 \times 0.400}{0.400}$$

$$= \frac{0.190}{0.400}$$

= 0.475 (same answer, therefore it does 'check')

Unit 25 **Task 25.1**

z score for 30 years service $= \dfrac{30 - 20}{7} = 1.43$ (to 2 decimal places)

Probability over 30 years service $=$ $1 - z$ score probability less than or equal to 30 years (from appendix 5)

$= 1 - 0.9236$

$= 0.0764$

Checkout operators eligible for early retirement $= 11000 \times 0.0764 = 840$

Task 25.2

z score for 3 years service $= \dfrac{3 - 20}{7} = -2.43$ (to 2 decimal places)

z score for 5 years service $= \dfrac{5 - 20}{7} = -2.14$ (to 2 decimal places)

Probability of less than or equal to 3 years of service is the probability that z is less than -2.43. As we do not have tabulated negative values of z we use the fact that the distribution is symmetrical and calculate the probability that z is greater than 2.43.

$= 1 - 0.9925 = 0.0075$

Checkout operators with 3 or less years service $= 11000 \times 0.0075 = 83$ redundancies.

Probability of less than or equal to 5 years of service is the probability that z is less than -2.14. As we do not have tabulated negative values of z we use the fact that the distribution is symmetrical and calculate the probability that z is greater than 2.14.

$= 1 - 0.9838 = 0.0162$

Checkout operators with 5 or less years service $= 11000 \times 0.0162 = 178$ redundancies.

Task 25.3

Probability of a checkout operator keeping their job $= 1 - (0.0764 + 0.0075)$

$= 1 - 0.0839$

$= 0.9161$

Number of checkout operators left after compulsory redundancies and early retirements

$= 11000 \times 0.9161 = 10{,}077$

Appendix 2: Answers to selected tasks in Section 3

Task 1.3

The report contains information as far as you (the assistant manager) are concerned.

As the assistant manager you could almost certainly interpret and understand the table and would find it useful for the feasibility study. The information is relevant and at the right level of detail. The sample size of 5,000 suggests that it should be sufficiently accurate. It is also timely as it was collected last January. It should be noted that you would require further information upon which to base the feasibility study.

Task 2.1

Your answer to this task will depend upon the random numbers you selected, and the way in which you numbered your sampling frame. However the process which you followed, and the pattern of each of the samples selected, is likely to be similar to that given below.

Staff members in sampling frame numbered starting at 0 (N.B. it is acceptable to number either along the rows or down the columns).

	Name	Ext.		Name	Ext.		Name	Ext.		Name	Ext.
0	Claire	7646	*13*	George	5454	*26*	Barry	6335	*38*	Chris	6664
1	Graham	6453	*14*	Maureen	4242	*27*	Sarah	4222	*39*	Mike	5332
2	Susan	5354	*15*	Jean	2245	*28*	Maria	7463	*40*	Martin	6424
3	Benjamin	5425	*16*	Mark	7355	*29*	Kenneth	5353	*41*	Val	5432
4	Sue	4245	*17*	Peter	5656	*30*	Jenny	4227	*42*	Sarah	7898
5	Sharon	7497	*18*	Julia	4690	*31*	Margaret	6789	*43*	Denise	6789
6	Sean	7567	*19*	Phil	5456	*32*	Pete	5588	*44*	Angela	6557
7	Mike	6336	*20*	Steve	5535	*33*	Derek	7554	*45*	John	4224
8	Keith	4648	*21*	Douglas	4478	*34*	Gregory	5353	*46*	Jemma	5353
9	Jane	5426	*22*	Stacey	5335	*35*	Paul	5757	*47*	Eliza	5568
10	June	5422	*23*	Andy	5352	*36*	Ann	4649	*48*	Jackie	7570
11	Adrian	5211	*24*	Joan	5400	*37*	Edward	5698	*49*	Ivan	3560
12	David	7970	*25*	Norman	5435						

Starting at randomly selected points, two sets of two digit 10 random numbers are read from the random number tables (appendix 3). If a number is selected twice, or it is outside the range 0 to 49 it is disregarded. For example these could be:

Set 1: 18, 46, 17, 02, 36, 40, 41, 06, 07, 32
Set 2: 14, 46, 39, 20, 48, 36, 25, 42, 02, 40

These are then marked on the sampling frame (in the example below set 1 is shaded, and set 2 is enclosed by a box):

	Name	Ext.		Name	Ext.		Name	Ext.		Name	Ext.
0	Claire	7646	*13*	George	5454	*26*	Barry	6335	*38*	Chris	6664
1	Graham	6453	*14*	Maureen	4242	*27*	Sarah	4222	*39*	Mike	5332
2	Susan	5354	*15*	Jean	2245	*28*	Maria	7463	*40*	Martin	6424
3	Benjamin	5425	*16*	Mark	7355	*29*	Kenneth	5353	*41*	Val	5432
4	Sue	4245	*17*	Peter	5656	*30*	Jenny	4227	*42*	Sarah	7898
5	Sharon	7497	*18*	Julia	4690	*31*	Margaret	6789	*43*	Denise	6789
6	Sean	7567	*19*	Phil	5456	*32*	Pete	5588	*44*	Angela	6557
7	Mike	6336	*20*	Steve	5535	*33*	Derek	7554	*45*	John	4224
8	Keith	4648	*21*	Douglas	4478	*34*	Gregory	5353	*46*	Jemma	5353
9	Jane	5426	*22*	Stacey	5335	*35*	Paul	5757	*47*	Eliza	5568
10	June	5422	*23*	Andy	5352	*36*	Ann	4649	*48*	Jackie	7570
11	Adrian	5211	*24*	Joan	5400	*37*	Edward	5698	*49*	Ivan	3560
12	David	7970	*25*	Norman	5435						

Your sets are likely to produce patterns which involve clustering around certain numbers in the sampling frame. However they may differ in the amount of clustering of sample points. In the example above the patterns are:

- set 1 (shaded): pattern is clustered around certain numbers in the sampling frame (2-7 and 40s) with larger gaps elsewhere;
- set 2 (boxed): pattern is clustered around certain numbers in the sampling frame (40s), elsewhere it is more dispersed.

The proportions of male and female staff members selected will depend upon your sample. In the example above the proportions are:

- set 1 (shaded): 50% males and 50% females from a total population of 54% males and 46% females;
- set 2 (boxed): 40% males and 60% females from a total population of 54% males and 46% females.

There is no bias in either sample, both have been selected at random. However in the case of this example the sample selected for set 2 (boxed) is less representative of the total population (in terms of gender) than that selected for set 1 (shaded). This has occurred entirely at random.

Task 2.2

Your answer to this task will depend upon the random number you select as the starting point for your systematic sample, and the way in which you numbered your sampling frame. However the process which you followed, and the pattern of each of the samples selected, is likely to be similar to that given below.

Staff members in sampling frame are numbered starting at 0 (N.B. it is acceptable to number either along the rows or down the columns). This is illustrated in the answer to task 2.1. As it is a 20% sample every fifth staff member needs to be selected. The starting point is selected using a random number between 0 and 4, in this case 3 (your starting point may differ). Once the staff member numbered 3 has been located every fifth staff member is selected:

3, 8, 13, 18, 23, 28, 33, 38, 43, 48

These are then marked on the sampling frame (in the example each sample member is enclosed by a box):

	Name	Ext.		Name	Ext.		Name	Ext.		Name	Ext.
0	Claire	7646	*13*	George	5454	*26*	Barry	6335	*38*	Chris	6664
1	Graham	6453	*14*	Maureen	4242	*27*	Sarah	4222	*39*	Mike	5332
2	Susan	5354	*15*	Jean	2245	*28*	Maria	7463	*40*	Martin	6424
3	Benjamin	5425	*16*	Mark	7355	*29*	Kenneth	5353	*41*	Val	5432
4	Sue	4245	*17*	Peter	5656	*30*	Jenny	4227	*42*	Sarah	7898
5	Sharon	7497	*18*	Julia	4690	*31*	Margaret	6789	*43*	Denise	6789
6	Sean	7567	*19*	Phil	5456	*32*	Pete	5588	*44*	Angela	6557
7	Mike	6336	*20*	Steve	5535	*33*	Derek	7554	*45*	John	4224
8	Keith	4648	*21*	Douglas	4478	*34*	Gregory	5353	*46*	Jemma	5353
9	Jane	5426	*22*	Stacey	5335	*35*	Paul	5757	*47*	Eliza	5568
10	June	5422	*23*	Andy	5352	*36*	Ann	4649	*48*	Jackie	7570
11	Adrian	5211	*24*	Joan	5400	*37*	Edward	5698	*49*	Ivan	3560
12	David	7970	*25*	Norman	5435						

Your sample should produce a regular pattern which, unlike the random samples, has no clustering around certain groups of numbers in the sampling frame.

Once the first point has been selected at random, the likelihood of any other member of staff in the sampling frame being selected has been fixed. In the example once the 3rd staff member had been selected then this determined that the 8th, 13th, 18th ... 48th staff members would also be selected. The likelihood of them being selected was 100%. By contrast the likelihood of the remaining staff members being selected was 0%.

Task 3.3

The bar chart below is drawn to facilitate a comparison between gender of employees, hence the bars for males and females are placed next to each other.

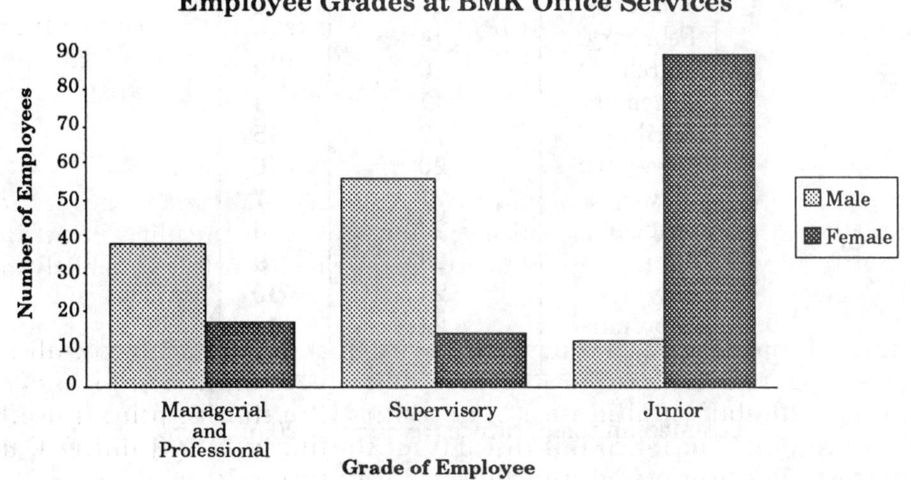

Source: Personnel Department 199-

The bar chart below is drawn to facilitate a comparison between grades of employees, hence the bars for each of the three grades are placed next to each other.

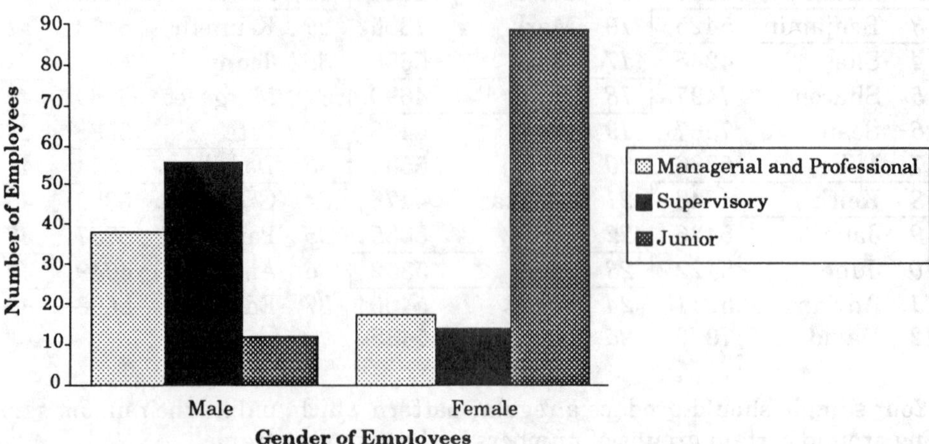

Source: Personnel Department 199-

Task 4.2

$$\text{Mean temperature} = \frac{13 + 14 + 16 + 19 + 21 + 23 + 24 + 25 + 24 + 22 + 20 + 17}{12}$$

$$= \frac{238}{12} = 19.8°\text{C (to 1 decimal place)}$$

$$\text{Median pointer} = \frac{12 + 1}{2} = 6.5 \text{ position (once the data has been ranked in ascending order)}$$

Month	Temperature	Rank
January	13	1
February	14	2
March	16	3
December	17	4
April	19	5
November	20	6
May	21	7
October	22	8
June	23	9
July	24	10
September	24	11
August	25	12

$$\text{Median temperature} = \frac{20 + 21}{2} = 20.5°\text{C}$$

Modal (average) temperature is 24°C

$$\text{Mean rainfall} = \frac{50 + 23 + 10 + 1 + 1 + 1 + 1 + 1 + 1 + 3 + 15 + 54}{12}$$

$$= \frac{161}{12} = 13.4 \text{ mm (to 1 decimal place)}$$

$$\text{Median pointer} = \frac{12 + 1}{2} = 6.5 \text{ position (once the data has been ranked in ascending order)}$$

Month	Rainfall	Rank
April	1	1
May	1	2
June	1	3
July	1	4
August	1	5
September	1	6
October	3	7
March	10	8
November	15	9
February	23	10
January	50	11
December	54	12

$$\text{Median rainfall} = \frac{1+3}{2} = 2 \text{ mm}$$

Modal (average) rainfall = 1mm

In both cases you would probably choose the mode. This gives the highest 'average' monthly temperature, and the lowest 'average' monthly rainfall, ideal for beach holidays.

Task 5.1

Calculations for rents in Southam:

Southam rents (£s)	Rank
4.89	1
5.87	2
5.98	3
6.98	4
7.20	5
7.37	6
7.40	7
7.80	8
8.65	9
8.82	10
9.36	11
9.50	12
10.34	13
10.40	14
10.93	15
11.04	16
11.10	17
11.40	18
11.80	19
13.00	20
13.25	21
15.92	22

$$\text{Median pointer} = \frac{22+1}{2} = \frac{23}{2} = 11.5$$

Therefore the median is halfway between the 11th and 12th rental.

$$\text{Median} = \frac{9.36 + 9.50}{2} = £9.43 \text{ per square foot}$$

$$\text{Lower quartile pointer} = \frac{22+1}{4} = \frac{23}{4} = 5.75$$

Therefore the lower quartile is 0.75 of the way between the 5th and 6th rental.

$$\begin{aligned}\text{Lower quartile} &= 7.20 + 0.75 \times (7.37 - 7.20)\\ &= 7.20 + 0.75 \times (0.17)\\ &= 7.20 + 0.1275\\ &= £7.33 \text{ per square foot (to 2 decimal places)}\end{aligned}$$

$$\text{Upper quartile pointer} = \frac{3 \times (22+1)}{4} = \frac{69}{4} = 17.25$$

Therefore the upper quartile is 0.25 of the way between the 17th and 18th rental.

$$\begin{aligned}\text{Upper quartile} &= 11.10 + 0.25 \times (11.40 - 11.10)\\ &= 11.10 + 0.25 \times (0.30)\\ &= 11.10 + 0.075\\ &= £11.18 \text{ per square foot (to 2 decimal places)}\end{aligned}$$

$$\text{Inter-quartile range} = 11.18 - 7.33 = £3.85 \text{ per square foot.}$$

Calculations for rents in Northam:

Northam rents (£s)	Rank
11.89	1
12.09	2
12.34	3
12.50	4
12.69	5
12.86	6
12.87	7
12.90	8
13.14	9
13.27	10
13.67	11
13.78	12
14.21	13
14.59	14
14.65	15
14.99	16
14.99	17

Median pointer $= \frac{17+1}{2} = \frac{18}{2} = 9$ Therefore the median is the 9th rental

Median = £13.14 per square foot

Lower quartile pointer $= \frac{17+1}{4} = \frac{18}{4} = 4.5$ Therefore the lower quartile is half way between the 4th and 5th rental.

Lower quartile $= \frac{12.50 + 12.69}{2} = £12.60$ per square foot (to 2 decimal places)

Upper quartile pointer = $\frac{3 \times (17+1)}{4} = \frac{54}{4} = 13.5$

Therefore the upper quartile is half way between the 13th and 14th rental.

Upper quartile = $\frac{14.21 + 14.59}{2}$ = £14.40 per square foot

Inter-quartile range = 14.40 – 12.60 = £1.80 per square foot.

Calculations for Westham:

Westham rents (£s)	Rank
6.59	1
6.99	2
7.20	3
7.40	4
7.44	5
8.09	6
8.28	7
8.70	8
9.53	9
9.71	10
9.75	11
9.97	12
9.99	13
10.40	14
10.57	15
10.60	16
10.70	17
10.90	18
11.99	19
11.99	20
12.71	21

Median pointer = $\frac{21+1}{2} = \frac{22}{2} = 11$ Therefore the median is the 11th rental.

Median = £9.75 per square foot

Lower quartile pointer = $\frac{21+1}{4} = \frac{22}{4} = 5.5$

Therefore the lower quartile is half way between the 5th and 6th rental.

Lower quartile = $\frac{7.44 + 8.09}{2}$ = £7.77 per square foot (to 2 decimal places)

Upper quartile pointer = $\frac{3 \times (21+1)}{4} = \frac{66}{4} = 16.5$

Therefore the upper quartile is halfway between the 16th and 17th rental.

Upper quartile = $\frac{10.60 + 10.70}{2}$ = £10.65 per square foot

Inter-quartile range = 10.65 – 7.77 = £2.88 per square foot.

Summary Statistics for Office Rental Per Square Foot for 3 Areas

Area	Median	Lower quartile	Upper quartile	Inter-quartile range
Southam	£9.43	£7.33	£11.18	£3.85
Northam	£13.14	£12.60	£14.40	£1.80
Westham	£9.75	£7.77	£10.65	£2.88

Source: Telephone Survey of Commercial Lettings Agencies 199-

As the company is relocating because of high current rents you can assume that they wish to locate to an area of low rents.

You should advise them not relocate to Northam as this has the highest median rent. In addition a comparison of the inter-quartile ranges show that rents in Northam vary less than in the other two areas and so it is unlikely that low rental property will be found.

The median rents for both Southam and Westham are at a similar level, £9.43 and £9.75 respectively. However the inter-quartile ranges show that rents in Southam vary more widely than those in Westham (the inter-quartile range for Southam is the larger).

Because of this you could advise them to do one of three things (all of which are right):

1. search for new office premises in Southam because the median rent is the lowest and there is a larger range of rents available;
2. search for new office premises in Westham because the median rent is still reasonably low and, as there is less variation in rentals, they can be more certain of what they would be likely to pay;
3. search for new office premises in both Southam and Westham as this will give them a wider choice of possible low rental premises.

Task 6.1

Calculation to determine the trend using a 3 period moving average:

(figures rounded to 2 decimal places when necessary)

Year	Output (million tonnes)	3 quarter total	3 period moving average (trend)
1981	11		
1982	15	34	11.33
1983	8	34	11.33
1984	11	35	11.67
1985	16	36	12.00
1986	9	38	12.67
1987	13	40	13.33
1988	18	42	14.00
1989	11	44	14.67
1990	15	44	14.67
1991	18	44	14.67
1992	11		

Calculation to determine the trend using a 5 period moving average:

Year	Output (million tonnes)	5 quarter total	5 period moving average (trend)
1981	11		
1982	15		
1983	8	61	12.2
1984	11	59	11.8
1985	16	57	11.4
1986	9	67	13.4
1987	13	67	13.4
1988	18	66	13.2
1989	11	75	15.0
1990	15	73	14.6
1991	18		
1992	11		

Quarry Output 1981 – 1992 and Overall Trends (3 and 5 period)

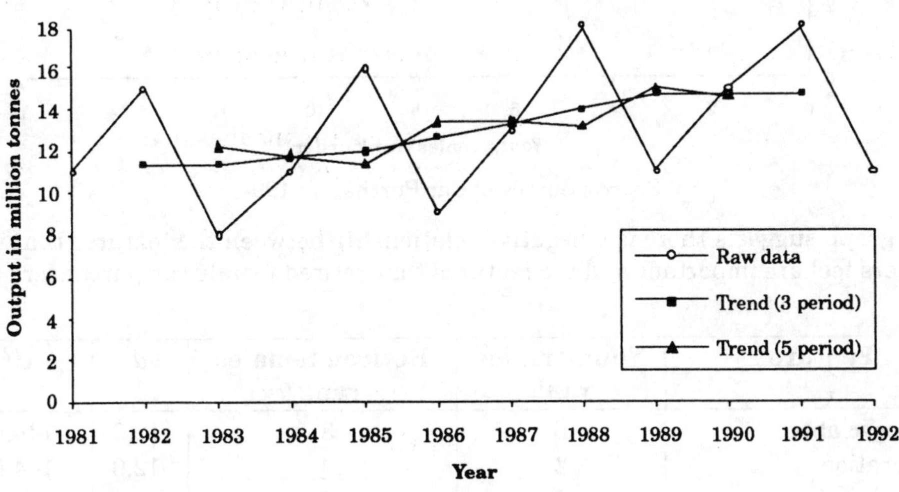

Source: Company Statistical Returns

The trend is of gradually increasing output.

The three period moving average is better for determining the trend as it removes the cyclical fluctuations in the data. This is because these fluctuations are on a three yearly rather than a five yearly cycle for this data.

Task 7.1

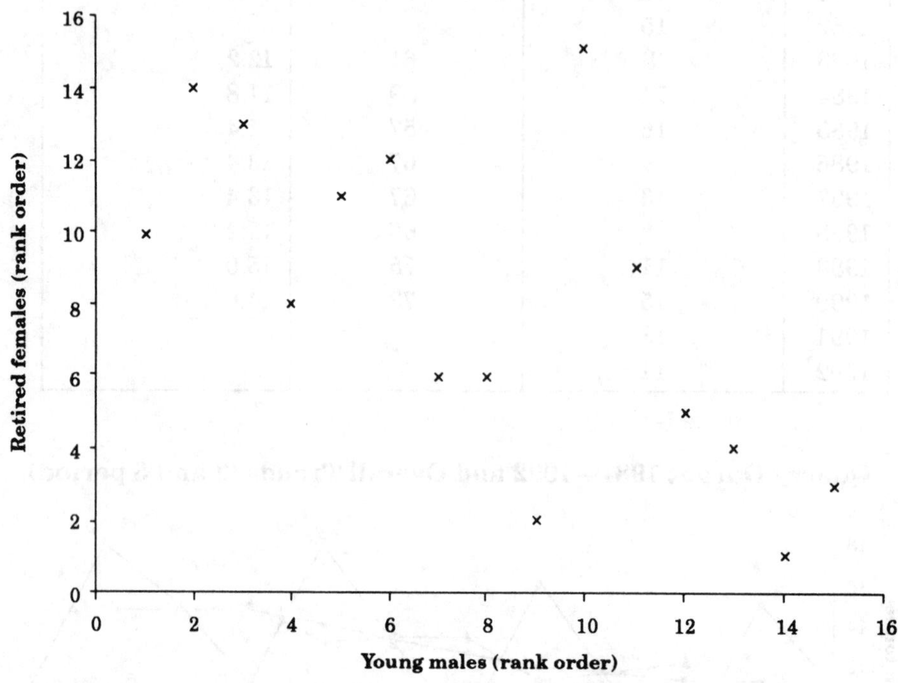

Source: Survey of Car Purchasers 199-

The scatter graph suggests there is a negative relationship between the features that young male car purchasers feel are important and the features that retired female car purchasers feel are important.

Feature	Young males rank	Retired females rank*	d	d^2
85% recyclable	15	3	12.0	144.00
Acceleration	2	14	-12.0	144.00
Boot size	7	6.5	0.5	0.25
Catalytic converter	12	5	7.0	49.00
Depreciation	9	2	7.0	49.00
Driver's air bag	13	4	9.0	81.00
Driving enjoyment	1	10	-9.0	81.00
Fuel economy	14	1	13.0	169.00
Handling and ride	3	13	-10.0	100.00
Insurance costs	4	8	-4.0	16.00
Metallic paint	10	15	-5.0	25.00
Price	5	11	-6.0	36.00
Quality and equipment	6	12	-6.0	36.00
Rear doors	11	9	2.0	4.00
Servicing costs	8	6.5	1.5	2.25
Total				936.50

* tied ranks are recorded as the sum of the tied ranks divided by (in this case) two.

$$\text{Spearman's rank correlation} = 1 - \frac{6 \times 936.5}{15(15^2 - 1)}$$

$$= 1 - \frac{5619}{15 \times (225 - 1)}$$

$$= 1 - \frac{5619}{15 \times 224}$$

$$= 1 - \frac{5619}{3360}$$

$$= 1 - 1.67 = -0.67 \text{ (to 2 decimal places)}$$

This means there is a reasonably strong negative correlation (-0.67) between the features that young male car purchasers feel are important and the features that retired female car purchasers feel are important. Manufacturers therefore need to emphasise the opposite features to each of these categories of purchasers.

Task 8.3

Total number of items purchased in typical week 3 years ago was 200.

Total number of items purchased in current typical week was 188.

The manager is therefore correct, the number of items sold has declined.

Base weighted (Laspeyre's) volume index:

Purchase	Unit price 3 yrs ago (p_o)	Quantity 3 yrs ago (q_o)	Quantity now (q_n)	Consumption 3 yrs ago ($p_o q_o$)	Consumption now ($p_o q_n$)
Vests	£4.80	40	32	192.00	153.60
Underpants	£0.80	75	60	60.00	48.00
Boxer shorts	£6.40	30	45	192.00	288.00
Hankies	£1.90	12	11	22.80	20.90
Ties	£8.10	12	11	97.20	89.10
Shirts	£9.80	20	19	196.00	186.20
Trousers	£14.00	11	10	154.00	140.00
Total				914.00	925.80

$$\text{Base weighted volume index} = \frac{925.80}{914.00} \times 100 = 101.29 \text{ (to 2 decimal places)}$$

Current weighted (Paasche's) volume index:

Purchase	Unit price now (p_n)	Quantity 3 yrs ago (q_o)	Quantity now (q_n)	Consumption 3 yrs ago ($p_n q_o$)	Consumption now ($p_n q_n$)
Vests	£7.30	40	32	292.00	233.60
Underpants	£1.90	75	60	142.50	114.00
Boxer shorts	£8.50	30	45	255.00	382.50
Hankies	£2.10	12	11	25.20	23.10
Ties	£9.50	12	11	114.00	104.50
Shirts	£12.60	20	19	252.00	239.40
Trousers	£17.00	11	10	187.00	170.00
Total				1267.70	1267.10

$$\text{Current weighted volume index} = \frac{1267.10}{1267.70} \times 100 = 99.95 \text{ (to 2 decimal places)}$$

The base weighted indexed is most appropriate to the argument that the shop be kept open as it shows a slight increase in the volume sold in terms of its value at base period prices.

Task 9.4

The first stage is to calculate the income and expenditure for each of the five sales levels if ingredients have been purchased for 200 cups of tea, and if ingredients have been purchased for 150 cups of tea. Expected profit can then be calculated.

Calculation for purchase of sufficient ingredients for 200 cups of tea:

Sales	Income[1]	Expenditure			Expected Profit	Prob-ability	
		Milk[2]	Other[3]	Total	(x)	(p)	($p\,x$)
0	0	£8.00	0	£8.00	-£8.00	0.1	-£0.80
50	£15.00	£8.00	£1.00	£9.00	£6.00	0.2	£1.20
100	£30.00	£8.00	£2.00	£10.00	£20.00	0.4	£8.00
150	£45.00	£8.00	£3.00	£11.00	£34.00	0.2	£6.80
200	£60.00	£8.00	£4.00	£12.00	£48.00	0.1	£4.80
Total							£20.00

1 **Income is 30p per cup of tea sold; therefore income is sales × 0.3.**

2 **Expenditure on milk is 4p per cup of tea for the total number for which sufficient ingredients have been purchased as any unused milk is thrown away at the end of the day; therefore expenditure on milk is 200 × 0.04 = £8.00.**

3 **Expenditure on other items is 2p per cup of tea sold; therefore expenditure is sales × 0.02.**

The expected profit for tea if he buys sufficient ingredients for 200 cups of tea is £20.00.

Calculation for purchase of sufficient ingredients for 200 cups of tea:

Sales	Income[1]	Expenditure			Expected Profit	Prob-ability	
		Milk[2]	Other[3]	Total	(x)	(p)	($p\,x$)
0	0	£6.00	0	£6.00	-£6.00	0.1	-£0.60
50	£15.00	£6.00	£1.00	£7.00	£8.00	0.2	£1.60
100	£30.00	£6.00	£2.00	£8.00	£22.00	0.4	£8.80
150	£45.00	£6.00	£3.00	£9.00	£36.00	0.2	£7.20
200	£45.00	£6.00	£3.00	£9.00	£36.00	0.1	£3.60
Total							£20.60

1 **Income is 30p per cup of tea sold up to 150 cups of tea. As sufficient ingredients have only been purchased for 150 cups of tea this is the maximum number that can be sold, hence the income for 200 cups of tea is the same as for 150 cups, £45.00.**

2 **Expenditure on milk is 4p per cup of tea for the total number for which sufficient ingredients have been purchased as any unused milk is thrown away at the end of the day; therefore expenditure on milk is 150 × 0.04 = £6.00.**

3 **Expenditure on other items is 2p per cup of tea sold; therefore expenditure is sales × 0.02 up to a maximum of 150 cups as sufficient milk has only been purchased for 150 cups.**

The expected profit for tea if he buys sufficient ingredients for 150 cups of tea is £20.60.

You would probably advise the cafe owner to buy sufficient ingredients for 150 cups of tea as this has the higher expected profit.

Appendix 3: Random Sampling Numbers

33865	04131	78302	22688	79034	01358	61724	98286	97086	21376
09356	09387	52825	93134	21731	93956	85324	68767	49490	11449
98243	37636	64825	43091	24906	13545	90172	31265	81457	93108
99052	61857	33938	86339	63531	77146	33252	81388	28302	18960
00713	24413	36920	03841	48047	04207	50930	84723	07400	81109
34819	80011	17751	03275	92511	70071	08183	72805	94618	46084
20611	34975	96712	32402	90182	94070	94711	94233	06619	34162
64972	86061	04685	53042	82685	45992	19829	45265	85589	83440
15857	73681	24790	20515	01232	25302	30785	95288	79341	54313
80276	67053	99022	36888	58643	96111	77292	03441	52856	95035
30548	51156	63914	64139	14596	35541	70324	20789	29139	66973
53530	79354	75099	89593	36449	66618	32346	37526	20084	52492
77012	18480	61852	82765	29602	10032	78925	71953	21661	95254
04304	40763	24847	07724	99223	77838	09547	47714	13302	17121
76953	39588	90708	67618	45671	19671	92674	22841	84231	59446
34479	85938	26363	12025	70315	58971	28991	35990	23542	74794
28421	16347	66638	25578	70404	67367	14730	37662	64669	16752
58160	17725	97075	99789	24304	63100	22123	83692	92997	58699
96701	73743	82979	69917	34993	36495	47023	48869	50611	61534
55600	61672	99136	73925	30250	12533	46280	03865	88049	13080
55850	38966	46303	37073	42347	36157	44357	52065	66913	06284
47089	83871	51231	32522	41543	22675	89316	38451	78694	01767
26035	86173	11115	22083	12083	43374	66542	23518	05372	33892
74920	35946	21149	70861	13235	02729	57485	23895	80607	11299
44498	00498	31354	39787	65919	61889	17690	10176	94138	95650
80045	71846	17840	23670	77769	84062	52850	20241	06073	20083
15828	95852	12124	95053	09924	91562	09419	27747	84732	81927
04100	75759	37926	70040	80884	48939	65228	60075	45056	56399
69257	48373	58911	78549	63693	43727	81058	53301	85945	54890
33915	26034	08166	59242	03881	88690	92298	48628	02698	94249
83497	62761	68609	85811	40695	08342	67386	63470	85643	68568
46466	15977	69989	90106	01432	59700	13163	56521	96687	41390
03573	87778	27696	35147	54639	20489	03688	72254	28402	98954
02046	44774	31500	30232	27434	14925	65901	34521	94104	54935
68736	12912	02579	34719	09568	21571	91111	81307	97866	76483
10817	35729	44825	67304	40180	51054	06745	35539	82764	44618
36715	32588	87768	70033	79187	69967	26494	01600	32800	03147
39125	18169	75335	47246	79137	87167	59804	25724	83782	55780
75285	49456	79438	45855	07117	62301	42452	12294	43591	83547

Appendix 4: Critical Values of Chi Square

d.f.	Significance Level .1	.05	.01
1	2.71	3.84	6.63
2	4.61	5.99	9.21
3	6.25	7.81	11.3
4	7.78	9.49	13.3
5	9.24	11.1	15.1
6	10.6	12.6	16.8
7	12.0	14.1	18.5
8	13.4	15.5	20.1
9	14.7	16.9	21.7
10	16.0	18.3	23.2
11	17.3	19.7	24.7
12	18.5	21.0	26.2
13	19.8	22.4	27.7
14	21.1	23.7	29.1
15	22.3	25.0	30.6
16	23.5	26.3	32.0
17	24.8	27.6	33.4
18	26.0	28.9	34.8
19	27.2	30.1	36.2
20	28.4	31.4	37.6
21	29.6	32.7	38.9
22	30.8	33.9	40.3
23	32.0	35.2	41.6
24	33.2	36.4	43.0
25	34.4	37.7	44.3
26	35.6	38.9	45.6
27	36.7	40.1	47.0
28	37.9	41.3	48.3
29	39.1	42.6	49.6
30	40.3	43.8	50.9
40	51.8	55.8	63.7
50	63.2	67.5	76.2
60	74.4	79.1	88.4
70	85.5	90.5	100
80	96.6	102	112
90	108	113	124
100	118	124	136

Appendix 5: Values of the Standard Normal distribution

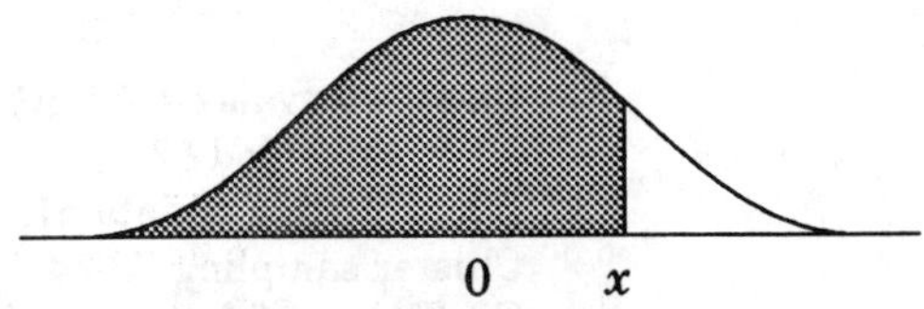

The table gives the probability that a standard Normal variable is less than or equal to x (which is equivalent to the shaded area on the figure).

x	0.00	0.01	0.02	0.03	0.04	0.05	0.06	0.07	0.08	0.09
0.0	.5000	.5040	.5080	.5120	.5160	.5199	.5239	.5279	.5319	.5359
0.1	.5398	.5438	.5478	.5517	.5557	.5596	.5636	.5675	.5714	.5754
0.2	.5793	.5832	.5871	.5910	.5948	.5987	.6026	.6064	.6103	.6141
0.3	.6179	.6217	.6255	.6293	.6331	.6368	.6406	.6443	.6480	.6517
0.4	.6554	.6591	.6628	.6664	.6700	.6736	.6772	.6808	.6844	.6879
0.5	.6915	.6950	.6985	.7019	.7054	.7088	.7123	.7157	.7190	.7224
0.6	.7258	.7291	.7324	.7357	.7389	.7422	.7454	.7486	.7518	.7549
0.7	.7580	.7612	.7642	.7673	.7704	.7734	.7764	.7794	.7823	.7852
0.8	.7881	.7910	.7939	.7967	.7996	.8023	.8051	.8078	.8106	.8133
0.9	.8159	.8186	.8212	.8238	.8264	.8289	.8315	.8340	.8365	.8389
1.0	.8413	.8438	.8461	.8485	.8508	.8531	.8554	.8577	.8599	.8621
1.1	.8643	.8665	.8686	.8708	.8729	.8749	.8770	.8790	.8810	.8830
1.2	.8849	.8869	.8888	.8907	.8925	.8944	.8962	.8980	.8997	.9015
1.3	.9032	.9049	.9066	.9082	.9099	.9115	.9131	.9147	.9162	.9177
1.4	.9192	.9207	.9222	.9236	.9251	.9265	.9279	.9292	.9306	.9319
1.5	.9332	.9345	.9357	.9370	.9382	.9394	.9406	.9418	.9429	.9441
1.6	.9452	.9463	.9474	.9484	.9495	.9505	.9515	.9525	.9535	.9545
1.7	.9554	.9564	.9573	.9582	.9591	.9599	.9608	.9616	.9625	.9633
1.8	.9641	.9649	.9656	.9664	.9671	.9678	.9686	.9693	.9699	.9706
1.9	.9713	.9719	.9726	.9732	.9738	.9744	.9750	.9756	.9761	.9767
2.0	.9772	.9778	.9783	.9788	.9793	.9798	.9803	.9808	.9812	.9817
2.1	.9821	.9826	.9830	.9834	.9838	.9842	.9846	.9850	.9854	.9857
2.2	.9861	.9864	.9868	.9871	.9875	.9878	.9881	.9884	.9887	.9890
2.3	.9893	.9896	.9898	.9901	.9904	.9906	.9909	.9911	.9913	.9916
2.4	.9918	.9920	.9922	.9925	.9927	.9929	.9931	.9932	.9934	.9936
2.5	.9938	.9940	.9941	.9943	.9945	.9946	.9948	.9949	.9951	.9952
2.6	.9953	.9955	.9956	.9957	.9959	.9960	.9961	.9962	.9963	.9964
2.7	.9965	.9966	.9967	.9968	.9969	.9970	.9971	.9972	.9973	.9974
2.8	.9974	.9975	.9976	.9977	.9977	.9978	.9979	.9979	.9980	.9981
2.9	.9981	.9982	.9982	.9983	.9984	.9984	.9985	.9985	.9986	.9986

3.0	3.1	3.2	3.3	3.4	3.5	3.6	3.7	3.8	3.9
.9987	.9990	.9993	.9995	.9997	.9998	.9998	.9999	.9999	1.0000

Index

All entries refer to coverage of these subjects in **Section 2: The information bank**